Glencoe

Algebra 1

Integration
Applications
Connections

Assessment and
Evaluation Masters

GLENCOE

McGraw-Hill

New York, New York   Columbus, Ohio   Woodland Hills, California   Peoria, Illinois

Glencoe/McGraw-Hill

A Division of The McGraw-Hill Companies

Send all inquiries to:
Glencoe/McGraw-Hill
8787 Orion Place
Columbus, OH 43240

Algebra I
Assessment and Evaluation Masters

ISBN: 0-02-824853-8

8 9 10 11 12 021 04 03 02 01 00 99

Contents

Book Materials

Math Learning Assessment

Chapter 1 Test, Form 1A

Write the letter for the correct answer in the blank at the right of each problem.

1. Write an algebraic expression for 10 less than d.
   A. $10 > d$ B. $10 < d$ C. $10 - d$ D. $d - 10$

   1. _____

2. Write an algebraic expression for the sum of the cube of a number and 5.
   A. $5x^3$ B. $5 \cdot 3x$ or $15x$ C. $5 + x^3$ D. $5 + 3x$

   2. _____

3. Write $6 \cdot 6 \cdot m \cdot m \cdot m \cdot y \cdot y \cdot y$ using exponents.
   A. $6^2 m^3 y^3$ B. $66 m^3 y^3$ C. $66 m y^3$ D. $6^2 m y^3$

   3. _____

4. What is the next number in the sequence $2x^2, 4x^2, 8x^2, 16x^2, \cdots$?
   A. $20x^2$ B. $24x^2$ C. $32x^2$ D. $48x^2$

   4. _____

5. What is the next figure in the following pattern?

      ...

   5. _____

   A.   B.   C.   D.

6. Evaluate $10(4 + 3 \cdot 2) \div (2 \cdot 6 - 7)$.
   A. 4   B. 20   C. 28   D. 100

   6. _____

7. Evaluate $4am - a^2$ when $a = \frac{1}{2}$ and $m = 5$.

   A. $10\frac{1}{4}$ B. $22\frac{1}{4}$ C. $9\frac{3}{4}$ D. 9

   7. _____

8. Evaluate $4v^2 - n(s - v)$ when $n = 3$, $s = 5$, and $v = 2$.
   A. 55   B. 39   C. 183   D. 7

   8. _____

9. Which set of data was used to make the stem-and-leaf plot?
   A. 14, 245, 36
   B. 4, 4, 5, 6
   C. 14, 24, 25, 36
   D. 1.4, 2.4, 2.5, 3.6

Stem	Leaf
1	4
2	4 5
3	6

   $1|4 = 14$

   9. _____

10. Solve $p = 148 - 3.7$.
    A. 145.7   B. 144.3   C. 11.1   D. 111

    10. _____

11. Solve $\frac{3}{8} + \frac{2}{3} = n$.

    A. $\frac{25}{24}$ B. $\frac{5}{11}$ C. $\frac{1}{4}$ D. $\frac{5}{24}$

    11. _____

12. Which property is illustrated by $4 + (3 - 1) = 4 + 2$?
    A. substitution property   B. associative property of addition
    C. additive identity property   D. reflexive property

    12. _____

13. Which of the following shows the symmetric property of equality?   13._____
    A. If $5 + 2 = 7$ and $7 = 1 + 6$, then $5 + 2 = 1 + 6$.
    B. If $2 + 9 = 11$, then $9 + 2 = 11$.
    C. If $13 = 5 + 8$, then $5 + 8 = 13$.
    D. $(x + y)4 = 4(x + y)$

14. What is the simplest form of $5x + x + 9$?   14._____
    A. $5x^2 + 9$ B. $6x + 9$ C. $5x + 9$ D. $15x$

15. What is the simplest form of $10y^2 + 2(y^2 + x)$?   15._____
    A. $12y^2 + 2x$ B. $12y^2 + x$ C. $12y^4 + 2x$ D. $12y^4 + x$

16. What is the simplest form of $9a^2 + 7a + 4a^2 + 2a$?   16._____
    A. $22a^6$ B. $13a^4 + 9a^2$ C. $22a^3$ D. $13a^2 + 9a$

17. Which property is illustrated by $6x^2 - 2x^2 = (6 - 2)x^2$?   17._____
    A. distributive property
    B. associative property of addition
    C. communicative property of addition
    D. reflexive property of equality

18. Which of the following illustrates the commutative property of addition?   18._____
    A. $7(wx + 3) = (wx + 3)7$ B. $7(wx + 3) = 7wx + 21$
    C. $7(wx + 3) = 7(xw + 3)$ D. $7(wx + 3) = 7(3 + wx)$

19. Which of the following best describes the graph?   19._____
    A. At first, the price of a share of the company's stock was unchanged. Then the price increased sharply.
    B. At first, the price of a share of the company's stock was unchanged. Then the price decreased sharply.
    C. The price of a share of the company's stock rose sharply and then leveled off.
    D. The price of a share of the company's stock declined sharply and then leveled off.

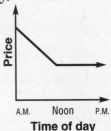

20. Identify the graph that matches the following statement: 20._____
    For many items, the number sold increases as the price decreases.
    A.   B.   C.   D.

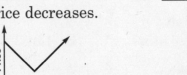

Bonus Simplify $\frac{5}{4}a + \frac{3}{4}[8(a^2 + 3b^2) - 24b^2] + \frac{1}{4}(8 - 5a)$.   **Bonus** _____

    A. $8a^2 + 4a$ B. $6a^2 + 2$ C. $2a^2 + 5a$ D. $5a^2 + 2$

NAME_____ DATE _____

Chapter 1 Test, Form 1B

Write the letter for the correct answer in the blank at the right of each problem.

1. Write $3 \cdot 3 \cdot a \cdot x \cdot x \cdot x \cdot x$ using exponents.
   A. $33ax^4$ **B.** 3^2ax^4 **C.** $3ax^4$ **D.** $3^2a^2x^4$
   1. _____

2. Write an algebraic expression for the product of 10 and a number, increased by 2.
   A. $10(n + 2)$ **B.** $10(2n)$ **C.** $10n + 2$ **D.** $10 - 2n$
   2. _____

3. Write an algebraic expression for 7 less than the square of a number.
   A. $7 < x^2$ **B.** $7 > x^2$ **C.** $7 - x^2$ **D.** $x^2 - 7$
   3. _____

4. Identify the next figure in the following pattern.
   A.   **B.**   **C.**   **D.**
   4. _____

5. What is the next number in the sequence $a + 1.7, a + 2.8, a + 3.9, a + 5, \cdots$?
   A. $a + 6$ **B.** $a + 6.1$ **C.** $a + 7$ **D.** $a + 7.1$
   5. _____

6. Evaluate $4 + 8 \div 2 - 3$.
   A. 5   **B.** 6   **C.** 3   **D.** 1
   6. _____

7. Evaluate $mn - p^2$ when $m = 9$, $n = \frac{2}{3}$, and $p = 2$.
   A. $3\frac{2}{3}$ **B.** $7\frac{2}{3}$ **C.** 4   **D.** 2
   7. _____

8. Evaluate $6a^2 + b(c - 3a)$ when $a = 3$, $b = 5$, and $c = 16$.
   A. 116   **B.** 89   **C.** 125   **D.** 71
   8. _____

9. What is the greatest number shown on the stem-and-leaf plot?
   A. 9
   B. 139
   C. 1569
   D. 131,569

Stem	Leaf
11	0
12	2 2 8
13	1 5 6 9

   $11|0 = 110$
   9. _____

10. Solve $154 - 0.32 = m$.
   A. 153.68   **B.** 153.32   **C.** 1.22   **D.** 122
   10. _____

11. Solve $n = \frac{3}{4} - \frac{5}{8}$.
   A. $\frac{1}{4}$ **B.** $\frac{3}{8}$ **C.** $\frac{1}{8}$ **D.** $\frac{3}{4}$
   11. _____

12. Which of the following illustrates the transitive property of equality?
   A. If $12 = 17 - 5$, then $17 - 5 = 12$.
   B. If $t = 4$ and $4 = 9 - 5$, then $t = 9 - 5$.
   C. $8(a + b) = 8(b + a)$
   D. If $5 + 6 = 11$, then $6 + 5 = 11$.
   12. _____

13. What is the simplest form of $7rs + 2rs + 3$?　　　　　　　13. _____
　　A. $9rs + 3$　　**B.** $12rs$　　**C.** $7r^2s^2 + 3$　　**D.** $9rs^2 + 3$

14. What is the simplest form of $6b + 3(2a^2 + b)$?　　　　　　14. _____
　　A. $2a^2 + 10b$　　**B.** $2a^2 + 9b$　　**C.** $6a^2 + 7b$　　**D.** $6a^2 + 9b$

15. Which property is illustrated by $7(6 \cdot 2) = (7 \cdot 6)2$?　　　　15. _____
　　A. distributive property
　　B. reflexive property of equality
　　C. commutative property of multiplication
　　D. associative property of multiplication

16. Which of the following illustrates the distributive property?　　16. _____
　　A. $5(xy + 4) = (xy + 4)5$　　　　**B.** $5(xy + 4) = 5(4 + xy)$
　　C. $5(xy + 4) = 5xy + 20$　　　　**D.** $5(xy + 4) = 5(xy) + 4(xy)$

17. What is the simplest form of $4[5t + 2(3t + 5)]$?　　　　　17. _____
　　A. $4(11t + 10)$　　**B.** $26t + 10$　　**C.** $44t + 40$　　**D.** $84t$

18. Which property is illustrated by $4n^2 + (6 + 2n) = 4n^2 + (2n + 6)$?　18. _____
　　A. distributive property
　　B. associative property of addition
　　C. commutative property of addition
　　D. reflexive property of equality

19. Which of the following best describes the graph?　　　　　19. _____
　　A. The price of a share of the company's stock
　　　　increased more in the morning than in
　　　　the afternoon.
　　B. The price of a share of the company's stock
　　　　decreased more in the morning than in the
　　　　afternoon.
　　C. The price of a share of the company's stock
　　　　increased more in the afternoon than in the morning.
　　D. The price of a share of the company's stock
　　　　decreased more in the afternoon than in the morning.

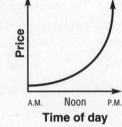

20. Identify the graph that matches the following statement:　　20. _____
　　The accident rate for middle-aged automobile drivers is lower
　　than the rate for younger and older drivers.

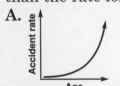

Bonus In some leagues, the equation $f = \frac{4}{5}(200 - m) + a$　　**Bonus a.** _____

is used to find a bowler's final score (f). In this equation, $m =$ the　　**b.** _____
bowler's average score and $a =$ the actual score. Find the final score if:
　a. Peter averages 110 but bowled a 132 this game.
　b. Rhonda averages 160 but bowled a 155 this game.

1

Chapter 1 Test, Form 1C

Write the letter for the correct answer in the blank at the right of each problem.

1. Write $4 \cdot 4 \cdot m \cdot m \cdot m \cdot m \cdot n$ using exponents.
   A. $44m^4n$ **B.** $4m^4n$ **C.** 4^4m^4n **D.** 4^2m^4n

   1. _____

2. Write an algebraic expression for the following verbal expression: 7 more than a number.
   A. $7 > n$ **B.** $n > 7$ **C.** $n + 7$ **D.** $7n$

   2. _____

3. Evaluate 2^3.
   A. 4   **B.** 6   **C.** 8   **D.** 9

   3. _____

4. Identify the next number in the following sequence:
   50, 45, 40, 35, $\cdots$
   A. 30   **B.** 34   **C.** 40   **D.** 50

   4. _____

5. Identify the next figure in the following pattern.

   A.   **B.**   **C.**   **D.**

   5. _____

6. Evaluate $6 + 2 \cdot 3 - 1$.
   A. 23   **B.** 10   **C.** 16   **D.** 11

   6. _____

7. Evaluate $2(11 - 5) + 3$.
   A. 18   **B.** 15   **C.** 30   **D.** 11

   7. _____

8. Evaluate $x^2 + 3xy$ when $x = 3$ and $y = 5$.
   A. 54   **B.** 51   **C.** 20   **D.** 70

   8. _____

9. What does the entry 20|1 represent in the following stem-and-leaf plot?
   A. 1
   B. 20.1
   C. 201
   D. 20,100

Stem	Leaf
19	0 0 7
20	1 4 5 5
21	7 8

   21|8 = 218

   9. _____

10. How many items are in the data set used to make the stem-and-leaf plot in question 9?
    A. 6   **B.** 7   **C.** 15   **D.** 9

    10. _____

11. Solve $5(3) + 7 = b$.
    A. 22   **B.** 50   **C.** 8   **D.** 23

    11. _____

12. Solve $\dfrac{10 - 4}{2} = m$.
    A. 7   **B.** 2   **C.** 3   **D.** 6

    12. _____

Algebra 1

13. Which of the following represents the multiplicative   13. _____
    inverse property?
    A. $9(2 + 0) = 9(2)$ **B.** $0 \cdot 16 = 0$ **C.** $1(48) = 48$ **D.** $3 \cdot \frac{1}{3} = 1$

14. What is the simplest form of $5x + 15x + 1$?   14. _____
    A. $21x$ **B.** $21x^2$ **C.** $20x + 1$ **D.** $20x^2 + 1$

15. What is the simplest form of $r^2 - 2r^3 + 3r^2$?   15. _____
    A. $4r^2 - 2r^3$ **B.** $2r$ **C.** $3r^2 - 2r^3$ **D.** $4r^2$

16. What property is illustrated by $4 + 5 = 5 + 4$?   16. _____
    A. distributive property
    B. commutative property of addition
    C. associative property of addition
    D. transitive property

17. Which of the following illustrates the distributive property?   17. _____
    A. $3(4x + 5) = (4x + 5)3$ **B.** $3(4x + 5) = 12x + 15$
    C. $3(4x + 5) = 3(5 + 4x)$ **D.** $3(4x + 5) = 3(4x) + 5(4x)$

18. Simplify $4(6x + y) - 3x$.   18. _____
    A. $3x + 4y$ **B.** $21x + 4y$ **C.** $24x$ **D.** $21x + y$

19. Which of the following best describes the graph?   19. _____
    A. The price of a share of the company's
       stock increased.
    B. The price of a share of the company's
       stock decreased.
    C. The price of a share of the company's
       stock did not change.
    D. The price of a share of the company's
       stock increased in the morning and
       decreased in the afternoon.

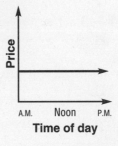

20. Which of the following graphs matches the following statement: 20. _____
    As the temperature increases, the number of cups of hot chocolate
    sold decreases.
    A.   **B.**   **C.**   **D.**

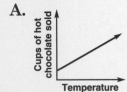 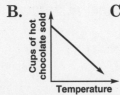 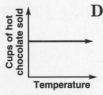

Bonus   Simplify $4x + \frac{3}{4}[12(x^2 + y^2) - 12y^2] + 2x(x + 1)$.   **Bonus** _____

   A. $9x^2 + 8x$ **B.** $11x^2 + 6x$ **C.** $17x^2$ **D.** $11x^2 + 6x + 18y^2$

NAME_____ DATE _____

Chapter 1 Test, Form 2A

Write an algebraic expression for each verbal expression.

1. the sum of the cube of a number and 12   1. _____

2. 14 less than a number   2. _____

3. 42 decreased by twice some number   3. _____

Rewrite each expression using exponents.

4. $7 \cdot 7 \cdot 7 \cdot 7$ 4. _____

5. $\frac{1}{4}y \cdot y \cdot m \cdot m$ 5. _____

Find the next item in each sequence.

6. $\frac{1}{32}, \frac{1}{16}, \frac{1}{8}, \frac{1}{4}, \cdots$ 6. _____

7.
_____   ...   7. _____

Evaluate each expression.

8. 9^3 8. _____

9. $24 + 8 \div 2 + 6$ 9. _____

10. $36 \div 4 \cdot 3$ 10. _____

11. $4[3^3 - 5(8 - 6)] \div 2 + 11$ 11. _____

Evaluate each expression when $w = 4$, $n = 8$, $v = 5$, and $t = 2$.

12. $w + n(v - t)$ 12. _____

13. $3nw - w^2$ 13. _____

14. The average monthly temperatures for Houston, Texas,   14.
    are given below. Make a stem-and-leaf plot of these data.

Month	Jan.	Feb.	Mar.	Apr.	May	June	July	Aug.	Sept.	Oct.	Nov.	Dec.
Temp. (°F)	51	55	61	69	75	81	83	83	78	70	60	54

15. Suppose the number 15,897 is rounded to 15,900 and   15. _____
    plotted using stem 15 and leaf 9. Write the stem and
    leaf for 9420 if this number is part of the same set of data.

Solve each equation.

16. $y = 12 - 1.4$ 16. _____

17. $\frac{3}{10} + \frac{1}{6} = m$ 17. _____

18. $w = 8\frac{1}{2} \div 4$ 18. _____

19. $\frac{5 \cdot 2^3 - 4 \cdot 3^2}{1 + 3} = x$ 19. _____

State the property illustrated by each statement.

20. $7y + y = 7y + 1y$ 20._____

21. $(3x + 7y) + 2y = 3x + (7y + 2y)$ 21._____

22. $9x + 4x = (9 + 4)x$ 22._____

23. $7(9t) = (7 \cdot 9)t$ 23._____

24. $5(4 + 7x) = 5(7x + 4)$ 24._____

25. $(6 + 9)x = 15x$ 25._____

Simplify each expression.

26. $9x^2 + 12x^2$ 26._____

27. $6n + n + 3$ 27._____

28. $5a + 7(2a + 3)$ 28._____

29. $3a^2 + 4a + 7a^2 + 5a$ 29._____

30. $3 + 6(5a + 4an) + 9na$ 30._____

Use the following graph for questions 31 and 32.

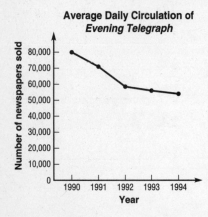

Average Daily Circulation of Evening Telegraph

31. Identify the variable represented along each axis. 31._____

32. Identify two points on the graph and write an ordered pair for each point. 32._____

33. Sketch a reasonable graph for the following situation. *For three months in a row, David deposited money into his savings account and made no withdrawals. Then, for the next four months, he withdrew money and made no deposits.* 33.

Bonus Simplify $\dfrac{6^2 + (3 + 4)^2 - (21 \div 3 + 4 \cdot 2)}{14 - 3 \cdot 1^4 + 2^3 - (5 + 1) \cdot 2}$. **Bonus** _____

Chapter 1 Test, Form 2B

Write an algebraic expression for each verbal expression.

1. the sum of the square of a number and 34

1._____

2. the product of 5 and twice a number

2._____

3. half a number decreased by 3

3._____

Rewrite each expression using exponents.

4. $5 \cdot 5 \cdot 5$

4._____

5. $2 \cdot b \cdot b \cdot b$

5_____

Find the next item in each sequence.

6. $3125, 625, 125, 25, \cdots$

6._____

7. ...

7._____

Evaluate each expression.

8. 10^2

8._____

9. $40 - 8 \div 4 + 12$

9._____

10. $24 \div [3(5 - 3)]$

10._____

11. $2^3[(15 - 7) \div 2]$

11._____

Evaluate each expression when $w = 4$, $n = 8$, $v = 5$, and $t = 2$.

12. $3w + (n - v)t$

12._____

13. $2nt - v^2$

13._____

14. Write the members of the data set used to make the stem-and-leaf plot.

Stem	Leaf
2	7 8
3	0 0 1 6
4	4

$4|4 = 44$

14._____

15. Suppose the number 1212 is rounded to 1210 and plotted using stem 12 and leaf 10. Write the stem and leaf for 1467 if this number is part of the same set of data.

15._____

Solve each equation.

16. $y = 4.5 - 1.25$

16._____

17. $\frac{3}{8} + \frac{1}{2} = c$

17._____

18. $m = 8 \div 4\frac{1}{4}$

18._____

19. $\frac{6 + 3^2 \cdot 4}{7 - 1} = y$

19._____

State the property illustrated by each statement.

20. $5 + 0 = 5$

20. _____

21. $w + (4 + 6) = w + 10$

21. _____

22. $7(8 - 3) = 7 \cdot 8 - 7 \cdot 3$

22. _____

23. $4(1) = 4$

23. _____

24. $7(6 \cdot 2) = (7 \cdot 6)2$

24. _____

25. If $9 = 5 + 4$, then $5 + 4 = 9$.

25. _____

26. $4n^2 + (6 + 2n^2) = 4n^2 + (2n^2 + 6)$

26. _____

Simplify each expression.

27. $6x + 7(y + x)$

27. _____

28. $15w + 14w^2 - 6w$

28. _____

29. $c^2 + 4d^2 + d(d + 3)$

29. _____

30. $3 + 2(8n + 4) + 9n$

30. _____

Use the following graph for questions 31 and 32.

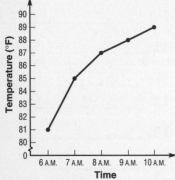

31. Identify the variable represented along each axis.

31. _____

32. Identify two points on the graph and write an ordered pair for each point.

32. _____

33. Sketch a reasonable graph for the following situation. *By the end of the day, almost everyone at school had heard the rumor.*

33.

Bonus Show how grouping symbols, exponents, and the symbols for addition, subtraction, multiplication, and division can be added to the digits 1, 9, 8, and 7 (in that order) to form expressions that will yield the following values when evaluated.

    a. 6

    b. 7

    c. 9

Bonus **a.** _____

b. _____

c. _____

Chapter 1 Test, Form 2C

Write an algebraic expression for each verbal expression.

1. the sum of half of a number and 13

2. x to the fourth power

3. 74 decreased by twice some number

Rewrite each expression using exponents.

4. $10 \cdot 10$

5. $5 \cdot n \cdot n \cdot n$

Find the next item in each sequence.

6. $30, 45, 60, 75, \cdots$

7. ...

Evaluate each expression.

8. 3^3

9. $30 \div 5 + 1$

10. $2(7 - 3) + 14$

11. $7 + [24 \div (3 + 9)]$

Evaluate each expression when $x = 7$, $y = 2$, and $z = 3$.

12. $2 + x(2y - z)$

13. $5xy - 3z$

Use the stem-and-leaf plot for questions 14 and 15.

14. What does the entry 3 | 0 represent?

15. What is the greatest number shown?

Stem	Leaf
1	7 8
2	2 2 5 6 9
3	0 1 1|7 = 17

Solve each equation.

16. $y = 23 - 5$

17. $\dfrac{1}{2} + \dfrac{1}{4} = a$

18. $t = 6 \div 1\dfrac{1}{2}$

19. $\dfrac{2^4 + 4}{3 - 1} = r$

State the property illustrated by each statement.

20. $3(0) = 0$

21. $b + 4 = 4 + b$

1. _____

2. _____

3. _____

4. _____

5. _____

6. _____

7. _____

8. _____

9. _____

10. _____

11. _____

12. _____

13. _____

14. _____

15. _____

16. _____

17. _____

18. _____

19. _____

20. _____

21. _____

22. $1 \cdot 25 = 25$ 22._____

23. $2x + 0 = 2x$ 23._____

24. $8(c + 2) = 8c + 16$ 24._____

25. $y^2 + (2y^2 + 6) = (y^2 + 2y^2) + 6$ 25._____

26. $9(2 + m) = 9(m + 2)$ 26._____

Simplify each expression.

27. $2x + 3x - 1$ 27._____

28. $3a^2 + 9a^2$ 28._____

29. $6(p^2 - 1) + 2p^2$ 29._____

30. $r^2 + 3s^2 + 8r + 5r^2$ 30._____

Use the following graph for questions 31 and 32.

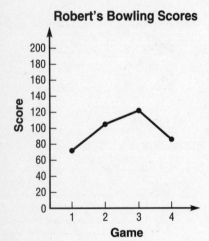

Robert's Bowling Scores

31. What does the ordered pair (1, 72) represent?   31._____

32. In which game was Robert's score 122?   32._____

33. Sketch a reasonable graph for the following situation.   33.
    *By the end of the day, the box office had only a few
    tickets left to sell.*

Bonus   Show how to insert brackets, parentheses,   **Bonus** _____
    and the symbols for addition, subtraction, and
    division in the following sequence of numbers so
    that its value is 4.

        2 5 1 4 1

NAME_____ DATE _____

Chapter 1 Calculator-Based Test

Evaluate each expression.

1. 11^2

2. 6^3

3. 3^6

4. $2 + 10 \div 2 - 1$

5. $44 - (12 + 17)$

6. $25 - 5 \cdot 4 + 1$

7. $7 \cdot 2(3^2 + 1)$

8. $9.5 + 1.2(4^3)$

9. $6(3)^2 + 5$

10. $6(2 \cdot 5)^2$

11. $\dfrac{(7-4)^2 + 12}{(3 \cdot 2^3) - 3}$

12. $2.75(1.5)^2 + 0.4(3.45)^3$

Evaluate each expression when r = 2 and s = 4.

13. $0.5r^2 + 1.25r$

14. $\dfrac{2r^3}{2r(r-1)}$

15. $\dfrac{3s^2 + 10}{0.5s}$

16. $17.95 + 4.5(s^2)$

Solve each equation.

17. $d = 9.165 + 0.1017$

18. $x = 3.2 - 1.687$

19. $\dfrac{1.5(4+3)}{8-2} = b$

20. $y = 17^3 - 5^2$

1. _____

2. _____

3. _____

4. _____

5. _____

6. _____

7. _____

8. _____

9. _____

10. _____

11. _____

12. _____

13. _____

14. _____

15. _____

16. _____

17. _____

18. _____

19. _____

20. _____

1 Chapter 1 Performance Assessment

Instructions: *Demonstrate your knowledge by giving a clear, concise solution to each problem. Be sure to include all relevant drawings and justify your answers. You may show your solution in more than one way or investigate beyond the requirements of the problem.*

1. Some important area formulas are given below.

   Area of a circle = πr^2, where r is the radius of the circle

   Area of a trapezoid = $\dfrac{(b_1 + b_2)}{2} \cdot h$, where b_1 and b_2 are the lengths of

   the bases and h is the height of the trapezoid

   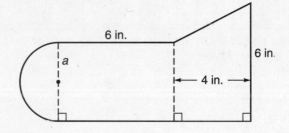

   a. Write a formula for the area of the figure shown at the right.

   b. Simplify the formula in part a. Justify each step in your simplification by naming the property used.

   c. State the order of operations indicated by the formula in part b. Then find the area when $a = 2$.

2. In each sentence, circle key words or phrases that indicate a mathematical operation and write the corresponding mathematical symbol above each. Then write an equation for each sentence.

   a. Three times a number decreased by four is equal to twenty-five.

   b. The sum of the square of a number and a second number is eighteen.

   c. A number multiplied by 7 and divided by three gives five more than the number.

   d. One-half of a number added to itself equals twice the difference of the number and five.

3. Think of a situation that could be modeled by this graph. Then label the axes of the graph and write several sentences describing the situation.

   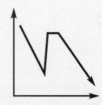

Chapter 1 Mid-Chapter Test (Lessons 1-1 through 1-5)

Write each expression as an expression with exponents.

1. $4 \cdot m \cdot m \cdot m \cdot m \cdot m$ 2. $\frac{1}{3} \cdot x \cdot x \cdot y \cdot y \cdot y \cdot y$

1. _____

2. _____

Write an algebraic expression for each verbal expression.

3. five times a number decreased by 2

4. twice the square of a number

3. _____

4. _____

Find the next item in each sequence.

5. 1, 3, 7, 13, 21, · · ·

5. _____

6.

6.

...

Evaluate each expression when m = 4, n = 12, p = $\frac{1}{4}$, q = 0.4.

7. $2mn - 5mp$ 8. $3m + 2(q + n)$

7. _____

8. _____

9. $5m^2 + (5m)^2$ 10. $2nq + m^2$

9. _____

10. _____

Evaluate each expression.

11. $120 \div [6(9 - 5)]$ 12. $\frac{17.2 + 15.8}{0.2 + 0.9}$

11. _____

12. _____

13. $\frac{4 \cdot 3 + 2}{1 + 2 \cdot 3}$ 14. $4\frac{1}{2} \div 3$

13. _____

14. _____

Use the stem-and-leaf plot for questions 15 and 16.

15. What does the entry 91|1 represent?

16. What is the greatest number of pages shown?

Stem	Leaf
89	4 7
90	6
91	1
92	2 8 8 90|6 = 906

15. _____

16. _____

Solve each equation.

17. $\frac{5^2 + 2^3}{11} = a$ 18. $n = 70 - 3(0.12)$

17. _____

18. _____

Find the solution set for each open sentence if the replacement set is $x = \left\{ \frac{2}{3}, 2, 3, 5 \right\}$.

19. $6x > 5$ 20. $3x - 4 < 2$

19. _____

20. _____

Bonus One generation back, your natural ancestors are your 2 parents. Two generations back, your natural ancestors are your 4 grandparents. Three generations back, your natural ancestors are your 8 great-grandparents.
  a. How many natural ancestors did you have 6 generations back?
  b. How many natural ancestors did you have 20 generations back? (Write this answer using a base and an exponent.)

Bonus a. _____

b. _____

Chapter 1, Quiz A (Lessons 1-1 through 1-3)

Write an algebraic expression for each verbal expression.

1. 8 to the fourth power increased by 6

2. three times the cube of a number

1. _____

2. _____

Evaluate each expression when $a = 2$, $b = 5$, and $c = 1$.

3. $a^3 + 2b^2$

4. $a(4b + c)$

3. _____

4. _____

Evaluate each expression.

5. 2^8

6. $4^2 + \frac{2}{3}(18 - 6)$

7. $62 - 3 \cdot 8 + 11$

8. $12 - [28 \div (3 + 4)]$

5. _____

6. _____

7. _____

8. _____

Give the next two items for each pattern.

9.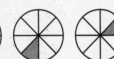

10. 10, 9, 11, 10, 12, · · ·

9. _____

10. _____

Chapter 1, Quiz B (Lessons 1-4 and 1-5)

1. The high temperatures for a particular day in 20 cities are shown below. Use these data to make a stem-and-leaf plot.

101	99
86	106
97	94
80	82
91	88
78	88
91	85
95	92
90	97
95	89

1.

Stem	Leaf

Solve each equation.

2. $4.5 - 1.25 = a$

3. $n = \frac{5}{8} + \frac{3}{4}$

2. _____

3. _____

Find the solution set for each open sentence if the replacement set is {2, 3, 4, 5}.

4. $\frac{10 - x}{2} < 4$

5. $t + 3 > 7$

4. _____

5. _____

Chapter 1, Quiz C (Lessons 1-6 and 1-7)

Name the property illustrated by each statement.

1. $3(x + 8) = 3x + 3 \cdot 8$

2. $9 + (1 + 5) = 9 + 6$

3. $38(0) = 0$

4. $aw = 1aw$

1. _____

2. _____

3. _____

4. _____

Simplify each expression, if possible. If not possible, write <u>in simplest form</u>.

5. $6a + 9(a + 3)$

6. $12x^2 - 3x^2$

7. $6a - b + 3ab$

8. $7 + 6(xy + 2m) + 2xy$

9. $4(3x + y) + 7(8y + 4x)$

10. $7c^2 + 9c + c + 14c^2$

5. _____

6. _____

7. _____

8. _____

9. _____

10. _____

Chapter 1, Quiz D (Lessons 1-8 and 1-9)

Name the property illustrated by each statement.

1. $6(x + y) = 6(y + x)$

1. _____

2. $10 + (a + b) = (10 + a) + b$

2. _____

3. $5(6x) = (5 \cdot 6)x$

3. _____

4. $8(v + 6w) = 8v + 48w$

4. _____

5. Identify the graph that best represents the cost of long-distance telephone calls if the rate per minute is $0.10. Explain your answer.

5. _____

_____

_____

a.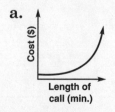

b.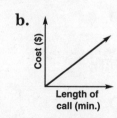

c.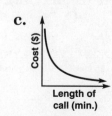

Choose the best answer. Write A, B, C, or D.

1. If $x = \frac{16}{24}$, which of the following is not an equivalent value of x?

   A. $\frac{2}{3}$ **B.** $\frac{3}{4}$ **C.** $\frac{12}{18}$ **D.** $\frac{32}{48}$

   1. _____

2. $5(b - d) =$
   A. $5(d - b)$ **B.** $5b - d$ **C.** $5(b + d)$ **D.** $5b - 5d$

   2. _____

3. Lynn has 4 more books than Jane. If Lynn gives Jane 6 of her books, how many more will Jane have than Lynn?
   A. 2   **B.** 4   **C.** 8   **D.** 10

   3. _____

4. What digit is represented by ☐ in this subtraction problem?

   $$6\bigcirc 4$$
   $$-\ 1\ 3\ 9$$
   $$\overline{\square\ 9\ 5}$$

   A. 2   **B.** 3   **C.** 4   **D.** 5

   4. _____

5. If $4 + 7 + 6 = 4 + 7 + 6 + n$, then $n =$
   A. 0.   **B.** 1.   **C.** 4.   **D.** 6.

   5. _____

6. If $a = 2$, $b = 6$, and $c = 4$, then $\frac{(4a - b)^2}{b + c} =$

   A. 4.   **B.** 0.4.   **C.** 40.   **D.** 0.04

   6. _____

7. How many cents do you have if you have p pennies, d dimes, and b dollar bills?
   A. $p + 10d + 100b$ **B.** $100p + 10d + b$
   C. $10pdb$ **D.** $10db + p$

   7. _____

8. Erin is twice as old as Jim, who is 5 years younger than Alyssa. If Alyssa is 15 years old, how old is Erin?
   A. 20   **B.** 30   **C.** 40   **D.** 50

   8. _____

9. How many eighths of an inch are in 8 inches?
   A. 1   **B.** 8   **C.** 16   **D.** 64

   9. _____

10. How many pens that cost 30¢ each can you buy with c cents?
    A. c **B.** $30c$ **C.** $\frac{30}{c}$ **D.** $\frac{c}{30}$

    10. _____

Chapter 1 Cumulative Review

1

Perform the indicated operations.

1. 27×42

2. $38 + 294 + 86$

3. $492 - 313$

4. $2210 \div 26$

5. $15 + 8.92$

6. $193.656 - 26.38$

7. 86.3×0.46

8. $12.084 \div 4.56$

9. $2.34 + 10.868 + 0.9$

10. $26 - 9.873$

11. $2\frac{1}{3} + 3\frac{2}{3}$

12. $4\frac{7}{8} - 2\frac{5}{8}$

13. $\frac{3}{8} \times 2\frac{7}{18}$

14. $1\frac{2}{3} \div 1\frac{1}{3}$

15. $\frac{2}{3} + \frac{5}{6} - \frac{1}{4}$

16. $12 - 2\frac{3}{7}$

1. _____

2. _____

3. _____

4. _____

5. _____

6. _____

7. _____

8. _____

9. _____

10. _____

11. _____

12. _____

13. _____

14. _____

15. _____

16. _____

Write an algebraic expression for each verbal expression.

17. six less than twice a number

18. two-thirds of the cube of a number

17. _____

18. _____

Find the next three numbers in each sequence.

19. 7, 6.5, 6, 5.5, $\cdots$

20. 2^2, 2^3, 2^4, 2^5, $\cdots$

19. _____

20. _____

Evaluate each expression.

21. $13 - \frac{1}{3}(11 - 5)$

22. $\frac{2x + c}{a}$ when $a = 5$, $c = 7$, $x = 14$

21. _____

22. _____

1

Write the stems that would be used for a stem-and-leaf plot of each set of data.

23. 56, 59, 48, 44, 60, 55, 62, 44

23. _____

24. 127, 112, 124, 133, 127, 127, 110, 115, 120

24. _____

Solve each equation.

25. $13.6 + 18.5 = a$

25. _____

26. $x = 2\frac{1}{2} \div 5$

26. _____

Name the property illustrated by each statement.

27. If $x + 1 = 9$, then $9 = x + 1$.

27. _____

28. $(a + b)c = ac + bc$

28. _____

29. $3(xy) = (3x)y$

29. _____

Simplify.

30. $3y + 2(2y - 1)$

30. _____

31. $5a^2 - 7b + 6a^2$

31. _____

Use the following graph for questions 32 and 33.

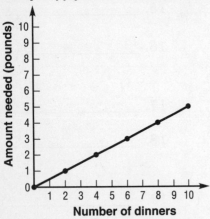

Daily Supply of Fish for Restaurant

32. What does the ordered pair (8, 4) represent?

32. _____

33. How many pounds of fish are needed for 4 dinners?

33. _____

Chapter 1 Answer Key

Form 1A

	Page 1		Page 2
1.	D	13.	C
2.	C		
3.	A	14.	B
4.	C	15.	A
5.	A	16.	D
		17.	A
6.	B	18.	D
7.	C		
		19.	D
8.	D		
9.	C		
10.	B		
11.	A	20.	A
12.	A	Bonus	B

Form 1B

	Page 3		Page 4
1.	B	13.	A
2.	C	14.	D
		15.	D
3.	D		
4.	C	16.	C
5.	B	17.	C
		18.	C
6.	A		
7.	D	19.	C
8.	B		
9.	B		
10.	A	20.	C
11.	C		
12.	B		
		Bonus a.	204
		b.	187

Chapter 1 Answer Key

Form 1C

1. **D**	13. **D**
2. **C**	14. **C**
3. **C**	15. **A**
4. **A**	16. **B**
5. **A**	
	17. **B**
6. **D**	18. **B**
7. **B**	19. **C**
8. **A**	
9. **C**	
10. **D**	20. **B**
11. **A**	
12. **C**	
	Bonus **B**

Form 2A

1. $x^3 + 12$
2. $h - 14$
3. $42 - 2a$
4. 7^4
5. $\frac{1}{4}y^2m^2$
6. $\frac{1}{2}$

7.

8. **729**
9. **34**
10. **27**
11. **45**
12. **28**
13. **80**

14.

Stem	Leaf
5	1 4 5
6	0 1 9
7	0 5 8
8	1 3 3

15. **stem: 9; leaf: 4**

16. **10.6**
17. $\frac{7}{15}$
18. $\frac{17}{8}$
19. **1**

20. **mult. ident.**
21. **assoc. of add.**
22. **distributive property**
23. **assoc. of mult.**
24. **comm. of add.**
25. **substit.**
26. $21x^2$
27. $7n + 3$
28. $19a + 21$
29. $10a^2 + 9a$
30. $30a + 33an + 3$

31. **x- axis: year; y-axis: number of newspapers sold**

32. **(1990, 79,950); (1991, 71,000)**

33.

Bonus **10**

Chapter 1 Answer Key

Form 2B

Page 9

1. $n^2 + 34$
2. $5(2x)$, or $10x$
3. $\frac{1}{2}a - 3$
4. 5^3
5. $2b^3$
6. 5
7.
8. 100
9. 50
10. 4
11. 32
12. 18
13. 7
14. 27, 28, 30, 30, 31, 36, 44
15. stem: 14; leaf: 70
16. 3.25
17. $\frac{7}{8}$
18. $\frac{32}{17}$, or $1\frac{15}{17}$
19. 7

Page 10

20. add. ident.
21. subst.
22. distributive
23. multi. ident.
24. assoc. of mult.
25. symmetric
26. comm. of add.
27. $13x + 7y$
28. $9w + 14w^2$
29. $c^2 + 5d^2 + 3d$
30. $25n + 11$
31. time; temperature (°F)
32. (6, 81); (7, 85)
33.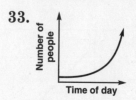

Bonus
a. $-(1 \cdot 9) + 8 + 7$
b. $1^{98} \cdot 7$
c. $1 + (9 - 8) + 7$

Algebra 1

Chapter 1 Answer Key

Form 2C

Page 11

1. $\frac{1}{2}n + 13$
2. x^4
3. $74 - 2n$
4. 10^2
5. $5n^3$
6. 90
7.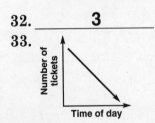
8. 27
9. 7
10. 22
11. 9
12. 9
13. 61
14. 30
15. 31
16. 18
17. $\frac{3}{4}$
18. 4
19. 10
20. mult. prop. of 0
21. commutative

Page 12

22. mult. ident.
23. add. ident.
24. distrib.
25. assoc. of add.
26. comm. of add.
27. $5x - 1$
28. $12a^2$
29. $8p^2 - 6$
30. $6r^2 + 3s^2 + 8r$

31. Robert's 1st game score
32. 3
33.

Bonus
$2[(5 - 1) \div 4 + 1]$

Calculator-Based

Page 13

1. 121
2. 216
3. 729
4. 6
5. 15
6. 6
7. 140
8. 86.3
9. 59
10. 600
11. 1
12. 22.61295
13. 4.5
14. 4
15. 29
16. 89.95
17. $d = 9.2667$
18. $x = 1.513$
19. $b = 1.75$
20. $y = 4888$

Scoring Guide
Chapter 1
Performance Assessment

Level	Specific Criteria
3 Superior	• Shows thorough understanding of the concepts of *evaluating and simplifying mathematical expressions, translating verbal expressions into mathematical expressions,* and *interpreting graphs.* • Uses appropriate strategies to solve problems. • Computations are correct. • Written explanations are exemplary. • Goes beyond requirements of some or all problems.
2 Satisfactory, with Minor Flaws	• Shows understanding of the concepts of *evaluating and simplifying mathematical expressions, translating verbal expressions into mathematical expressions,* and *interpreting graphs.* • Uses appropriate strategies to solve problems. • Computations are mostly correct. • Written explanations are effective. • Satisfies all requirements of problems.
1 Nearly Satisfactory, with Serious Flaws	• Shows understanding of most of the concepts of *evaluating and simplifying mathematical expressions, translating verbal expressions into mathematical expressions,* and *interpreting graphs.* • May not use appropriate strategies to solve problems. • Computations are mostly correct. • Written explanations are satisfactory. • Satisfies most requirements of problems.
0 Unsatisfactory	• Shows little or no understanding of the concepts of *evaluating and simplifying mathematical expressions, translating verbal expressions into mathematical expressions,* and *interpreting graphs.* • May not use appropriate strategies to solve problems. • Computations are incorrect. • Written explanations are not satisfactory. • Does not satisfy requirements of problems.

Chapter 1 Answer Key
Performance Assessment

Sample Solutions: Many of the test questions in this booklet are open-ended, allowing for alternate solutions, differing explanations, and expressions of personal opinion.
What follows are sample solutions that may often vary greatly from correct responses by students. The rubric provided with each chapter test will usually be a better scoring guide than direct comparison of student answers with answers given here.

Page 14

1. a. $A = \frac{1}{2}\pi a^2 + 6(2a) + \frac{2a+6}{2} \cdot 4$

b. $A = \frac{1}{2}\pi a^2 + 12a + 4a + 12$ distributive property

$A = \frac{1}{2}\pi a^2 + 16a + 12$ combining like terms

c. Let $a = 2$. $A = \frac{1}{2}\pi 2^2 + 16(2) + 12$

Perform powers. $A = \frac{1}{2}\pi(4) + 16(2) + 12$

Then multiply. $A = 2\pi + 32 + 12$
Add. $A = 2\pi + 44$
If 3.14 is used for π, $A = 50.28$ in^2.

2. a.   3 $\times$ n $-$ 4
   Three   times   a   number   decreased by   four

      $=$ 25
   is   equal   to   twenty-five.
   Equation: $3n - 4 = 25$

b. $+$ a^2
   The   sum   of the   square of a number   and

         b $=$ 18
   a second   number   is   eighteen.
   Equation: $a^2 + b = 18$

c. x $\times$ 7 $\div$
   A   number   multiplied   by   7   and   divided   by

      3      $=$ 5 $+$ x
   three   gives   five   more than   the   number.
   Equation: $\frac{7x}{3} = x + 5$

d. $\frac{1}{2}$ $\times$ n $+$ n $=$

   One half   of   a   number   added   to   itself   equals

      $2\times$ $n - 5$
   twice   the   difference of the number and five.
   Equation: $\frac{1}{2}n + n = 2(n - 5)$

3. See students' descriptions; students should describe a situation in which a decrease in some amount is followed by a rapid increase and then another decrease.

Chapter 1 Answer Key

Mid-Chapter Test
Page 15

1. $4m^5$
2. $\frac{1}{3}x^2y^4$
3. $5x - 2$
4. $2n^2$
5. 31
6. [grid figure]
7. 91
8. 36.8
9. 480
10. 25.6
11. 5
12. 30
13. 2
14. $1\frac{1}{2}$
15. 911
16. 928
17. 3
18. 69.64
19. $\{2, 3, 5\}$
20. $\left\{\frac{2}{3}\right\}$

Bonus: a. $2^6 = 64$
b. 2^{20}

Quiz A
Page 16

1. $8^4 + 6$
2. $3x^3$
3. 58
4. 42
5. 256
6. 24
7. 49
8. 8
9.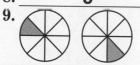
10. 11, 13

Quiz B
Page 16

1.

Stem	Leaf
7	8
8	0 2 5 6 8 8 9
9	0 1 1 2 4 5 5 7 7 9
10	1 6

2. 3.25
3. $1\frac{3}{8}$
4. $\{3, 4, 5\}$
5. $\{5\}$

Quiz C
Page 17

1. distributive
2. substitution
3. zero property of multiplication
4. multiplicative identity
5. $15a + 27$
6. $9x^2$
7. in simplest form
8. $7 + 8xy + 12m$
9. $40x + 60y$
10. $21c^2 + 10c$

Quiz D
Page 17

1. comm. of add.
2. assoc. of add.
3. assoc. of mult.
4. distributive
5. b; cost increases by same amount each minute

Chapter 1 Answer Key

1. __B__

2. __D__

3. __A__

4. __C__

5. __A__

6. __B__

7. __A__

8. __A__

9. __D__

10. __D__

1. __1134__

2. __418__

3. __179__

4. __85__

5. __23.92__

6. __167.276__

7. __39.698__

8. __2.65__

9. __14.108__

10. __16.127__

11. __6__

12. __$2\frac{1}{4}$__

13. __$\frac{43}{48}$__

14. __$1\frac{1}{4}$__

15. __$1\frac{1}{4}$__

16. __$9\frac{4}{7}$__

17. __$2n - 6$__

18. __$\frac{2}{3}x^3$__

19. __5, 4.5, 4__

20. __$2^6, 2^7, 2^8$__

21. __11__

22. __7__

23. __4, 5, 6__

24. __11, 12, 13__

25. __32.1__

26. __$\frac{1}{2}$__

27. __symmetric__

28. __distributive__

29. __assoc.; mult.__

30. __$7y - 2$__

31. __$11a^2 - 7b$__

32. __4 lbs of fish needed for 8 dinners__

33. __2 lbs__

Chapter 2 Test, Form 1A

Write the letter for the correct answer in the blank at the right of each problem.

1. What set of numbers is graphed below?

   A. {even integers}   **B.** $\{-4, -2, 2, 4\}$
   C. $\{\cdots, -4, -2, 0\}$ **D.** $\{4, 2, 0, \cdots\}$

   1. _____

2. Which of the following is the graph of {integers less than 0}?

   A.   **B.**

   C.   **D.**

   2. _____

3. You are making a line plot. Each unit on the line stands for 10 points. Where will you plot 28 points?

   3. _____

4. Use a number line to find the sum of -5 and (-25).
   A. 30   **B.** -30 **C.** 20   **D.** -20

   4. _____

5. What is the value of $-286 + 347$?
   A. 61   **B.** -61 **C.** 633   **D.** -633

   5. _____

6. What is the value of $-53 + |-32|$?
   A. 85   **B.** -85 **C.** 21   **D.** -21

   6. _____

7. Find $9 - (-21)$.
   A. -30 **B.** 30   **C.** -12 **D.** 12

   7. _____

8. What is the value of $-31 + (-26) + 79 + (-8)$?
   A. -144 **B.** -30 **C.** 14   **D.** none of these

   8. _____

9. What fractions are written in order from least to greatest?
   A. $\frac{7}{13}, \frac{6}{11}, \frac{9}{14}$ **B.** $\frac{6}{11}, \frac{7}{13}, \frac{9}{14}$ **C.** $\frac{9}{14}, \frac{6}{11}, \frac{7}{13}$ **D.** $\frac{7}{13}, \frac{9}{14}, \frac{6}{11}$

   9. _____

10. Which of the following is a rational number between $\frac{5}{13}$ and $\frac{7}{9}$?
    A. $\frac{3}{11}$ **B.** $\frac{68}{117}$ **C.** $\frac{104}{117}$ **D.** $\frac{34}{117}$

    10. _____

Exercises 11 through 13: What symbol can replace the __?__ to make each sentence true?

11. $\frac{7}{3}$ __?__ -7

    A. =   B. >   C. <

11. _____

12. $\frac{4}{15}$ __?__ $\frac{5}{19}$

    A. =   B. >   C. <

12. _____

13. $-\frac{11}{5}$ __?__ $-\frac{17}{8}$

    A. =   B. >   C. <

13. _____

14. Find $\begin{bmatrix} -2.8 & 0 \\ 4.7 & -5.1 \end{bmatrix} - \begin{bmatrix} -7.4 & -1.6 \\ 0.9 & -3.2 \end{bmatrix}$.

    A. $\begin{bmatrix} 4.6 & 1.6 \\ 3.8 & -1.9 \end{bmatrix}$ B. $\begin{bmatrix} -10.2 & -1.6 \\ 5.6 & -8.3 \end{bmatrix}$ C. $\begin{bmatrix} -1.2 & 7.4 \\ 7.9 & -6 \end{bmatrix}$ D. $\begin{bmatrix} 7.4 & -1.2 \\ -6 & 7.9 \end{bmatrix}$

14. _____

15. Find $\left(\frac{5}{6}\right)\left(-\frac{3}{25}\right)$.

    A. $-\frac{2}{31}$ B. $\frac{2}{31}$ C. $-\frac{1}{10}$ D. $\frac{1}{10}$

15. _____

16. Find $18 \div \left(-\frac{2}{3}\right)$.

    A. -27 B. 27 C. -12 D. 12

16. _____

17. Simplify $\frac{-3x + 12}{-6}$.

    A. $3x + 2$ B. $-3x - 2$ C. $-\frac{1}{2}x + 2$ D. $\frac{1}{2}x - 2$

17. _____

18. Simplify $\pm \sqrt{0.0081}$.

    A. ± 9 B. ± 0.9 C. ± 0.09 D. ± 0.009

18. _____

19. Which number is irrational?

    A. $0.\overline{35}$ B. $\sqrt{0.25}$ C. $0.12323\cdots$ D. $4.163124\cdots$

19. _____

20. Willie's weight is 2 pounds less than twice his son's weight. Willie weighs 174 pounds. Which of the following equations can be used to find the son's weight?

    A. $174 = 2 + 2x$ B. $174 = 2 - 2x$
    C. $174 = 2x - 2$ D. $174 = 3x - 2$

20. _____

Bonus Simplify $\frac{(-1)^1 + (-1)^3 + (-1)^5 + \cdots + (-1)^{99}}{(-1)^2 + (-1)^4 + (-1)^6 + \cdots + (-1)^{100}}$.

Bonus _____

NAME_____ DATE _____

Chapter 2 Test, Form 1B

Write the letter for the correct answer in the blank at the right of each problem.

1. What set of numbers is graphed below?   1. _____

-5 -4 -3 -2 -1 0 1 2 3

   A. {negative integers}   B. {· · ·, −3, −2, −1, 0}
   C. { −4, −3, −2, −1, 0, · · ·}   D. none of these

2. Which of the following is the graph of {integers greater than −2}?   2. _____
   A.   B.

   C.   D.

3. You are making a line plot. Each unit on the line stands   3. _____
for \$100. Where will you plot \$5.16?

4. Use a number line to find the sum of −9 and (−13).   4. _____
   A. −22   B. 22   C. −4   D. 4

5. What is the value of −387 + 432?   5. _____
   A. −45   B. 45   C. −9   D. 9

6. Find the value of $-|w + 12|$ if $w = -82$.   6. _____
   A. −70   B. 70   C. −94   D. 94

7. Find −0.007 + 0.02.   7. _____
   A. −0.09   B. 0.13   C. −0.027   D. 0.013

8. Simplify $16a + (-7a) + (-12a) + a$.   8. _____
   A. 0   B. $-20a$ C. $-2a$ D. $-3a$

9. Which fractions are written in order from least to greatest?   9. _____

   A. $\frac{4}{25}, \frac{3}{19}, \frac{5}{27}$ B. $\frac{3}{19}, \frac{5}{27}, \frac{4}{25}$ C. $\frac{5}{27}, \frac{4}{25}, \frac{3}{19}$ D. $\frac{3}{19}, \frac{4}{25}, \frac{5}{27}$

10. Which of the following is a rational number between $\frac{2}{9}$ and $\frac{11}{40}$?   10. _____

   A. $\frac{2}{11}$ B. $\frac{9}{31}$ C. $\frac{179}{360}$ D. $\frac{179}{720}$

       Algebra 1

Exercises 11 through 13: What symbol can replace the __?__ to make each sentence true?

11. -4 __?__ $\frac{4}{3}$

    A. $=$ **B.** $<$ **C.** $>$

11. _____

12. $(2.1)(-1)$ __?__ -5

    A. $=$ **B.** $<$ **C.** $>$

12. _____

13. $\frac{3}{4}$ __?__ $\frac{5}{7}$

    A. $=$ **B.** $<$ **C.** $>$

13. _____

14. Find $\begin{bmatrix} 3 & -4 \\ 2.1 & 1.7 \end{bmatrix} + \begin{bmatrix} 6.6 & -1 \\ -5 & 0.5 \end{bmatrix}$.

14. _____

    A. $\begin{bmatrix} 2 & 2.6 \\ 2.6 & -3.3 \end{bmatrix}$ **B.** $\begin{bmatrix} 2.6 & 2 \\ -3.3 & 2.6 \end{bmatrix}$ **C.** $\begin{bmatrix} -2 & -3.5 \\ 8.7 & 0.7 \end{bmatrix}$ **D.** $\begin{bmatrix} 9.6 & -5 \\ -2.9 & 2.2 \end{bmatrix}$

15. Find $\left(-\frac{1}{3}\right)\left(-\frac{6}{7}\right)$.

15. _____

    A. $\frac{7}{10}$ **B.** $\frac{2}{7}$ **C.** $-\frac{2}{7}$ **D.** $-\frac{7}{10}$

16. Find $-\frac{1}{4} \div 6$.

16. _____

    A. $-\frac{1}{24}$ **B.** $-\frac{3}{2}$ **C.** $\frac{1}{24}$ **D.** $\frac{3}{2}$

17. Simplify $\frac{24k - 6}{-6}$.

17. _____

    A. $-4k - 6$ **B.** $-4k + 1$ **C.** $-24k - 1$ **D.** $24k - 1$

18. Simplify $\sqrt{\frac{81}{256}}$.

18. _____

    A. $\frac{9}{16}$ **B.** $\pm\frac{9}{16}$ **C.** $\frac{3}{4}$ **D.** $\pm\frac{3}{4}$

19. Which number is irrational?

19. _____

    A. $\sqrt{\frac{4}{9}}$ **B.** $9.737737773\cdots$

    C. $8.888\cdots$ **D.** They are all irrational.

20. Which equation can be used to solve the following problem? The Sears Tower in Chicago is 40 feet taller than the Empire State Building in New York. The sum of their heights is 2868 feet. How tall is the Empire State Building?

20. _____

    A. $x + 40 = 2868$ **B.** $x = 2868 - 40$

    C. $x + (x + 40) = 2868$ **D.** $x - 40 = 2868$

Bonus What is the opposite of the reciprocal of the multiplicative inverse of the additive inverse of 5?

Bonus _____

2

Chapter 2 Test, Form 1C

Write the letter for the correct answer in the blank at the right of each problem.

1. What set of numbers is graphed below?

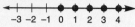

   A. {0, 1, 2, 3, 4}   B. {· · ·, 0, 1, 2, 3, 4}
   C. {integers}   D. {0, 1, 2, 3, 4,· · ·}

   1. _____

2. Which of the following is the graph of {integers greater than 1}?

   A. ← | | | | |●| | | →
      -3 -2 -1 0 1 2 3 4

   B. ← ●|●|●|●| | | | →
      -3 -2 -1 0 1 2 3 4

   C. ← | | | | | |●|●|●| →
      -3 -2 -1 0 1 2 3 4

   D. ← | | | | |○━━━━→
      -3 -2 -1 0 1 2 3 4

   2. _____

3. You are making a line plot. Each unit on the line stands for 10 points. Where will you plot 50 points?

   ```
        A.      B.        C.  D.
      | | | | | | |
      1   2   3   4   5   6
   ```

   3. _____

4. Use a number line to find the sum of −4 and (−5).
   A. 9   B. −9   C. 1   D. −1

   4. _____

5. What is the value of −50 + 120?
   A. 70   B. −70   C. 170   D. −170

   5. _____

6. What is the value of −25 + |−10|?
   A. −15   B. 15   C. −35   D. 35

   6. _____

7. Find −2 − (−7).
   A. −9   B. 9   C. −5   D. 5

   7. _____

8. What is the value of −15 + 7 + (−4)?
   A. −26   B. −4   C. −12   D. none of these

   8. _____

9. What fractions are written in order from least to greatest?
   A. $\frac{1}{2}, \frac{2}{3}, \frac{3}{5}$ B. $\frac{2}{3}, \frac{3}{5}, \frac{1}{2}$ C. $\frac{3}{5}, \frac{1}{2}, \frac{2}{3}$ D. $\frac{1}{2}, \frac{3}{5}, \frac{2}{3}$

   9. _____

10. Which of the following is a rational number between $\frac{1}{2}$ and $\frac{3}{4}$?

    A. $\frac{2}{7}$ B. $\frac{1}{3}$ C. $\frac{5}{8}$ D. $\frac{7}{9}$

    10. _____

Algebra 1

Exercises 11 through 13: What symbol can replace the __?__ to make each sentence true?

11. $\frac{5}{3}$ __?__ -5

    A. $=$ B. $>$ C. $<$

11. _____

12. $\frac{2}{3}$ __?__ $\frac{5}{6}$

    A. $=$ B. $>$ C. $<$

12. _____

13. $\frac{-1}{2}$ __?__ $\frac{-3}{6}$

    A. $=$ B. $>$ C. $<$

13. _____

14. Find $\frac{-1}{4} - \frac{3}{8}$.

    A. $\frac{-5}{8}$ B. $\frac{-1}{8}$ C. $\frac{1}{8}$ D. $\frac{5}{8}$

14. _____

15. Find $\left(\frac{-2}{3}\right)\left(\frac{-3}{4}\right)$.

    A. $\frac{-5}{7}$ B. $\frac{5}{7}$ C. $\frac{1}{2}$ D. $\frac{-1}{2}$

15. _____

16. Find $-9 \div \left(\frac{3}{4}\right)$.

    A. 12 B. -12 C. 1 D. -1

16. _____

17. Simplify $\frac{12x - 8}{4}$.

    A. $12x - 2$ B. $-12x + 2$ C. $3x - 2$ D. $-3x + 2$

17. _____

18. Simplify $\sqrt{\frac{49}{100}}$.

    A. $\pm\frac{7}{10}$ B. $\frac{7}{10}$ C. $\frac{7}{50}$ D. $\pm\frac{7}{50}$

18. _____

19. Which number is irrational?

    A. $0.44444\cdots$ B. $\sqrt{36}$ C. $\frac{3}{5}$ D. All are rational.

19. _____

20. Wanda scored 85 on a test. This was 17 points more than Winnie. Which of the following equations can be used to find Winnie's test score?

    A. $85 = 17 + x$ B. $85 + 17 = x$ C. $x - 17 = 85$ D. $17 - x = 85$

20. _____

Bonus Simplify $\sqrt{\sqrt{\sqrt{256}}}$.

Bonus _____

2 Chapter 2 Test, Form 2A

Graph the following sets on the number lines provided.

1. $\{\cdots, -2, -1, 0, 1\}$

1.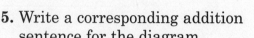

2. {negative integers}

2. ────────────────
-4-3-2-1 0 1 2 3 4

3. the solution set of $x > -2$

3. ────────────────
-4-3-2-1 0 1 2 3 4

4. Name the coordinate of point P.

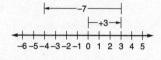

4. _____

5. Write a corresponding addition sentence for the diagram.

5. _____

6. Make a line plot of the data listed below.
53,000; 51,000; 46,000; 45,000; 46,000; 46,000; 48,000

6. ────────────────

Find each sum or difference.

7. $35 + (-27)$

8. $-1471 + (-3296)$

7. _____

8. _____

9. $-2.6 + 0.49$

10. $-45 + (-91) + 23 + (-9)$

9. _____

10. _____

11. $-11 - 19$

12. $\begin{bmatrix} 7 & -1 \\ -5 & 0 \end{bmatrix} - \begin{bmatrix} -8 & 2 \\ 11 & -5 \end{bmatrix}$

11. _____

12. _____

13. $\frac{9}{16} + \left(-\frac{3}{4}\right)$

14. $\left(-\frac{3}{7}\right) + \left(-\frac{6}{5}\right)$

13. _____

14. _____

15. $|-38 + 21|$

16. $-\left|-18 + |-12|\right|$

15. _____

16. _____

Evaluate each expression if $a = -\frac{11}{5}$, $b = 20$, and $c = 361$.

17. $|a|$

18. $c - ab$

17. _____

18. _____

19. $\frac{3}{5} - a$

20. $-\sqrt{c}$

19. _____

20. _____

Replace each __?__ with <, >, or = to make each sentence true.

21. 3 __?__ − 8   21. _____

22. (3.6)(−0.4) __?__ − 14.4   22. _____

23. $\frac{7}{11}$ __?__ $\frac{2}{3}$ 23. _____

24. Find a number between $\frac{3}{16}$ and $\frac{5}{12}$.   24. _____

25. Find $\frac{1}{3}\begin{bmatrix} 9 & 15 & 3 \\ -6 & 2 & -12 \end{bmatrix}$.   25. _____

Simplify.

26. $\frac{7(-32)}{-4}$ 27. $\frac{3}{4}\left(-\frac{1}{2}\right) - \left(-\frac{3}{2}\right)\left(\frac{1}{4}\right)$ 26. _____

                                                                                            27. _____

28. $\frac{2}{5}(20a - 10b) + \frac{1}{9}(27a - 18b)$ 29. $\frac{-5}{\frac{3}{7}}$ 28. _____

                                                                                            29. _____

30. $\frac{14y + 35}{-7}$ 31. $\pm\sqrt{\frac{16}{625}}$ 30. _____

                                                                                            31. _____

32. Which of the following numbers are irrational?   32. _____

    −4   2.$\overline{73}$ −$\sqrt{20}$ $\sqrt{\frac{36}{49}}$ 3.838838883· · ·

33. Define the variable. Then write an equation for the   33. _____
    following. Do *not* try to solve.
    In captivity, the average life span of an elephant is 25 years
    more than that of an elk. The sum of the two ages is 55 years.
    What is the average life span of an elk in captivity?

Bonus   Melinda's father pays her 10 cents for each   **Bonus a.** _____
right answer on her algebra homework, and he collects 7
cents from her for each wrong answer. After her 34 problems   **b.** _____
were corrected, they did not owe each other anything.
    a. If *c* stands for the number of right answers, write an   **c.** _____
        expression for the number of wrong answers.
                                                                                        d. _____
    b. Write an expression for the money Melinda collects
        for her right answers.

    c. Write an expression for the money Melinda owes her
        father for her wrong answers.

    d. Write an equation for this problem using your answers
        from **a, b,** and **c.**

2

Chapter 2 Test, Form 2B

Graph the following sets on the number lines provided.

1. {integers greater than -1}

1. <number line from -4 to 5>

2. {1, 3, 5, $\cdots$}

2. <number line from -4 to 5>

3. the solution set of $y \neq 5$

3. <number line from -3 to 6>

4. Name the coordinate of point P.   <number line from -4 to 4 with point at 3>

4. _____

5. Write a corresponding addition sentence for the diagram.

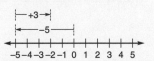

5. _____

6. Make a line plot of the average monthly temperatures for New York City as shown in the table below.

6. <number line>

Month	Jan.	Feb.	Mar.	Apr.	May	June	July	Aug.	Sept.
N.Y.C. (°F)	32	33	41	53	62	71	77	75	68

Find each sum or difference.

7. $-8 + (-8)$

8. $-279 + 191$

7. _____

8. _____

9. $\frac{3}{4} + \left(-\frac{7}{12}\right)$

10. $-6.4 + (-0.64) + 64$

9. _____

10. _____

11. $\begin{bmatrix} 0 & -2 \\ 6 & 4 \end{bmatrix} + \begin{bmatrix} 5 & 3 \\ -1 & 9 \end{bmatrix}$

12. $0 - 57$

11. _____

12. _____

13. $|-10 + (-2)|$

14. $-6 + (20 - 71)$

13. _____

14. _____

15. $\frac{5}{9} + \frac{2}{3} + \left(-\frac{4}{27}\right)$

15. _____

16. $15.62 + (-10) + (-3.8) + (0.52)$

16. _____

Evaluate each expression if $a = 64$, $m = -2$, and $n = -0.7$.

17. am

18. $|a - m|$

17. _____

18. _____

19. $n - m$

20. $\pm\sqrt{a}$

19. _____

20. _____

Replace each ___?___ with <, >, or = to make each sentence true.

21. -9 ___?___ -1

22. $(6.4) - (-0.04)$ ___?___ 6.44

21. _____

22. _____

23. $\dfrac{5}{6}$ ___?___ $\dfrac{13}{15}$

23. _____

24. Arrange these fractions in order from least to greatest.

$\dfrac{11}{21}, \dfrac{7}{15}, \dfrac{8}{17}$

24. _____

25. Find $-3\begin{bmatrix} -1.5 & 2 \\ 7 & -4 \end{bmatrix}$.

25. _____

Simplify.

26. $-\dfrac{5}{8}(16)(3)(-4)$ **27.** $-\dfrac{5}{12} - \dfrac{3}{10}$

26. _____

27. _____

28. $(0.35)(0.6) - 5(-0.8)$ **29.** $\dfrac{-6}{\frac{2}{9}}$

28. _____

29. _____

30. $\dfrac{30w - 18}{-6}$ **31.** $\sqrt{\dfrac{64}{81}}$

30. _____

31. _____

32. Which of the following numbers are rational?

$\sqrt{49}$ $\pm\sqrt{7}$ $2.\overline{23}$ $2.040506\cdots$

32. _____

33. Define the variable, then write an equation for the following. Do *not* try to solve.

During the year, a school gained 54 students who moved into the district. It lost 29 students who moved out of the district and lost 42 students who dropped out. The final number of students was 2538. How many students began the year?

33. _____

Bonus   Most historical records do not include a year zero. Thus, the year before 1 A.D. is labeled 1 B.C., not 0 B.C. If Rome celebrated its 1000th anniversary in 248 A.D., when was Rome founded?

Bonus _____

② Chapter 2 Test, Form 2C

Graph the following sets on the number lines provided.

1. {−2, −1, 0, 1, 2, 3}   2. {positive integers}

1. number line −3 −2 −1 0 1 2 3 4

2. number line −3 −2 −1 0 1 2 3 4

3. the solution set of $x > 1$

3. number line −3 −2 −1 0 1 2 3 4

4. Name the coordinate of point P.   number line with point P at 2: −3 −2 −1 0 1 2 3 4

4. _____

5. Write a corresponding addition sentence for the diagram.   diagram: ←−4→, 6→, number line −3 −2 −1 0 1 2 3 4 5 6 7

5. _____

6. Make a line plot of the data listed below.
4, 7, 5, 4, 2, 4, 6, 7

6. number line 2 3 4 5 6 7

Find each sum or difference.

7. $25 + (-15)$ 8. $-143 + (-143)$

7. _____

8. _____

9. $\dfrac{1}{2} - \left(\dfrac{-1}{4}\right)$ 10. $-2.45 + 6.8$

9. _____

10. _____

11. $-4 - 7$ 12. $5 - 13$

11. _____

12. _____

13. $-18.5 - 10.25$ 14. $\dfrac{5}{9} + \dfrac{2}{3} + \left(\dfrac{-4}{9}\right)$

13. _____

14. _____

15. $|-9 + 5|$ 16. $20 - 14 + 3 - 10$

15. _____

16. _____

Evaluate each expression if $a = -\dfrac{1}{7}$, $b = 49$, and $c = 12$.

17. $14 - c$ 18. $|c - b|$

17. _____

18. _____

19. $\dfrac{6}{7} - a$ 20. $-\sqrt{b}$

19. _____

20. _____

Replace each ___?___ with <, >, or = to make each sentence true.

21. -5 ___?___ 2

22. $(0.3)(-0.7)$ ___?___ -2.1

21. _____

22. _____

23. $\dfrac{3}{5}$ ___?___ $\dfrac{5}{8}$

23. _____

24. Arrange these fractions in order from least to greatest. $\dfrac{5}{6}, \dfrac{2}{3}, \dfrac{4}{5}$

24. _____

25. Find $2\begin{bmatrix} 4 & -1 \\ 5 & 0 \end{bmatrix}$.

25. _____

Simplify.

26. $\dfrac{6(-5)}{10}$

27. $\dfrac{-4}{5} \div 4$

26. _____

27. _____

28. $5a + \dfrac{1}{2}(2a - 6)$

29. $(-0.6)(0.9) + 0.54$

28. _____

29. _____

30. $\dfrac{12w - 10}{-2}$

31. $\sqrt{\dfrac{16}{25}}$

30. _____

31. _____

32. Which of the following numbers are rational?
$\sqrt{25}$ 3.65 $\sqrt{2}$ $1.010010001\cdots$

32. _____

33. Define the variable, then write an equation for the following. Do *not* try to solve. Seven boys and six girls were added to the cast of the school play. This made a total number of 25 students in the play. How many students were in the play originally?

33. _____

Bonus Two students started at 0 on a number line. One student walked to the left a units and the other student walked to the right b units. Write an expression that describes how far apart the students are.

Bonus _____

2

Chapter 2 Calculator-Based Test

Find each sum or difference.

1. $-2583 + 967$

1. _____

2. $17,961 + (-8455)$

2. _____

3. $-4972 - (-6972)$

3. _____

4. $45,486 - 12,955$

4. _____

Use <, >, or = to make each sentence true.

5. $\dfrac{28}{69}$ _____ $\dfrac{41}{89}$

5. _____

6. $(1.46)(-0.73)$ _____ $(-0.025)(40)$

6. _____

Simplify.

7. $\left(\dfrac{40}{63}\right)\left(\dfrac{-27}{50}\right)$

7. _____

8. $\dfrac{-12}{23} - \dfrac{11}{25}$

8. _____

9. $-6.04 \div (-0.0302)$

9. _____

10. $0.03(21x - 2.5) + 4(0.12x - 1.75)$

10. _____

11. $\dfrac{-51}{95} \div \left(\dfrac{-119}{57}\right)$

11. _____

12. $\dfrac{11}{15} - \dfrac{13}{16} + \left(\dfrac{-19}{24}\right)$

12. _____

Find each square root. Round to the nearest hundredth, if necessary.

13. $\sqrt{5000}$

13. _____

14. $-\sqrt{0.000004}$

14. _____

15. $\sqrt{1,234,321}$

15. _____

16. Which of the following numbers are integers?

    $-\sqrt{1000}$ $\dfrac{-441}{21}$ $\dfrac{700}{-0.035}$

16. _____

NAME_____ DATE _____

Chapter 2 Performance Assessment

Instructions: *Demonstrate your knowledge by giving a clear, concise solution to each problem. Be sure to include all relevant drawings and justify your answers. You may show your solution in more than one way or investigate beyond the requirements of the problem.*

1. Draw a diagram to show each sum or difference.

   a. $4 + (-7)$ **b.** $-3 - 4$ **c.** $3\frac{1}{2} - \left(-2\frac{3}{4}\right)$ **d.** $|5| - |-8|$

2. Ching, Alex, Ellen, and Ashley are playing in a local golf tournament. For the first two days of the tournament, both of Ching's scores were under -2. Alex had scores under par, or zero. Ellen's scores were less than Ching's scores and Ashley's scores were par or greater.

   a. Draw a graph showing possible scores for Ching.

   b. Are Ashley's scores greater than Ching's? Explain your reasoning.

   c. Were Alex's scores greater than Ching's? Explain your reasoning.

   d. Were Ellen's scores less than Ashley's? Explain your reasoning.

3. Replace each ● with <, >, or = to make a true sentence. Explain your reasoning.

   a. $\left(-\frac{3}{4}\right)\left(\frac{7}{8}\right) ● \left(-\frac{4}{5}\right)\left(-\frac{5}{6}\right)$

   b. $(-5)(7)(-3) - \left(\frac{2}{3}\right)(360) ● \frac{3}{8}(-24)(5)(3)$

   c. $-8 \div \left(-\frac{9}{14}\right) ● \frac{7}{\frac{2}{5}}$

   d. $\frac{-15x + 21}{3} ● \frac{6 - 10x}{2}$

4. Write a short paragraph describing the set of data shown in the line plot below.

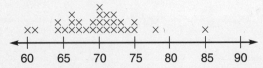

NAME_____ DATE _____

Chapter 2 Mid-Chapter Test (Lessons 2-1 through 2-5)

Name the set of numbers graphed.

1.

2.

1. _____

2. _____

3. Graph the following set on the number line provided. {odd integers less than 2}

3.

4. Make a line plot for the data. 15, 22, 8, 13, 15, 20, 16

4.

Find each sum or difference.

5. $-61 + 18$

6. $-2.6 - 3.5$

7. $|-17 + (-5)|$

8. $38 + (-38)$

9. $12 - (-63)$

10. $\frac{1}{5} - \frac{1}{2}$

11. $\begin{bmatrix} 5 & -2 \\ 3 & 8 \end{bmatrix} - \begin{bmatrix} 1 & -4 \\ -3 & 6 \end{bmatrix}$

12. $-18 + 46 + (-5) + (-21)$

5. _____

6. _____

7. _____

8. _____

9. _____

10. _____

11. _____

12. _____

Evaluate each expression if $m = -2$ and $y = -51$.

13. $|-12 + m|$ 14. $-39 - y$

13. _____

14. _____

Replace each __?__ with <, >, or = to make each sentence true.

15. -7 __?__ -1

16. 3 __?__ $\frac{14}{3}$

17. $\frac{2}{3}$ __?__ $\frac{5}{8}$

18. 0.37 __?__ -2.65

19. Find a number between $\frac{5}{6}$ and $\frac{3}{4}$.

20. Arrange the fractions in order from least to greatest. $\frac{1}{3}, \frac{3}{8}, \frac{4}{9}$

15. _____

16. _____

17. _____

18. _____

19. _____

20. _____

Bonus Julius Caesar was born in 100 B.C. and died in 44 B.C. How many years did he live?

Bonus _____

Name the set of numbers graphed.

1.
   $-3\ -2\ -1\ 0\ 1\ 2\ 3\ 4$

2.
   $-4\ -3\ -2\ -1\ 0\ 1\ 2\ 3\ 4$

1. _____

2. _____

Graph each set of numbers on the number line provided.

3. $\{-5, 2, 4\}$ 4. $\{2, 4, 6, 8, \cdots\}$

3.
   $-5\ -4\ -3\ -2\ -1\ 0\ 1\ 2\ 3\ 4$

4.
   $-2\ -1\ 0\ 1\ 2\ 3\ 4\ 5\ 6$

5. Make a line plot of the data.
   60, 75, 58, 65, 66, 70, 72, 69, 59, 60, 67, 66

5.
   $55\ 57\ 59\ 61\ 63\ 65\ 67\ 69\ 71\ 73\ 75\ 77$

Find each sum or difference.

6. $5 + (-2)$ 7. $-54 - 23$ 8. $-151 + 47$

6. _____

7. _____

9. $-8n - (-12n)$

8. _____

9. _____

10. Evaluate $-|a + y|$ if $a = -17$ and $y = -13$.

10. _____

Replace each __?__ with <, >, or = to make each sentence true.

1. 4 __?__ -8 2. -0.66 __?__ -0.67

1. _____

2. _____

3. $\frac{5}{13}$ __?__ $\frac{6}{14}$ 4. $\frac{2.3}{2}$ __?__ $\frac{6.9}{6}$

3. _____

4. _____

5. Write the following fractions in order from least to greatest. $\frac{5}{13}, \frac{4}{23}, \frac{7}{27}$

5. _____

6. Find a number between $\frac{3}{7}$ and $\frac{5}{6}$.

6. _____

Find each sum or difference.

7. $2.7 + (-1.372)$ 8. $-\frac{3}{8} + \left(-\frac{5}{4}\right)$

7. _____

8. _____

9. $\frac{2}{5} - \left(-\frac{5}{7}\right)$ 10. $-8.6m - 2.4m$

9. _____

10. _____

NAME_____ DATE _____

Chapter 2, Quiz C (Lessons 2-6 and 2-7)

Find each product.

1. $(7)(-31)$

2. $\left(-\dfrac{1}{2}\right)\left(-\dfrac{2}{3}\right)\left(\dfrac{6}{7}\right)$

1. _____

2. _____

Simplify.

3. $4.1(-5.3) + 2.4(-1.04)$

4. $(-3a)(-4b) - (-2a)(7b)$

3. _____

4. _____

5. $6(7x + 2x) - 5(3x + 4x)$

6. $\dfrac{-42}{6}$

5. _____

6. _____

7. $\dfrac{49a}{-7}$

8. $\dfrac{(-5)(4)}{-2}$

7. _____

8. _____

9. $\dfrac{-9}{\frac{3}{2}}$

10. $\dfrac{-9x - 15y}{-3}$

9. _____

10. _____

NAME_____ DATE _____

Chapter 2, Quiz D (Lessons 2-8 and 2-9)

Find each square root. Use a calculator if necessary. Round to the nearest hundredth if the result is not a whole number.

1. $\sqrt{144}$

2. $\sqrt{0.0036}$

1. _____

2. _____

3. $\sqrt{169}$

4. $-\sqrt{49}$

3. _____

4. _____

5. $\pm\sqrt{\dfrac{121}{25}}$

6. $\sqrt{54}$

5. _____

6. _____

7. Graph $n \geq -4$ on the number line provided.

7. ←++++++++++++→
   $-5\,-4\,-3\,-2\,-1\ 0\ 1\ 2\ 3$

8. Which of the following numbers are rational?
   0.465 -2.1 $3.89\overline{2}$ $43.56143562435634\cdots$

8. _____

Define a variable. Then write an equation for the problem. Do _not_ try to solve.

9. A science-fiction book has three times as many pages as a mystery book. Together the books have 624 pages. How many pages are there in the mystery book?

9. _____

10. It takes a plane about 3 hours to fly 1500 miles. What is the approximate speed of the plane?

10. _____

NAME_____ DATE _____

Chapter 2 Standardized Test Practice

Choose the best answer. Write A, B, C, or D.

1. If $x = \frac{-3}{12}$ which of the following is not a value of x?

   A. $\frac{-1}{4}$ **B.** $-\frac{1}{4}$ **C.** $-\left(\frac{-1}{4}\right)$ **D.** $-\left(\frac{-1}{-4}\right)$

                                                       1. _____

2. $-6(a - c) =$ 2. _____

   A. $6(c - a)$ **B.** $-6a - 6c$ **C.** $-6(c - a)$ **D.** $6(a + c)$

3. The sum of three odd numbers is   3. _____

   A. always odd.   **B.** sometimes odd.

   C. always even.   **D.** always a prime number.

4. How many integers between 100 and 200 are divisible by 3?   4. _____

   A. 32   **B.** 33   **C.** 34   **D.** 66

5. What is the value of x in the sequence 3, 6, 18, 72, x, 2160?   5. _____

   A. 75   **B.** 144   **C.** 350   **D.** 360

6. In a group of 28 animals, 12 are dogs. What part of the group   6. _____
   does not consist of dogs?

   A. $\frac{3}{7}$ **B.** $\frac{3}{4}$ **C.** $\frac{1}{2}$ **D.** $\frac{4}{7}$

7. If $16(24 + y) = 1600$, then $y =$ 7. _____

   A. 66.   **B.** 76.   **C.** 1200.   **D.** 1216.

8. $\dfrac{7(1.4 - 7.9) - (1.4 - 7.9)}{-3} =$ 8. _____

   A. -39 **B.** -13 **C.** 13   **D.** 39

9. If $2x = 11$, the value of $6x - 3$ is   9. _____

   A. 0.   **B.** 19.   **C.** 30.   **D.** 36.

10. Loa is two years younger than three times Mary's age. If   10. _____
    Mary's age in six years will be $3x - 6$, what is Loa's age now?

    A. $6x - 12$ **B.** $9x - 38$ **C.** $9x - 12$ **D.** $6x - 8$

Write an algebraic expression for each verbal expression. (Lesson 1-1)

1. 7 more than the square of a number

1. _____

2. 5 less than 4 times a number

2. _____

Evaluate each expression. (Lesson 1-3)

3. $6 - 2^2 + 14 \cdot 3 \div 7$

3. _____

4. $3a^2(a^2 - b^2)$ if $a = 4$ and $b = 3$

4. _____

Solve each equation. (Lesson 1-5)

5. $a = \frac{3}{5} \cdot 15$

5. _____

6. $\frac{84 \div 14}{27 \div 9} = m$

6. _____

Name the property illustrated by each statement. (Lessons 1-6, 1-7, and 1-8)

7. If $x = 7 + 2$ and $7 + 2 = w$, then $x = w$.

7. _____

8. $6 + (7 \cdot 5) = 6 + 35$

8. _____

9. $3(4a + b) = 12a + 3b$

9. _____

10. $(7 + x) + a = (x + 7) + a$

10. _____

Simplify. (Lesson 1-7)

11. $6a^2 + 11a^2 - 3$

11. _____

12. $2(2x + y) + 6(x + 2y)$

12. _____

Translate each sentence into an equation, inequality, or formula. (Lesson 2-9)

13. y is the product of a and b, increased by c.

13. _____

14. The number m equals the square of the difference of n and p.

14. _____

Replace each __?__ with <, >, or = to make each sentence true. (Lesson 2-4)

15. -3 __?__ -6

15. _____

16. $\frac{4}{13}$ __?__ $\frac{3}{11}$

16. _____

17. Name the set of numbers graphed below. (Lesson 2-1)

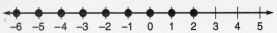

17. _____

18. Graph $\{-3, -1, 0, 2\}$ on the number line provided. (Lesson 2-1)

18. ⟵ +++++++ ⟶
    -4 -3 -2 -1 0 1 2 3

19. Graph the solution set of $w \le 3$ on the number line. (Lesson 2-1)

19. ⟵ +++++++ ⟶
    -3 -2 -1 0 1 2 3 4

Find each sum or difference. (Lessons 2-3 and 2-5)

20. $-15 + a$ if $a = -10$

20. _____

21. $-13 + 6 + (-8)$

21. _____

22. $4m + (-3m) + (-12m)$

22. _____

23. $\begin{bmatrix} -3 & -\frac{2}{7} \\ 2.7 & 12 \end{bmatrix} + \begin{bmatrix} -18 & \frac{11}{14} \\ -5.4 & 6 \end{bmatrix}$

23. _____

24. Make a line plot for the following data. (Lesson 2-2)
21, 20, 29, 29, 22, 20, 24, 27, 29, 26.

24. ⟵ ++++++++++ ⟶
    20   25   30

Find each scalar product. (Lesson 2-6)

25. $4 \begin{bmatrix} -3 & -\frac{3}{4} \\ 2.6 & 12 \end{bmatrix}$

25. _____

26. $-\frac{2}{3} \begin{bmatrix} 9.6 & \frac{9}{4} & -12 \end{bmatrix}$

26. _____

27. Find $\sqrt{38}$ to the nearest hundredth. (Lesson 2-8)

27. _____

Simplify. (Lessons 2-6 and 2-7)

28. $5(-7) + (-3)(6)$

28. _____

29. $3(5t - t) + 4(2t + t)$

29. _____

30. $\left(-\frac{1}{3}\right)\left(\frac{3}{7}\right) + \left(\frac{5}{6}\right)\left(\frac{12}{35}\right)$

30. _____

31. $\frac{5a - 10}{5}$

31. _____

Define a variable, then write an equation for each problem. Do not try to solve. (Lesson 2-9)

32. Wayne bought a suit on sale and saved $15.35. The regular price was $139.29. What was the sale price?

32. _____

33. Lisa is 5 years older than Susan. The sum of their ages is 25. How old is Susan?

33. _____

Chapter 2 Answer Key

Form 1A

Page 29	Page 30
1. __B__	11. __B__
	12. __B__
2. __A__	13. __C__
	14. __A__
3. __C__	
4. __B__	15. __C__
5. __A__	16. __A__
6. __D__	17. __D__
7. __B__	18. __C__
8. __C__	19. __D__
9. __A__	20. __C__
10. __B__	Bonus __−1__

Form 1B

Page 31	Page 32
1. __B__	11. __B__
	12. __C__
2. __D__	13. __C__
	14. __D__
3. __A__	15. __B__
4. __A__	16. __A__
5. __B__	17. __B__
6. __A__	18. __A__
7. __D__	19. __B__
8. __C__	20. __C__
9. __D__	
10. __D__	Bonus __5__

Chapter 2 Answer Key

Form 1C

Page 33

1. **D**

2. **C**

3. **C**

4. **B**

5. **A**

6. **A**

7. **D**

8. **C**

9. **D**

10. **C**

Page 34

11. **B**

12. **C**

13. **A**

14. **A**

15. **C**

16. **B**

17. **C**

18. **B**

19. **D**

20. **A**

Bonus **2**

Form 2A

Page 35

1.

2.

3.

4. **-2**

5. **$3 + (-7) = -4$**

6.

7. **8**

8. **-4767**

9. **-2.11**

10. **-122**

11. **-30**

12. $\begin{bmatrix} 15 & -3 \\ -16 & 5 \end{bmatrix}$

13. $\dfrac{-3}{16}$

14. $\dfrac{-57}{35}$, or $-1\dfrac{22}{35}$

15. **17**

16. **-6**

17. $\dfrac{11}{5}$

18. **405**

19. $\dfrac{14}{5}$, or $2\dfrac{4}{5}$

20. **-19**

Page 36

21. **$>$**

22. **$>$**

23. **$<$**

24. **sample:** $\dfrac{29}{96}$

25. $\begin{bmatrix} 3 & 5 & 1 \\ -2 & \frac{2}{3} & -4 \end{bmatrix}$

26. **56**

27. **0**

28. **$11a - 6b$**

29. $\dfrac{-35}{3}$, or $-11\dfrac{2}{3}$

30. **$-2y - 5$**

31. $\pm\dfrac{4}{25}$

32. **$-\sqrt{20}$, 3.838838883···**

33. **Let $e =$ life span of elk; $e + (e + 25) = 55$.**

Bonus a. **$34 - c$**

b. **$10c$**

c. **$7(34 - c)$**

d. **$10c = 7(34 - c)$**

Chapter 2 Answer Key

Form 2B

Page 37

1.

2.

3.

4. **3**

5. **$-5 + 3 = -2$**

6.

7. **-16**

8. **-88**

9. **$\dfrac{1}{6}$**

10. **56.96**

11. **$\begin{bmatrix} 5 & 1 \\ 5 & 13 \end{bmatrix}$**

12. **-57**

13. **12**

14. **-57**

15. **$\dfrac{29}{27}$, or $1\dfrac{2}{27}$**

16. **2.34**

17. **-128**

18. **66**

19. **1.3**

20. **± 8**

Page 38

21. **$<$**

22. **$=$**

23. **$<$**

24. **$\dfrac{7}{15}, \dfrac{8}{17}, \dfrac{11}{21}$**

25. **$\begin{bmatrix} 4.5 & -6 \\ -21 & 12 \end{bmatrix}$**

26. **120**

27. **$\dfrac{-43}{60}$**

28. **4.21**

29. **-27**

30. **$-5w + 3$**

31. **$\dfrac{8}{9}$**

32. **$\sqrt{49}, 2.\overline{23}$**

33. **Let s = number of beginning students;
$s + 54 - 29 - 42 = 2538$.**

Bonus **753 B.C.**

Chapter 2 Answer Key

Form 2C		Calculator-Based
Page 39	Page 40	Page 41

Form 2C

Page 39

1. (number line, -3 to 4)

2. (number line, -3 to 4)

3. (number line, -3 to 4)

4. **2**

5. $6 + (-4) = 2$

6. (number line, 2 to 7)

7. **10**

8. **−286**

9. $\dfrac{3}{4}$

10. **4.35**

11. **−11**

12. **−8**

13. **−28.75**

14. $\dfrac{7}{9}$

15. **4**

16. **−1**

17. **2**

18. **37**

19. **1**

20. **−7**

Page 40

21. **<**

22. **>**

23. **<**

24. $\dfrac{2}{3}, \dfrac{4}{5}, \dfrac{5}{6}$

25. $\begin{bmatrix} 8 & -2 \\ 10 & 0 \end{bmatrix}$

26. **−3**

27. $\dfrac{-1}{5}$

28. $6a - 3$

29. **0**

30. $-6w + 5$

31. $\dfrac{4}{5}$

32. $\sqrt{25}, 3.65$

33. **Let n = number of students; $n + 7 + 6 = 25$.**

Bonus $|a - b|$ or $|b - a|$

Calculator-Based

Page 41

1. **−1616**

2. **9506**

3. **2000**

4. **32,531**

5. **<**

6. **<**

7. $\dfrac{-12}{35}$

8. $\dfrac{-553}{575}$

9. **200**

10. $1.11x - 7.075$

11. $\dfrac{9}{35}$

12. $\dfrac{-209}{240}$

13. **70.71**

14. **−0.002**

15. **1111**

16. $\dfrac{-441}{21}, \dfrac{700}{-0.035}$

Scoring Guide
Chapter 2
Performance Assessment

Level	Specific Criteria
3 Superior	• Shows thorough understanding of the concepts of *adding, subtracting, and comparing rational numbers; absolute value; graphing inequalities;* and *line plot.* • Uses appropriate strategies to solve problems. • Computations are correct. • Written explanations are exemplary. • Graphs and diagrams are accurate and appropriate. • Goes beyond requirements of some or all problems.
2 Satisfactory, with Minor Flaws	• Shows understanding of the concepts of *adding, subtracting, and comparing rational numbers; absolute value; graphing inequalities;* and *line plot.* • Uses appropriate strategies to solve problems. • Computations are mostly correct. • Written explanations are effective. • Graphs and diagrams are mostly accurate and appropriate. • Satisfies all requirements of problems.
1 Nearly Satisfactory, with Serious Flaws	• Shows understanding of most of the concepts of *adding, subtracting, and comparing rational numbers; absolute value; graphing inequalities;* and *line plot.* • May not use appropriate strategies to solve problems. • Computations are mostly correct. • Written explanations are satisfactory. • Graphs and diagrams are mostly accurate and appropriate. • Satisfies most requirements of problems.
0 Unsatisfactory	• Shows little or no understanding of the concepts of *adding, subtracting, and comparing rational numbers; absolute value; graphing inequalities;* and *line plot.* • May not use appropriate strategies to solve problems. • Computations are incorrect. • Written explanations are not satisfactory. • Graphs are not accurate or appropriate. • Does not satisfy requirements of problems.

Chapter 2 Answer Key
Performance Assessment

Page 42

1. a. $4 + (-7) = -3$

b. $-3 - 4 = -7$

c. $3\frac{1}{2} - \left(-2\frac{3}{4}\right) = 6\frac{1}{4}$

d. $|5| - |-8| = 5 - 8 = -3$

2. a.

b. Yes; Ashley's scores are greater than Ching's because Ashley's scores were 0 or greater, while Ching's scores were less than -2.

c. We do not have enough information to answer this question. Alex's scores could be any number less than zero. If Alex's score is -1, his score is greater than Ching's. If it is -2, it is equal to Ching's. If it is -3 or less, it is less than Ching's.

d. Yes; Ashley's scores were par or greater, making her score non-negative. Ellen's scores were less than Ching's, whose were less than -2. Thus, Ellen's scores are negative. A negative value (Ellen) is less than a non-negative value (Ashley).

3. a. $<$, because the first product is negative and the second is positive.

For parts **b–d,** you simplify each side of the sentence to determine which sign to use.

b. $(-5)(7)(-3) - \left(\frac{2}{3}\right)(360) \bullet \frac{3}{8}(-24)(5)(3)$

$$-135 \bullet -135$$
$$-135 = -135$$

c. $-8 \div \left(-\frac{9}{14}\right) \bullet \frac{7}{\frac{2}{5}}$

$$-8\left(-\frac{14}{9}\right) \bullet 7 \cdot \frac{5}{2}$$
$$12\frac{4}{9} \bullet 17\frac{1}{2}$$
$$12\frac{4}{9} < 17\frac{1}{2}$$

d. $\frac{-15x + 21}{3} \bullet \frac{6 - 10x}{2}$

$$\frac{3(-5x + 7)}{3} \bullet \frac{2(3 - 5x)}{2}$$
$$-5x + 7 \bullet 3 - 5x$$
$$7 \bullet 3$$
$$7 > 3$$

4. Students will probably mention that the data ranges from 60 to 85 and that 70 occurs most frequently. They may also give the number of values in the data set.

Chapter 2 Answer Key

Mid-Chapter Test
Page 43

1. $\{-4, 2\}$
2. {integers greater than -3}
3.
4.
5. -43
6. -6.1
7. 22
8. 0
9. 75
10. $\dfrac{-3}{10}$
11. $\begin{bmatrix} 4 & 2 \\ 6 & 2 \end{bmatrix}$
12. 2
13. 14
14. 12
15. $<$
16. $<$
17. $>$
18. $>$
19. sample: $\dfrac{19}{24}$
20. $\dfrac{1}{3}, \dfrac{3}{8}, \dfrac{4}{9}$

Bonus   56 years

Quiz A
Page 44

1. $\{-3, 0, 4\}$
2. $\{\cdots, -2, -1, 0, 1, 2\}$
3.
4.
5.
6. 3
7. -77
8. -104
9. $4n$
10. -30

Quiz B
Page 44

1. $>$
2. $>$
3. $<$
4. $=$
5. $\dfrac{4}{23}, \dfrac{7}{27}, \dfrac{5}{13}$
6. sample: $\dfrac{53}{84}$
7. 1.328
8. $\dfrac{-13}{8}$, or $-1\dfrac{5}{8}$
9. $\dfrac{39}{35}$, or $1\dfrac{4}{35}$
10. $-11m$

Quiz C
Page 45

1. -217
2. $\dfrac{2}{7}$
3. -24.226
4. $26ab$
5. $19x$
6. -7
7. $-7a$
8. 10
9. -6
10. $3x + 5y$

Quiz D
Page 45

1. 12
2. 0.06
3. 13
4. -7
5. $\pm\dfrac{11}{5}$
6. 7.35
7.
8. $0.465, -2.1, 3.892$
9. Let m = no. of myst. pages; $m = 624 - 3m$.
10. Let s = speed; $s = \dfrac{1500}{3} = 500$ miles per hour.

Chapter 2 Answer Key

     Cumulative Review

Page 46	Page 47	Page 48
1. __C__	1. $n^2 + 7$	17. {integers less than 3}
2. __A__	2. $4n - 5$	18.
3. __A__	3. 8	19.
4. __B__	4. 336	20. -25
5. __D__	5. 9	21. -15
6. __D__	6. 2	22. $-11m$
7. __B__	7. transitive	23. $\begin{bmatrix} -21 & \frac{1}{2} \\ -2.7 & 18 \end{bmatrix}$
8. __C__	8. substitution	24.
9. __C__	9. distributive	25. $\begin{bmatrix} -12 & -3 \\ 10.4 & 48 \end{bmatrix}$
10. __B__	10. commutative of add.	26. $\begin{bmatrix} -6.4 & -\frac{3}{2}\,8 \end{bmatrix}$
	11. $17a^2 - 3$	27. 6.16
	12. $10x + 14y$	28. -53
	13. $y = ab + c$	29. $24t$
	14. $m = (n - p)^2$	30. $\frac{1}{7}$
	15. $>$	31. $a - 2$
	16. $>$	32. Let s = sales price; $s = 139.29 - 15.35$
		33. Let s = Susan's age; $s + (s + 5) = 25$

Write the letter for the correct answer in the blank at the right of each problem.

1. What is the solution of $y + (-18) = -3$?
   A. -21 B. 21 C. -15 D. 15 1. _____

2. What is the solution of $m - 13 = 8$?
   A. 21 B. -21 C. 5 D. -5 2. _____

3. The difference of two integers is 26. The lesser integer is -50. What is the greater integer?
   A. 76 B. -76 C. 24 D. -24 3. _____

4. What is the solution of $5w = -75$?
   A. -15 B. -80 C. 15 D. 80 4. _____

5. What is the solution of $-\dfrac{3}{8}y = -24$?
   A. -9 B. 9 C. -64 D. 64 5. _____

6. What is the solution of $-\dfrac{n}{4} + 5 = -16$?
   A. 40 B. 44 C. 59 D. 84 6. _____

7. What is the solution of $8 - 3x = -16$?
   A. $-\dfrac{8}{3}$ B. $\dfrac{8}{3}$ C. 8 D. -8 7. _____

8. What is the solution of $\dfrac{a + 2}{5} = -9$?
   A. 47 B. -47 C. -55 D. 55 8. _____

9. What is the complement of an angle whose measure is $56°$?
   A. $34°$ B. $44°$ C. $124°$ D. $144°$ 9. _____

10. What is the supplement of an angle whose measure is $(x - 5)°$?
    A. $95 - x$ B. $85 - x$ C. $175 - x$ D. $185 - x$ 10. _____

11. A triangle has two angles with measures of $25°$ and $50°$. What is the measure of the third angle?
    A. $75°$ B. $105°$ C. $15°$ D. $25°$ 11. _____

12. What is the solution of $3(x - 1) - x = 3 + 2(x - 3)$?　　　　12. _____
A. 0　　　　　　　　　　　**B.** 4
C. There are no solutions.　**D.** The equation is an identity.

13. What is the solution of $2n - \frac{5}{6} = \frac{3}{4}n$?　　　　13. _____

A. $-\frac{10}{7}$　　**B.** -5　　**C.** $\frac{2}{3}$　　**D.** $\frac{10}{21}$

14. What is the solution of $1.8x - 5 = 4.3x - 7.75$?　　　14. _____
A. 1.1　　**B.** -1.1　　**C.** 0.11　　**D.** -0.11

15. Six is subtracted from a number. Then the result is divided by 4.　15. _____
The new result is added to 10 to give a final result of 30. What is
the number?
A. 4　　**B.** 80　　**C.** 86　　**D.** 16

16. Find the greatest of four consecutive integers if the least integer　16. _____
decreased by twice the greatest integer is 14.
A. -20　　**B.** -26　　**C.** -5　　**D.** -17

17. What is the solution for x of $ax - 5 = b$?　　　　17. _____

A. $a(b+5)$　　**B.** $\frac{b-5}{a}$　　**C.** $\frac{b+5}{a}$　　**D.** $a(b-5)$

18. Find the mode of these data: 7 5 5 3 9 8 9 4 9.　　　18. _____
A. 5　　**B.** 7　　**C.** 6.6　　**D.** 9

19. Find the mean of these data: 95.2, 94.8, 91.8, 97.8, 92.4, 88.4, 103.9.　19. _____
A. 97.8　　**B.** 94.8　　**C.** 94.9　　**D.** no mean

20. If all the numbers in a set of data occur the same number　20. _____
of times, then the set has no
A. mean.　　　　**B.** median.
C. mode.　　　　**D.** central tendency.

Bonus　　　　　　　　　　　　　　　Bonus _____

Solve for n: $an + bn = w$.

3

Chapter 3 Test, Form 1B

Write the letter for the correct answer in the blank at the right of each problem.

1. What is the solution of $m - (-4) = 7$?
   A. 3   B. 23   C. 11   D. 211

   1. _____

2. What is the solution of $-11 = n - (-11)$?
   A. 0   B. 22   C. -22 D. none of these

   2. _____

3. The sum of two integers is -46. The greater integer is 13. What is the lesser integer?
   A. 59   B. -59 C. -33 D. 33

   3. _____

4. What is the solution of $-26y = 884$?
   A. 910   B. 858   C. 34   D. -34

   4. _____

5. What is the solution of $\frac{3}{5}x - 15$?

   A. 45   B. 5   C. 25   D. 75

   5. _____

6. What is the solution of $5x + 3 = 23$?
   A. 4   B. -4 C. 5   D. -5

   6. _____

7. What is the solution of $\frac{n}{3} - 8 = -2$?

   A. -30 B. 30   C. -18 D. 18

   7. _____

8. What is the solution of $-14 = \frac{c + 12}{-6}$?

   A. -72 B. 72   C. 96   D. -96

   8. _____

9. What is the supplement of an angle whose measure is $(x - 28)°$?
   A. $(62 - x)°$ B. $(118 - x)°$ C. $(208 - x)°$ D. $(152 - x)°$

   9. _____

10. What is the measure of an angle that is twice its complement?
    A. 30°   B. 60°   C. 90°   D. 120°

    10. _____

11. The measures of two angles of a triangle are 44° and 32°. What is the measure of the third angle?
    A. 76°   B. 14°   C. 44°   D. 104°

    11. _____

3

Chapter 3 Test, Form 1B (continued)

12. What is the solution of $2x + 7 = 5x + 16$?

    A. -3 **B.** $\frac{2}{3}$ **C.** $-\frac{23}{3}$ **D.** 3

12._____

13. What is the solution of $\frac{2}{3}(6x - 3) = x + 5(x + 8) - 2x$?

    A. identity   **B.** no solution   **C.** 6   **D.** 0

13._____

14. What is the solution of $-3(h - 6) = 5(2h + 3)$?

    A. $-\frac{3}{13}$ **B.** $\frac{3}{13}$ **C.** $-\frac{9}{13}$ **D.** $\frac{9}{13}$

14._____

15. Let x represent the lesser of two consecutive even integers. Which equation would you use to find the two integers if their sum is 126?

    A. $x + (x + 2) = 126$ **B.** $x + 2x = 126$
    C. $(x + 2) + (x + 4) = 126$ **D.** $x(x + 2) = 126$

15._____

16. A number is added to 9. The result is then multiplied by 4 to give a new result of 120. What is the number?

    A. $27\frac{3}{4}$ **B.** 489   **C.** 39   **D.** 21

16._____

17. What is the solution for x of $2x - y = y$?

    A. $2y - 2$ **B.** $y - 2$ **C.** y **D.** 0

17._____

18. Find the mean of the set of data 4, 6, 7, 7, 9, 11, 17, 21, 25 rounded to the nearest tenth.

    A. 7   **B.** 9   **C.** 11.9   **D.** 11.5

18._____

19. Find the median of the set of data 5.11, 7.07, 8.95, 6.89, 8.63, 8.95.

    A. 7.85   **B.** 8.95   **C.** 7.60   **D.** no median

19._____

20. Which is affected by extremely high or low values in a set of data?

    A. median   **B.** mode   **C.** mean   **D.** All are affected.

20._____

Bonus

Bonus

A high school team had just won a conference mathematics contest. A reporter from the local paper asked the team captain, "How many gold, silver, and bronze medals did the team win?" The captain replied, "The product of the three numbers is 72 and their sum is the same as today's date." The reporter thought for a while and said, "I know today is the 18th, but I still can't find the answer." The captain exclaimed, "I'm sorry. I forgot to tell you that the smallest number of medals was of bronze and the greatest number of medals was gold." "Thank you," replied the reporter, who then left to write the story. How many medals of each type were won?

_____

_____

_____

Chapter 3 Test, Form 1C

Write the letter for the correct answer in the blank at the right of each problem.

1. Which of the following equations has a solution that is different than the others?
   A. $2x + 7 = -21$ **B.** $5x = 70$
   C. $x + 19 = 5$ **D.** All solutions are the same.

   1. _____

2. Which of the following equations has a solution that is different than the others?
   A. $3t - 7 = t - 2$ **B.** $4(t + 1) = 6t - 1$
   C. $10 - t = 3t$ **D.** All solutions are the same.

   2. _____

3. Which of the following equations has a solution that is different than the others?
   A. $5(g - 2) - g = 6(g - 4)$ **B.** $\frac{g + 5}{2} = 20 - 2g$
   C. $2(g + 5) + 1 = 4 + g$ **D.** All solutions are the same.

   3. _____

4. Which of the following equations has no solutions?
   A. $2(y - 6) = 3(y + 4) - y$ **B.** $\frac{2}{3}y + \frac{1}{2} = \frac{1}{4}y - \frac{1}{3}$
   C. $3(y - 2) = 6(y - 1) - 3y$ **D.** All equations have solutions.

   4.

5. Which of the following equations has more than one solution?
   A. $3(a + 7) = 7 - 4a$ **B.** $\frac{3}{4}a + 7 = 2 - a$
   C. $2(4 - a) = 3(a + 1) - 5(a - 1)$
   D. No equation has more than one solution.

   5. _____

6. The measure of an angle is 24 less than twice its supplement. If $x =$ the measure of the angle, which equation must be true?
   A. $x = 2(90 - x) - 24$ **B.** $x + 24 = 2(180 - x)$
   C. $x = 2(x - 180) - 24$ **D.** $x + 24 = 2(x - 90)$

   6. _____

7. Two-thirds times a number plus 7 equals 7 minus the number. Find the number.
   A. -1 **B.** 0 **C.** 1 **D.** no solution

   7. _____

8. Find the greatest of four consecutive integers if the least minus twice the greatest equals 8.
   A. 14   **B.** 11   **C.** -11 **D.** -14

   8. _____

9. Heather bought a winter coat for $6 less than half its original price. Heather paid $65 for the coat. What was the original price?
   A. $118   **B.** $124   **C.** $136   **D.** $142

   9. _____

10. Tony and Roberto bought 25 pounds of apples and $5.25 worth of fruit punch for the party. If Tony's half of the bill is $5.75, what is the price of a pound of apples?
    A. 20¢   **B.** 25¢   **C.** 30¢   **D.** 35¢

    10. _____

11. Find the measure of an angle that is two-thirds of its supplement.
  A. 36°   **B.** 54°   **C.** 72°   **D.** 108°   11. _____

12. Find the measure of an angle that is 27° more than twice its complement.
  A. 21°   **B.** 51°   **C.** 69°   **D.** 129°   12. _____

13. One angle of a triangle measures 10° more than the second. The measure of the third angle is twice the sum of the first two angles. Find the measure of the angle in the triangle that has the greatest measure.
  A. 90°   **B.** 120°   **C.** 135°   **D.** 140°   13. _____

14. The measure of the vertex angle of an isosceles triangle is 5° less than twice the measure of a base angle. Find the measure of a base angle.
  A. 43.75°   **B.** 46.25°   **C.** 87.5°   **D.** 92.5°   14. _____

15. Solve $\frac{x+b}{c} = a + e$ for x.

  A. $x = ac + ec - b$ **B.** $x = \dfrac{c(a+e)}{b}$

  C. $x = ac + e - b$ **D.** $x = \dfrac{a+e-b}{c}$ 15. _____

16. Solve $ay - b = c + dy$ for y.
  A. $y = \dfrac{c+d}{a-b}$ **B.** $y = \dfrac{a-d}{c+b}$

  C. $y = \dfrac{c+d+b}{a}$ **D.** $y = \dfrac{c+b}{a-d}$ 16. _____

17. Find the mode of the following set of data: 5, 5, 5, 6, 6, 6.
  A. 5   **B.** 5.5   **C.** 6   **D.** 5 and 6   17. _____

18. Find the median of the following set of data: 1, 1, 1, 2, 5, 7, 7, 9.
  A. 1   **B.** 3.5   **C.** 4.125   **D.** no median   18. _____

19. Find the mean of the following set of data: 4, 7, 11, 13, 14.
  A. 9.8   **B.** 11   **C.** 12   **D.** no mean   19. _____

20. Find the mean, median, and mode of the following batting   20. _____
averages. Then choose the correct response.
0.185, 0.225, 0.234, 0.240, 0.253, 0.275, 0.286, 0.297, 0.312, 0.333
  A. The mean is greater than the median.
  B. The mode is greater than the median.
  C. Exactly two of them are equal.
  D. All of them are equal.

Bonus   Bonus _____

Use what you know about the sum of the angles of a triangle to determine the sum of the angles of a hexagon (a six-sided figure). Justify your answer.

NAME_____ DATE _____

Chapter 3 Test, Form 2A

Solve each equation.

1. $n + 39 = 12$

2. $w + (-8) = -21$

3. $24 = m - 8.6$

4. $18 = 7 - p$

5. $-\frac{5}{9} = w - \left(\frac{3}{4}\right)$

6. $-6n = 16$

7. $\frac{3}{4}w = -48$

8. $-13 = \frac{n}{-4}$

9. $9 - 4w = -11$

10. $\frac{p}{-6} + 7 = -14$

11. $9 = \frac{t - 8}{4}$

12. $6 - \frac{3}{5}y = 9$

13. $6 - 2y = 7y + 13$

14. $3x - 5(x - 6) = 2(10 - x)$

15. $\frac{3}{5}x - 4 = \frac{1}{2}x$

16. $2.6n - 5 = 2.1n + 4.5$

17. Find the complement of an angle whose measure is 47°.

18. Find the supplement of an angle whose measure is 81°.

19. Find the supplement of an angle whose measure is $v°$.

20. Find the complement of an angle whose measure is $(x - 35)°$.

21. Find the measure of the third angle of the triangle.

Solve for x.

22. $ax - n = v$

23. $\frac{4x + t}{r} = s$

1. _____

2. _____

3. _____

4. _____

5. _____

6. _____

7. _____

8. _____

9. _____

10. _____

11. _____

12. _____

13. _____

14. _____

15. _____

16. _____

17. _____

18. _____

19. _____

20. _____

21. _____

22. _____

23. _____

Algebra 1

Define a variable, write an equation, and solve each problem.

24. A number is decreased by 45. The result is then divided by 12. Then 20 is added to this new result to give a final result of 25. What is the number?

24. _____

_____

_____

25. Lorna had a 91 on today's test. This was 17 points higher than her score on last week's test. Find her score on last week's test.

25. _____

_____

_____

26. Some number subtracted from 14 yields 71. What is the number?

26. _____

_____

_____

27. The greatest temperature variation recorded in a day occurred at Browning, Montana, in 1916. The temperature began at 44°F and dropped 100°F. To what temperature did it drop?

27. _____

_____

_____

28. Find four consecutive even integers whose sum is four.

28. _____

_____

_____

29. Twice the lesser of two consecutive integers is 12 less than three times the greater integer. Find the lesser integer.

29. _____

_____

_____

30. The length of a rectangle is 10 more than three times its width. The perimeter of the rectangle is 108. Find the dimensions of the rectangle.

30. _____

_____

_____

Use the stem-and-leaf plot at the right to answer each question. (8|2 represents 82.)

Stem	Leaf
5	4
6	7 9
7	1 3 3 3 7 9
8	2 2 8

31. What is the mean of the data?

31. _____

32. What is the median of the data?

32. _____

33. What is the mode of the data?

33. _____

Bonus

Solve for x: $5[x - 4(1 - 2x) - 6] - 3(x + 10) = 40x - 12$.

Bonus _____

③ Chapter 3 Test, Form 2B

Solve each equation.

1. $12 + r = 3$

2. $-12 = 7 - p$

3. $n - (-8) = 3$

4. $d + (-11) = -4$

5. $-\dfrac{3}{4} - p = \dfrac{1}{2}$

6. $-7b = -35$

7. $31 = -\dfrac{1}{6}n$

8. $-\dfrac{5}{8}w = -9$

9. $-3a + 4 = -14$

10. $3.2n + 2.6 = -23$

11. $\dfrac{x}{-4} + 5 = 1$

12. $2 = \dfrac{-2y - (-6)}{13}$

13. $6y - 3 = 6y + 8$

14. $1.4f + 1.1 = 8.3 - f$

15. $-4(p + 2) + 8 = 2(p - 1) - 7p + 15$

16. $\dfrac{n}{3} + \dfrac{3}{4} = \dfrac{5}{6}n - 1$

17. Find the complement of an angle whose measure is 33°

18. Find the supplement of an angle whose measure is 85°.

19. Find the supplement of an angle whose measure is $(y - 13)°$.

20. Find the complement of an angle whose measure is $(40 + a)°$.

21. Find the measure of the third angle of the triangle.

Solve for x.

22. $\dfrac{a}{b}x - c = 0$

23. $\dfrac{x + a}{b} = c$

1. _____

2. _____

3. _____

4. _____

5. _____

6. _____

7. _____

8. _____

9. _____

10. _____

11. _____

12. _____

13. _____

14. _____

15. _____

16. _____

17. _____

18. _____

19. _____

20. _____

21. _____

22. _____

23. _____

Define a variable, write an equation, and solve each problem.

24. A number is subtracted from −6. If the answer is 55, find the number.

24. _____

_____

_____

25. In 1989, the Chicago Cubs pitching staff had 50 saves. Williams had 36 saves while Lancaster had 8 saves. How many saves did the rest of the pitching staff have?

25. _____

_____

_____

26. A number is divided by 3 and the result added to 1. The new result is doubled to give a final result of 80. What is the number?

26. _____

_____

_____

27. Find two consecutive even integers whose sum is 98.

27. _____

_____

_____

28. Find three consecutive integers such that the sum of the first and third is 84.

28. _____

_____

_____

29. Four times a number decreased by 6 is 150. What is the number?

29. _____

_____

_____

30. The length of a rectangle is 5 less than twice the width. The perimeter of the rectangle is 80. Find the dimensions of the rectangle.

30. _____

_____

_____

The table below gives the average monthly temperatures over nine months for San Francisco.

Month	Jan.	Feb.	Mar.	Apr.	May	June	July	Aug.	Sept.
SF(°F)	49	52	53	55	58	61	62	63	64

31. Find the mean of the average monthly temperatures.

31. _____

32. Find the median of the average monthly temperatures.

32. _____

33. Find the mode of the average monthly temperatures.

33. _____

Bonus

Bonus _____

$$\frac{97}{9+7} = 6.06 \qquad \frac{42}{4+2} = 7 \qquad \frac{61}{6+1} = 8.714$$

Find the greatest two-digit whole number that when divided by the sum of its digits gives the greatest result.

Chapter 3 Test, Form 2C

Solve each equation.

1. $-16 = \dfrac{c - 6}{-3}$

2. $2b + 2.5 = -0.5(b - 1.5)$

1. _____

2. _____

3. $-\dfrac{x}{3} + 4 = x + 6$

4. $5n + 4 = 7(n + 1) - 2n$

3. _____

4. _____

5. $\dfrac{3}{5}a - \dfrac{3}{4} = -\dfrac{1}{2}a + 3$

6. $5(w + 3) + 9 = 3(w - 2) + 6$

5. _____

6. _____

7. $\dfrac{k - 7}{5} + 2 = \dfrac{k + 8}{10}$

8. $5(12 - 3p) = 15p + 60$

7. _____

8. _____

Solve for x.

9. $a = \dfrac{bx + c}{d}$

10. $ax + 5 = bx - c$

9. _____

10. _____

Solve each problem.

11. Shyam sold the family car for $200 more than half of the original price of the car. If he sold the car for $4950, what was the original price?

11. _____

12. A soccer field is 75 yards shorter than 3 times its width. Its perimeter is 370 yards. Find its dimensions.

12. _____

13. Irene gave half of her marbles to Patty and then 8 marbles to Maria. She had 16 marbles left. How many marbles did she have at the beginning?

13. _____

14. The perimeter of a triangle is 51 centimeters. The lengths of its sides are consecutive odd integers. Find the lengths of all three sides.

14. _____

15. Three times a number minus 5 equals half the sum of ten and the number. Find the number.

15. _____

16. The telephone rate between two calling zones is $0.45 for the first three minutes and $0.10 for each additional minute. If a call between the two zones costs $0.95, what was the length of the call?

16. _____

17. Three times the least of four consecutive integers minus the greatest of the integers equals the next to the least integer. Find the integers.

17. _____

18. An angle measures 17° more than its complement. Find the measure of the angle.

18. _____

19. An angle measures 5° more than three times its supplement. Find the measure of the angle.

19. _____

20. The first angle of a triangle measures 5° more than the second. The measure of the third angle is half of the measure of the second. Find the measures of the angles of the triangle.

20. _____

21. Find the measures of the angles of the triangle.

21. _____

22. Participants in diving events have each of their dives rated by seven judges using a scale from 0 to 10. A diver's score is computed by eliminating the highest and lowest ratings of the judges and then finding the mean of the remaining scores. This rating is then multiplied by a number that represents the difficulty of the dive attempted. Wendy received ratings of 8.2, 9.0, 7.3, 8.2, 7.7, 8.6, and 8.3 on a dive with difficulty 3.3. What was her score?

22. _____

23. Of the 40 employees at Speedy Pizza, sixteen earn $5.00 an hour, four earn $5.50 an hour, four earn $6.50 an hour, eight earn $5.25 an hour, and eight earn $6.00 an hour. Find the mean, median, and mode of the hourly wages.

23. _____

24. The annual salaries of the twelve employees at CompuSoftware Inc. are $38,500, $34,000, $27,500, $38,500, $63,500, $125,000, $31,500, $30,000, $38,500, $31,500, $92,500, and $31,000. Suppose you are the personnel director trying to convince someone that the company is a good place to work. Would you quote the median, mean, or mode as the "average" salary of the employees? Why?

24. _____

25. Suppose you represent a group of employees from the company in exercise 24. You are trying to argue that the employees need a raise. Would you quote the median, mean, or mode as the "average" salary of the employees? Why?

25. _____

Bonus

Bonus _____

Paloma Rey drove to work on Wednesday at 40 miles per hour and arrived one minute late. She left home at the same time on Thursday, drove 45 miles per hour, and arrived one minute early. How far does Ms. Rey drive to work?

NAME_____ DATE _____

Chapter 3 Calculator-Based Test

Solve each equation.

1. $x + 457.32 = 202$

2. $t - (-5.7832) = 34.776$

3. $0.8963 = w - 1.8896$

4. $-3.776c = -21.3344$

5. $\dfrac{g}{3.562} = -4.45$

6. $\dfrac{0.25t}{4.18} = 62.5$

7. $\dfrac{0.5k}{0.334} - 1.332 = 2.563$

8. $\dfrac{z + 34.7}{6.65} = 8.88$

9. $7.1r + 8.3 = 6.3r - 9.4$

10. $2.3y + 5(0.3y - 1.6) = -4(1.25y - 0.2)$

11. Find the complement of an angle whose measure is 72.354°.

12. Find the supplement of an angle whose measure is $(x + 5.334)°$.

13. A triangle has two angles with measures of 32.67° and 78.82°. Find the measure of the third angle.

14. Solve $5x + a = dc$ for x.

Find each measure of central tendency for the following data.

56.82, 77.89, 91.23, 68.76, 49.83, 81.65, 91.23, 75.14

15. mean

16. median

17. mode

Define a variable, write an equation, and solve each problem.

18. The area of a rectangle is 77.6 square feet. If the width is 3.2 feet, find the length.

19. A number is decreased by 7.13. The result is then divided by 5.62. Then 14.08 is added to the new result to give a final result of 3.5. What is the number?

20. Find three consecutive numbers such that the sum of the first and twice the third is equal to 445.

1. _____

2. _____

3. _____

4. _____

5. _____

6. _____

7. _____

8. _____

9. _____

10. _____

11. _____

12. _____

13. _____

14. _____

15. _____

16. _____

17. _____

18. _____

_____

_____

19. _____

_____

_____

20. _____

_____

_____

Algebra 1

Chapter 3 Performance Assessment

Instructions: *Demonstrate your knowledge by giving a clear, concise solution to each problem. Be sure to include all relevant drawings and justify your answers. You may show your solution in more than one way or investigate beyond the requirements of the problem.*

1. Use the equation $10x + 18 = 48$ for parts a–d.

   a. Add 4 to each side of the equation. Tell, in your own words, how you know that the two sides of the equation are still equal.

   b. How are the solutions of the original equation and the equation in part a related? What does the term *equivalent equations* mean?

   c. Use subtraction, multiplication, and division to form three equations equivalent to the original equation.

   d. Solve the original equation. Explain each step in finding the solution.

2. Use the equation $\frac{1}{2}(x - 3) = \frac{1}{3}x + 1$ for parts a–c.

   a. How can you eliminate the fraction from each side of the equation to make finding the solution easier?

   b. Write a word problem for the equation.

   c. Solve the equation. Explain each step and give the meaning of the answer.

3. a. Solve $ry + s = tx - m$ for y. Explain each step in your solution.

   b. Would there be any limitations for the value of each variable? If so, explain the limitation.

4. The opening day scores in a local golf tournament are 78, 83, 70, 84, 89, 67, 84, 92, 78, 91, 85, 77, 68, 80, 71, 78, 99, 81, 75, 88, 90, 71, 73. Find the mean, median, and mode for the set of scores. Give a reason for finding each of these values.

3

Chapter 3 Mid-Chapter Test (Lessons 3-1 through 3-3)

Solve and check each equation.

1. $y + (-16) = -12$

2. $n + \left(-\dfrac{1}{2}\right) = \dfrac{3}{4}$

3. $-18.5 = v - (-4.6)$

4. $-6d = -42$

5. $\dfrac{3}{5}y = -9$

6. $3.2x = 8.96$

7. $-18.4 + n = -51.8$

8. $5n = 2\dfrac{3}{4}$

9. $3t - 5 = 46$

10. $\dfrac{2}{5}x + 8 = 9$

11. $0.4p - 3 = -1$

12. $\dfrac{2d + 3}{8} = -2$

13. $\dfrac{a}{-6} + 5 = 2$

14. $0.5c - 1.2 = 0.7$

1. _____

2. _____

3. _____

4. _____

5. _____

6. _____

7. _____

8. _____

9. _____

10. _____

11. _____

12. _____

13. _____

14. _____

Define a variable, write an equation, and solve each problem.

15. Some number added to 7 is equal to 22. What is the number?

16. The temperature reached a high reading of 72° at mid-afternoon. By 7:00 P.M., the temperature dropped 23°. What was the reading at 7:00 P.M.?

17. Three-fourths of a number is 5.673. What is the number?

18. The area of a rectangle is $42\dfrac{3}{4}$ ft². The length is $9\dfrac{1}{2}$ ft. What is the width?

19. Find three consecutive integers whose sum is -27.

20. Four less than 5 times a number is 12. Find the number.

15. _____

_____

_____

16. _____

_____

_____

17. _____

_____

_____

18. _____

_____

_____

19. _____

_____

_____

20. _____

_____

_____

Bonus

The number of inches in the perimeter of a certain square is the same as the number of square inches in its area. What is the length of one side?

Bonus _____

NAME_____ DATE _____

Chapter 3, Quiz A (Lessons 3-1 and 3-2)

Solve and check each equation.

1. $-3.2 + q = -12.3$

2. $-28 = 21 - p$

3. $d - \dfrac{8}{5} = \dfrac{6}{5}$

4. $-7x = 63$

5. $\dfrac{t}{-5} = -8$

6. $\dfrac{4}{5}d = -32$

1. _____

2. _____

3. _____

4. _____

5. _____

6. _____

Define a variable, write an equation, and solve each problem.

7. Three CDs are missing from the music room. If 21 CDs are in the room, how many CDs should be there?

8. A number increased by 8 is -9. What is the number?

9. Negative six times a number is -15.42. Find the number.

10. Find the missing measure if the area is 54m^2.

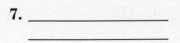

12 m

7. _____

_____

_____

8. _____

_____

9. _____

_____

10. _____

_____

_____

NAME_____ DATE _____

Chapter 3, Quiz B (Lessons 3-3 and 3-4)

Solve and check each equation.

1. $3x + 8 = 29$

2. $\dfrac{a}{6} - 5 = 9$

3. $5r - 14 = -42$

4. $\dfrac{-2m + 3}{-5} = 25$

1. _____

2. _____

3. _____

4. _____

Find the complement of each angle measure.

5. $39°$

6. $41°$

5. _____

6. _____

Find the supplement of each angle measure.

7. $56°$

8. $(25 - x)°$

7. _____

8. _____

Find the measure of the third angle of each triangle in which the measures of two angles of the triangle are given.

9. $26°, 105°$

10. $38°, x°$

9. _____

10. _____

3

Chapter 3, Quiz C (Lessons 3-5 and 3-6)

Solve and check each equation.

1. $7n + 6 = 4n - 9$

2. $5 - 3(w + 4) = w - 7$

3. $\frac{3}{4}x + \frac{1}{2} = \frac{2}{3}$

4. $-6(2r + 8) = -12(r - 3)$

5. $1.6y - 3 = 2.4y + 1.8$

6. $2x - 5(x - 3) = 2(x - 10)$

1. _____
2. _____
3. _____
4. _____
5. _____
6. _____

Solve for x.

7. $nx - m = p$

8. $\frac{x - b}{a} = c$

7. _____
8. _____

Define a variable, write an equation, and solve each problem.

9. The sum of the least and greatest of three consecutive integers is equal to 35 plus the middle integer. Find the integers.

9. _____
_____
_____

10. One-half of a number decreased by two-thirds is two less than one-fifth of the number. Find the number.

10. _____
_____
_____

3

Chapter 3, Quiz D (Lesson 3-7)

The heights (in inches) of the students in Mrs. Graham's class are 60, 75, 58, 65, 66, 70, 72, 69, 59, 60, 67, and 66.

1. Find the mean of the data.

1. _____

2. Find the median of the data.

2. _____

3. Find the mode(s) of the data.

3. _____

List five numbers that satisfy each set of data.

4. The mean is 5, the median is 4, and the mode is 4.

4. _____
_____
_____
_____
_____

5. The mean is 4, the median is 4, and the mode is 1.

5. _____
_____
_____
_____
_____

Chapter 3 Standardized Test Practice

Choose the best answer. Write A, B, C, or D.

1. Which of the following fractions is less than $\frac{1}{7}$?

    A. $\frac{3}{10}$ B. $\frac{2}{15}$ C. $\frac{26}{137}$ D. $\frac{25}{78}$

    1. _____

2. Which group of numbers is arranged in ascending order?

    A. $\frac{2}{3}, \frac{4}{7}, \frac{8}{9}, \frac{3}{5}$ B. $\frac{3}{5}, \frac{8}{9}, \frac{4}{7}, \frac{2}{3}$ C. $\frac{4}{7}, \frac{3}{5}, \frac{2}{3}, \frac{8}{9}$ D. $\frac{2}{3}, \frac{4}{7}, \frac{3}{5}, \frac{8}{9}$

    2. _____

3. If $36y(6) = 18$, then $y =$

    A. $\frac{1}{12}$.   B. $\frac{1}{6}$.   C. $\frac{1}{2}$.   D. $\frac{1}{3}$.

    3. _____

4. If $\frac{x}{6} + 2 = 4$, the value of $\frac{x}{2}$ is

    A. 6.   B. 12.   C. 18.   D. 36.

    4. _____

5. How many integers are between, but not including, 15 and 995?

    A. 969   B. 979   C. 980   D. 981

    5. _____

6. Which of the following numbers is the greatest?

    A. $\frac{1}{4}$ B. $\frac{2}{5}$ C. $\frac{3}{7}$ D. $\frac{2}{9}$

    6. _____

7. Three-eighths is how many ninths?

    A. $\frac{8}{27}$ B. $3\frac{3}{8}$ C. 24   D. $2\frac{2}{3}$

    7. _____

8. If $-[-(8 + 3 - 6 \cdot 5 \div 3 - 10)] = -9$, then $-(8 + 3 - 6 \cdot 5 \div 4 - 10) =$

    A. -9.   B. $-\frac{5}{3}$.   C. $\frac{5}{3}$.   D. 9.

    8. _____

9. If $m + 1 < n$, then

    A. $n > m$.   B. $m > n$.   C. $m = n$.   D. $n + 1 < m$.

    9. _____

10. If $a = b$, then $236 (a - b) =$

    A. 236.   B. 0.   C. -236.   D. none of these

    10. _____

11. If $\frac{x}{12} = 7$, then $\frac{x}{7} =$

    A. $\frac{1}{12}$.   B. $\frac{1}{7}$.   C. 12.   D. 84.

    11. _____

NAME_____ DATE _____

Chapter 3 Cumulative Review

1. Write an algebraic expression for a number decreased by 21. (Lesson 1-1)

1. _____

2. Evaluate $d^2 - x$ if $d = -\frac{1}{3}$ and $x = \frac{1}{2}$. (Lesson 1-3)

2. _____

3. Solve $a = 3\frac{1}{2} \div 2$. (Lesson 1-5)

3. _____

State the property illustrated by each of the following. (Lessons 1-6 and 1-8)

4. $6(0) = 0$

4. _____

5. $(a + 3) + 2 = a + (3 + 2)$

5. _____

Simplify. (Lesson 1-7)

6. $6(4a + 7b - 6b)$

6. _____

7. $3x^2 + 7x + x^2 + z^2$

7. _____

8. Translate the following sentence into an equation. m is the product of r and d, decreased by s. (Lesson 2-9)

8. _____

9. There are 150 juniors and seniors attending Monroe High School. If there are x juniors, how many seniors are there? (Lesson 2-9)

9. _____

10. Define a variable and write an equation. Then solve the following problem.
A number is 6 less than another number. Their sum is 86. Find the numbers. (Lesson 3-3)

10. _____
_____
_____

11. Graph $\{\cdots, -1, 0, 1, 2, 3\}$ on the number line. (Lesson 2-1)

11. ◄─┼─┼─┼─┼─┼─┼─┼─►
-1 0 1 2 3 4 5 6

Find each sum or difference. (Lesson 2-5)

12. $\begin{bmatrix} 32 & -15.3 \\ 4.7 & -3 \end{bmatrix} + \begin{bmatrix} -11 & -4.2 \\ 5.8 & 41 \end{bmatrix}$

12. _____

13. $\begin{bmatrix} -2.6 & 3.7 \\ 15 & -4 \end{bmatrix} - \begin{bmatrix} -8.6 & 1.3 \\ -3 & 7 \end{bmatrix}$

13. _____

Use the data 6, 10, 7, 6, 9, 8, 6, and 8 for exercises 14–16. (Lesson 3-7)

14. Find the mode of the data.

14. _____

15. Find the median of the data.

15. _____

16. Find the mean of the data.

16. _____

Solve each equation. (Lesson 3-1)

17. $y + 5 = -10$

17. _____

18. $a - 12 = 25$ 18. _____

19. $-27 = -6 - p$ 19. _____

Define a variable, write an equation, and solve each problem. (Lesson 3-1)

20. Jane is reading a book that is 350 pages long. She has read 85 pages. How many pages does she have left to read?   20. _____
_____

21. In the 1988 Olympics, Carl Lewis won the 100-meter run in a time of 9.92 seconds. This time is 0.08 seconds faster than the winning time for the race in 1964, run by Bob Hayes. What was Hayes's winning time?   21. _____
_____
_____

22. 35 less than some number is -43. Find the number.   22. _____

23. Find the complement and supplement of a 70° angle. (Lesson 3-4)   23. _____

Name the set or sets of numbers to which each real number belongs. Use N for natural numbers, W for whole numbers, Z for integers, Q for rational numbers, and I for irrational numbers. (Lesson 2-8)

24. -46 24. _____

25. $\sqrt{15}$ 25. _____

Simplify. (Lessons 2-6 and 2-7)

26. $\left(\frac{2}{3}\right)\left(-\frac{3}{5}\right)\left(-\frac{1}{2}\right)$ 26. _____

27. $\frac{-12x + (-14y)}{-2}$ 27. _____

Solve each equation. (Lessons 3-2, 3-3, and 3-5)

28. $\frac{n}{4} = -6$ 28. _____

29. $8 - 7x = 11$ 29. _____

30. $7a + 2 = 3a - 10$ 30. _____

31. $q = mn + p$ for m 31. _____

32. A rectangular city lot has a perimeter of 540 feet. The width of the lot is 150 feet less than its length. Find the length and the width. (Lesson 3-3)   32. _____

33. Find three consecutive odd integers such that the sum of the least and greatest is 78. (Lesson 3-3)   33. _____

Chapter 3 Answer Key

Form 1A		Form 1B	
Page 57	**Page 58**	**Page 59**	**Page 60**

Form 1A

Page 57

1. __D__
2. __A__
3. __D__
4. __A__
5. __D__
6. __D__
7. __C__
8. __B__
9. __A__
10. __D__
11. __B__

Page 58

12. __D__
13. __C__
14. __A__
15. __C__
16. __D__
17. __C__
18. __D__
19. __C__
20. __C__

Bonus $\dfrac{w}{a+b}$

Form 1B

Page 59

1. __A__
2. __C__
3. __B__
4. __D__
5. __C__
6. __A__
7. __D__
8. __B__
9. __C__
10. __B__
11. __D__

Page 60

12. __A__
13. __B__
14. __B__
15. __A__
16. __D__
17. __C__
18. __C__
19. __A__
20. __C__

Bonus __9 gold__

__8 silver__

__1 bronze__

Chapter 3 Answer Key

Page 61	Page 62	Page 63	Page 64
1. __B__	11. __C__	1. __-27__	24. n = the number
	12. __C__	2. __-13__	$\dfrac{n-45}{12} + 20 = 25$
2. __D__		3. __32.6__	$n = 105$
		4. __-11__	25. s = the score
	13. __B__	5. __$\dfrac{7}{36}$__	$91 = s + 17$
3. __C__		6. __$-\dfrac{8}{3}$__	$74 = s$
	14. __B__	7. __-64__	26. n = the number
		8. __52__	$14 - n = 71$
4. __A__		9. __5__	$n = -57$
		10. __126__	27. t = final temp.
	15. __A__	11. __44__	$44 - 100 = t$
5. __C__		12. __-5__	$-56°F = t$
		13. __$-\dfrac{7}{9}$__	28. n = least integer
	16. __D__	14. __no soln.__	$n + (n+2) +$
		15. __40__	$(n+4) + (n+6) = 4$
6. __B__	17. __D__	16. __19__	$-2, 0, 2, 4$
		17. __43°__	29. n = lesser integer
	18. __B__	18. __99°__	$2n = 3(n+1) - 12$
7. __B__			$n = 9$
	19. __A__	19. __$(180 - v)°$__	30. w = width, $2w +$
8. __C__	20. __C__	20. __$(125 - x)°$__	$2(10 + 3w) = 108$
	Bonus The sum of the angles of a hexagon is 720° because it can be divided into 4 triangles: $(4x)(180) = 720$.	21. __118°__	width: 11 length: 43
9. __D__			31. __74__
			32. __73__
			33. __73__
10. __B__		22. $x = \dfrac{v + n}{a}$	Bonus __34__
		23. $x = \dfrac{sr - t}{4}$	

Chapter 3 Answer Key

Form 2B

<table>
<tr><td>

Page 65

1. -9

2. 19

3. -5

4. 7

5. $-\dfrac{5}{4}$

6. 5

7. -186

8. $\dfrac{72}{5}$

9. 6

10. -8

11. 16

12. -10

13. no soln.

14. 3

15. 13

16. $\dfrac{7}{2}$

17. $57°$

18. $95°$

19. $(193 - y)°$

20. $(50 - a)°$

21. $135°$

22. $x = \dfrac{cb}{a}$

23. $x = cb - a$

</td><td>

Page 66

24. n = the number
$-6 - n = 55$
$n = -61$

25. s = no. of saves
$36 + 8 + s = 50$
$s = 6$

26. n = the number
$\left(1 + \dfrac{n}{3}\right)2 = 80$
$n = 117$

27. n = lesser integer
$n + (n + 2) = 98$
$n = 48, 50$

28. n = least integer
$n + (n + 2) = 84$
$n = 41, 42, 43$

29. n = the number
$4n - 6 = 150$
$n = 39$

30. w = width
$2w + 2(2w - 5) = 80$
width: 15
length: 25

31. about 57.4°F

32. 58°F

33. none

Bonus   90

</td></tr>
</table>

Chapter 3 Answer Key

Page 67   **Page 68**   **Page 69**

1. 54

2. −0.7

3. $-\dfrac{3}{2}$

4. no soln.

5. $\dfrac{75}{22}$

6. −12

7. 2

8. 0

9. $x = \dfrac{ad - c}{b}$

10. $x = \dfrac{c + 5}{b - a}$

11. $9500

12. 65 yd by 120 yd

13. 48 marbles

14. 15 cm, 17 cm, 19 cm

15. 4

16. 8 min.

17. 4, 5, 6, 7

18. 53.5°

---

19. 136.25°

20. 75°, 70°, 35°

21. 20°, 80°, 80°

22. 27.06

23. $5.45, $5.25, $5.00

24. The mean; it is higher.

25. The median; it is lower.

Bonus 12 miles

---

1. −255.32

2. 28.9928

3. 2.7859

4. 5.65

5. −15.8509

6. 1045

7. 2.60186

8. 24.352

9. −22.125

10. 1

11. 17.646°

12. $(174.666 - x)°$

13. 68.51°

14. $x = \dfrac{dc - a}{5}$

15. 74.06875

16. 76.515

17. 91.23

18. l = length
$3.2l = 77.6$
$l = 24.25$ ft

19. n = the number
$\dfrac{n - 7.13}{5.62} + 14.08 = 3.5$
$n = -52.3296$

20. n = least integer
$n + 2(n + 2) = 445$
147, 148, 149

Scoring Guide
Chapter 3
Performance Assessment

Level	Specific Criteria
3 Superior	• Shows thorough understanding of the concepts of *solving equations, solving formulas for a given variable,* and *finding measures of central tendency.* • Uses appropriate strategies to solve problems. • Computations are correct. • Written explanations are exemplary. • Word problem concerning equation is appropriate and makes sense. • Goes beyond requirements of all or some problems.
2 Satisfactory, with Minor Flaws	• Shows understanding of the concepts of *solving equations, solving formulas for a given variable,* and *finding measures of central tendency.* • Uses appropriate strategies to solve problems. • Computations are mostly correct. • Written explanations are effective. • Word problem concerning equation is appropriate and makes sense. • Satisfies all requirements of problems.
1 Nearly Satisfactory, with Serious Flaws	• Shows understanding of most of the concepts of *solving equations, solving formulas for a given variable,* and *finding measures of central tendency.* • May not use appropriate strategies to solve problems. • Computations are mostly correct. • Written explanations are satisfactory. • Word problem concerning equation is mostly appropriate and sensible. • Satisfies most requirements of problems.
0 Unsatisfactory	• Shows little or no understanding of the concepts of *solving equations, solving formulas for a given variable,* and *finding measures of central tendency.* • May not use appropriate strategies to solve problems. • Computations are incorrect. • Written explanations are not satisfactory. • Word problem concerning equation is not appropriate or sensible. • Does not satisfy requirements of problems.

Chapter 3 Answer Key
Performance Assessment

Page 70

1. **a.** Adding 4 to each side of the equation $10x + 18 = 48$ results in the equation $10x + 22 = 52$; students may say that according to the addition property of equality, if the exact same value is added to both sides of an equation, the equation remains balanced.

   b. The solutions are exactly the same. Equivalent equations are equations that have the same solution set.

   c. Sample answers: $10x = 30$, $-40x = -120$, $12x + 18 = 48 + 2x$

   d. $10x + 18 = 48$ original equation
   $10x = 30$ subtract 18 from both sides, subtraction property
   $x = 3$ divide both sides by 10, division property

2. **a.** Multiply both sides of the equation by the LCD of 2 and 3, which is 6.

   b. Sample answer: John and Jake have the same number of marbles. They determined that if John added 1 marble to $\frac{1}{3}$ of his marbles and Jake took $\frac{1}{2}$ of 3 less than his total number of marbles, then that would equal the same number. How many marbles did John and Jake each have?

   c. $\frac{1}{2}(x - 3) = \frac{1}{3}x + 1$ original equation

   $3(x - 3) = 2x + 6$ multiply both sides by 6, multiplication property

   $3x - 9 = 2x + 6$ distributive property
   $x - 9 = 6$ subtract $2x$ from both sides, subtraction property
   $x = 15$ add 9 to both sides, addition property
   They each had 15 marbles.

3. **a.** $ry + s = tx - m$ original equation
   $ry = tx - m - s$ subtract s from both sides, subtraction property
   $y = \dfrac{tx - m - s}{r}$ divide both sides by r, division property

   b. $r = 0$

4. mean: 80.5 (used as long as there aren't extreme score values to find the average score); median: 80 (used to find the score for which there is an equal number of higher and lower scores); mode: 78 (used to find the score that occurred most often)

Chapter 3 Answer Key

Mid-Chapter Test
Page 71

1. 4
2. $\dfrac{5}{4}$
3. -23.1
4. 7
5. -15
6. 2.8
7. -33.4
8. $\dfrac{11}{20}$
9. 17
10. $\dfrac{5}{2}$
11. 5
12. -9.5
13. 18
14. 3.8
15. $n =$ the number
$7 + n = 22$
$n = 15$
16. $t =$ temp at 7 P.M.
$72 - 23 = t$
$49° = t$
17. $n =$ the number
$\dfrac{3}{4}n = 5.673$
$n = 7.564$
18. $w =$ width
$9\dfrac{1}{2}w = 42\dfrac{3}{4}$
$w = 4\dfrac{1}{2}$ ft
19. $n =$ least integer
$n + (n + 1) + (n + 2) = -27,$
$-10, -9, -8$
20. $n =$ the number
$5n - 4 = 12$
3.2

Bonus 4 in.

Quiz A
Page 72

1. -9.1
2. 49
3. $\dfrac{14}{5}$
4. -9
5. 40
6. -40
7. $r =$ no. of CDs
$r - 3 = 21$
24
8. $n =$ the number
$n + 8 = -9$
-17
9. $n =$ the number
$-6n = -15.42$
2.57
10. $m =$ missing measure, $12m = 54$
4.5

Quiz B
Page 72

1. 7
2. 84
3. -5.6
4. 64
5. $51°$
6. $49°$
7. $124°$
8. $(155 + x)°$
9. $49°$
10. $(142 - x)°$

Quiz C
Page 73

1. -5
2. 0
3. $\dfrac{2}{9}$
4. no soln.
5. -6
6. 7
7. $x = \dfrac{p + m}{n}$
8. $x = ac + b$
9. $n =$ least integer
$n + (n + 2) = 35 + (n + 1)$; 34, 35, 36
10. $n =$ the number
$\dfrac{1}{2}n - \dfrac{2}{3} = \dfrac{1}{5}n - 2$
$-\dfrac{40}{9}$

Quiz D
Page 73

1. about 65.6
2. 66
3. 60 and 66
4. See students' work.
5. See students' work.

Chapter 3 Answer Key

Standardized Test Practice

Page 74

1. __B__
2. __C__
3. __A__
4. __A__
5. __B__
6. __C__
7. __B__
8. __D__
9. __A__
10. __B__
11. __C__

Cumulative Review

Page 75

1. $n - 21$
2. $-\dfrac{7}{18}$
3. $1\dfrac{3}{4}$
4. multiplicative of zero
5. associative of add.
6. $24a + 6b$
7. $4x^2 + 7x + z^2$
8. $m = rd - s$
9. $150 - x$
10. n = larger number; $n + (n - 6) = 86$; 40, 46
11.
12. $\begin{bmatrix} 21 & -19.5 \\ 10.5 & 38 \end{bmatrix}$
13. $\begin{bmatrix} 6 & 2.4 \\ 18 & -11 \end{bmatrix}$
14. 6
15. 7.5
16. 7.5
17. -15

Page 76

18. 37
19. 21
20. x = pages left; $85 + x = 350$; 265
21. x = Hayes's time; $9.92 = x - 0.08$; 10.0 seconds
22. n = number; $n - 35 = -43$; -8
23. 20°; 110°
24. Z, Q
25. I
26. $\dfrac{1}{5}$
27. $6x + 7y$
28. -24
29. $-\dfrac{3}{7}$
30. -3
31. $m = \dfrac{q - p}{n}$
32. 210 ft; 60 ft
33. 37, 39, 41

Chapter 4 Test, Form 1A

Write the letter for the correct answer in the blank at the right of each problem.

1. Solve the proportion $\frac{x}{7} = \frac{13}{42}$.

    A. 91   **B.** 6   **C.** $2\frac{1}{6}$ **D.** $\frac{6}{13}$

1. _____

2. Solve the proportion $\frac{8}{6} = \frac{a+4}{a-1}$.

    A. 16   **B.** 12   **C.** 24   **D.** 32

2. _____

3. After 105 games, a major-league baseball player had 28 home runs. At this rate, how many home runs would the player have at the end of the 162-game schedule?

    A. 57   **B.** 607.5   **C.** 18.4   **D.** 43

3. _____

In exercises 4 and 5, triangles ABC and DEF are similar.

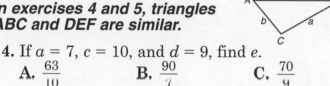 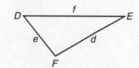

4. If $a = 7$, $c = 10$, and $d = 9$, find e.

    A. $\frac{63}{10}$ **B.** $\frac{90}{7}$ **C.** $\frac{70}{9}$ **D.** not enough information

4. _____

5. If $b = 4$, $d = 8$, $e = 6$, and $f = 9$, find a and c.

    A. $a = 12$, $c = \frac{27}{2}$ **B.** $a = \frac{27}{2}$, $c = 12$

    C. $a = 6$, $c = \frac{16}{3}$ **D.** $a = \frac{16}{3}$, $c = 6$

5. _____

For exercises 6 and 7, XYZ is a right triangle and angle X is the right angle.

6. If $x = 34$, $y = 16$, and $z = 30$, find sin Y.

    A. $\frac{17}{8}$ **B.** $\frac{8}{17}$ **C.** $\frac{15}{17}$ **D.** $\frac{17}{15}$

6. _____

7. If $y = 24$, and $z = 32$, what is the measure of $\angle Z$ to the nearest degree?

    A. 41°   **B.** 49°   **C.** 37°   **D.** 53°

7. _____

8. The access ramp to an expressway is 850 feet long. The measure of the angle of elevation is 4°. About how high is the expressway from the horizontal at the beginning of the ramp?

    A. 85.2 ft   **B.** 121.8 ft   **C.** 848 ft   **D.** 59.3 ft

8. _____

9. What is 30% of 72?

    A. 24   **B.** 21.6   **C.** 2160   **D.** 240

9. _____

10. Twenty-one is 12% of what number?

    A. 175   **B.** 2.52   **C.** 252   **D.** 25.2

10. _____

11. The price of a television was reduced from $450 to $360. What was the percent of decrease?

    A. 75%   **B.** 20%   **C.** 80%   **D.** 25%

11. _____

12. Jody paid $48.23 for a jacket. The price included a 6% sales tax.   12. _____
    Which expression represents the price in dollars of the jacket
    without the tax?
    A. $\frac{48.23}{1.06}$ **B.** $(48.23)(1.06)$ **C.** $\frac{48.23}{0.94}$ **D.** $48.23 - (0.06)(48.23)$

13. Rick's salary has been increased by 12%. His salary was $15,905.   13. _____
    What is his new salary?
    A. $1908.60   **B.** $19,806   **C.** $16,095.86   **D.** $17,813.60

14. A computer randomly selects a digit from 0 to 9. What is the   14. _____
    probability that the digit selected will be greater than 1?
    A. $\frac{7}{9}$ **B.** $\frac{7}{10}$ **C.** $\frac{1}{5}$ **D.** $\frac{4}{5}$

15. The probability in favor of an event is $\frac{5}{11}$. What are the odds   15. _____
    that the event will not occur?
    A. $11:6$ **B.** $5:6$ **C.** $6:11$ **D.** $6:5$

16. Which of the following events has a probability of 1?   16. _____
    A. You will be younger tomorrow than today.
    B. The Chicago Cubs will win the World Series this year.
    C. Your mother will always be older than you.
    D. You will be elected president of the United States
       before your eighteenth birthday.

17. Mandy begins bicycling west at 30 mi/h at 11 A.M. If Liz leaves   17. _____
    from the same point 20 minutes later bicycling west at 36 mi/h,
    when will she catch Mandy?
    A. 2:00 P.M.   **B.** 1:00 P.M.   **C.** 1:30 P.M.   **D.** 2:30 P.M.

18. Calvin invested $7500 for one year, part at 12% annual interest   18. _____
    and the rest at 10% annual interest. His total interest for the
    year was $890. How much money did he invest at 12%?
    A. $6334   **B.** $4045   **C.** $7000   **D.** $6250

19. If y varies directly as x and $x = 8$ when $y = 5$, what is y when   19. _____
    $x = 9$?
    A. $\frac{72}{5}$ **B.** $\frac{45}{8}$ **C.** $\frac{40}{9}$ **D.** 6

20. Matt, who weighs 144 pounds, is seated 8 feet from the fulcrum   20. _____
    of a seesaw. Todd is seated 6 feet from the fulcrum. If the seesaw
    is balanced, how much does Todd weigh?
    A. 108 lb   **B.** 146 lb   **C.** 152 lb   **D.** 192 lb

Bonus Wanda has read 80 of the 118 pages in a book. It took   **Bonus** _____
    her 2 h, 40 min. It is 8:30 P.M. now. When will she finish?

4

Chapter 4 Test, Form 1B

Write the letter for the correct answer in the blank at the right of each problem.

1. Solve the proportion $\frac{5}{4c} = \frac{1}{3}$.

   A. $\frac{4}{15}$ **B.** $\frac{1}{15}$ **C.** $3\frac{3}{4}$ **D.** $\frac{4}{3}$ 1. _____

2. A 12-ounce can of cola contains 150 calories. How many ounces   2. _____
   should you drink if your diet limits you to 100 calories?
   A. 12   **B.** 50   **C.** 10   **D.** 8

3. By federal law, the ratio of the width to the length of the U. S. flag   3. _____
   is 10 to 19. If you want to make a flag with an 8-foot width, what
   should be its length?
   A. 23.75 ft   **B.** 15.2 ft   **C.** 4.21 ft   **D.** 152 ft

Triangles ABC and DEF are similar. Use the information for exercises 4 and 5.

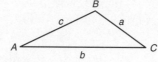 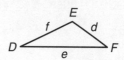

4. If $a = 10$, $b = 12$, and $d = 6$, find e.   4. _____
   A. 7.2   **B.** 3.6   **C.** 6   **D.** not enough information

5. If $a = 4$, $d = 6$, $e = 4$, and $f = 3$, find b and c.   5. _____
   A. $b = 6$, $c = \frac{9}{2}$ **B.** $b = \frac{9}{2}$, $c = 6$ **C.** $b = \frac{8}{3}$, $c = 2$ **D.** $b = 2$, $c = \frac{8}{3}$

Use the triangle at the right for exercises 6 and 7.

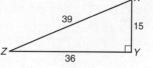

6. What is $\sin X$?   6. _____
   A. $\frac{13}{12}$ **B.** $\frac{5}{12}$ **C.** $\frac{12}{13}$ **D.** $\frac{12}{5}$

7. What is the measure of angle Z to the nearest degree?   7. _____
   A. 43°   **B.** 23°   **C.** 67°   **D.** 5°

8. An inclined plane links Johnstown, Pennsylvania, to suburban   8. _____
   Westmont 504 feet above. Cable cars move up and down an incline
   895 feet long. Find the measure of the angle of the incline to the
   nearest degree.
   A. 34°   **B.** 29°   **C.** 56°   **D.** 61°

9. What is 14% of 32?   9. _____
   A. 4480   **B.** 4.48   **C.** 228   **D.** 43.75

10. Ninety is what percent of 200?   10. _____
    A. 55%   **B.** 40.5%   **C.** 45%   **D.** 20%

11. Lonnie earns 6% of the value of each house he sells. His com-   11. _____
    mission on a sale was $8700. What was the value of the house?
    A. $52,200   **B.** $152,000   **C.** $450,000   **D.** $145,000

12. The price of a pair of ski boots was reduced from $160 to $120. What was the percent of decrease?

    A. 75%   **B.** 30%   **C.** 25%   **D.** $33\frac{1}{3}$%

    12. _____

13. Sharon paid $40.28 for cosmetics. This included a 6% sales tax. What was the cost before the sales tax?

    A. $38.00   **B.** $37.86   **C.** $33.57   **D.** $36.00

    13. _____

14. If the probability of rain is $\frac{3}{11}$, what are the odds in favor of rain?

    A. 8 : 11   **B.** 11 : 8   **C.** 8 : 3   **D.** 3 : 8

    14. _____

15. Suppose you are tossing a die. What is the probability that you will get a number less than 5?

    A. $\frac{1}{6}$ **B.** $\frac{5}{6}$ **C.** $\frac{1}{3}$ **D.** $\frac{2}{3}$

    15. _____

16. Which of the following events has a probability of 0?
    A. It will rain every day for a year in Los Angeles, California.
    B. The next president of the United States will be a woman.
    C. A dropped object will fall down.
    D. You will win a gold medal in the 1980 Summer Olympics.

    16. _____

17. Two airplanes leave Indianapolis at the same time in opposite directions. One plane travels at 270 mi/h and the other at 250 mi/h. When will they be 1560 miles apart?

    A. in $3\frac{5}{7}$ hours **B.** in 78 hours **C.** in 3 hours   **D.** in 4 hours

    17. _____

18. A chemist has 12 liters of a 25% acid solution. How many liters of water must be added to obtain a 20% acid solution?

    A. $\frac{3}{4}$ **B.** $\frac{4}{3}$ **C.** $1\frac{1}{4}$ **D.** 3

    18. _____

19. If y varies inversely as x and $y = 3$ when $x = 10$, find x when $y = 8$.

    A. $\frac{80}{3}$ **B.** $\frac{12}{5}$ **C.** $\frac{15}{4}$ **D.** none of these

    19. _____

20. The amount a spring stretches varies directly as the weight of the object attached to it. If an 8-ounce weight stretches a spring 10 cm, how much weight will stretch it 15 cm?

    A. 16 oz   **B.** 6 oz   **C.** 10 oz   **D.** 12 oz

    20. _____

Bonus   Twenty-five artisans can produce 180 figurines in a week. What will the total weekly production be if 10 new artisans are hired?

Bonus _____

4 Chapter 4 Test, Form 1C

Write the letter for the correct answer in the blank at the right of each problem.

1. Solve the proportion $\frac{2}{7} = \frac{x}{42}$.

   A. $\frac{1}{12}$ B. 12 C. $\frac{2}{7}$ D. 6

   1. _____

2. Find x if $\frac{x+2}{x} = \frac{3}{2}$.

   A. 4 B. $\frac{1}{4}$ C. 6 D. $\frac{1}{6}$

   2. _____

3. Emilio read 56 pages in 3 hours. At that same rate, find the number of hours it will take him to read the next 140 pages.

   A. $7\frac{1}{2}$ B. $2613\frac{1}{3}$ C. 28 D. $10\frac{1}{2}$

   3. _____

In exercises 4 and 5, triangles ABC and DEF are similar.

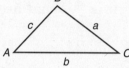 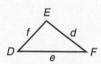

4. If $c = 8$, $f = 4$, and $b = 12$, find e.

   A. 24 B. 8 C. 6 D. not enough information

   4. _____

5. If $d = 6$, $a = 9$, and $e = 10$, find b.

   A. 15 B. 13 C. $6\frac{2}{3}$ D. 5

   5. _____

Use the triangle at the right for exercises 6 and 7.

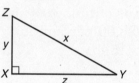

6. If $x = 34$, $y = 16$, and $z = 30$, find $\cos Y$.

   A. $\frac{15}{8}$ B. $\frac{8}{15}$ C. $\frac{15}{17}$ D. $\frac{17}{15}$

   6. _____

7. If the measure of $\angle Y = 37°$ and $y = 6$, find z to the nearest tenth.

   A. 4.5 B. 4.8 C. 8.0 D. 3.6

   7. _____

8. A radio station's signal is transmitted from a tall tower. The tower casts a shadow 135 meters long when the measure of the angle of elevation of the sun is 32°. Approximately how tall is the tower?

   A. 216 meters B. 114 meters C. 72 meters D. 84 meters

   8. _____

9. What number is 10% of 120?

   A. 1.2 B. 10 C. 12 D. 1200

   9. _____

10. Twelve is what percent of 48?

    A. 12% B. 25% C. 75% D. 400%

    10. _____

11. Dolores earned $67.56 interest on a one-year investment at 12% annual interest. How much money did Dolores invest?

    A. $8107 B. $563 C. $1776 D. $5360

    11. _____

12. A price increased from $30.00 to $34.50. What was the percent
of increase?
 A. 1.5% **B.** 4.5% **C.** 15% **D.** 45%

12._____

13. The cost of a pair of shorts was $45. They have been marked
down 40%. What is the price after the discount?
 A. $5 **B.** $18 **C.** $22.50 **D.** $27

13._____

14. Suppose you are tossing a die. What is the probability that you
will get a 6?
 A. 0 **B.** $\frac{1}{6}$ **C.** $\frac{5}{6}$ **D.** 1

14._____

15. The probability in favor of an event is $\frac{3}{5}$. What are the odds that
the event will occur?
 A. 3 : 5 **B.** 5 : 3 **C.** 3 : 2 **D.** 2 : 3

15._____

16. What is the probability that it will rain in your area tomorrow?
 A. 0 **B.** 1 **C.** between 0 and 1 **D.** greater than 1

16._____

17. How many pounds of nuts costing $2.50 per pound should be
mixed with 2 pounds of nuts costing $4.50 per pound to obtain
a mixture costing $3.00 per pound?
 A. 6 lb **B.** 15 lb **C.** 2 lb **D.** 1.5 lb

17._____

18. Paula leaves home driving 40 mi/h. One hour later, Dan drives
50 mi/h in the same direction. How long will it take Dan to catch
up to Paula?
 A. 1 hour **B.** 4 hours **C.** 5 hours **D.** 10 hours

18._____

19. If y varies inversely as x, and $y = 10$ when $x = 4$, find x when
$y = 8$.
 A. 2 **B.** 5 **C.** 6 **D.** 20

19._____

20. A driver's distance varies directly as the amount of time
traveled. After 6 hours, a driver had traveled 390 miles.
How far had the driver traveled after 4 hours?
 A. 260 miles **B.** 650 miles **C.** 130 miles **D.** 220 miles

20._____

Bonus Find the value of x.

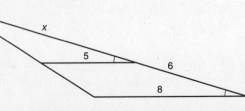

Bonus _____

Chapter 4 Test, Form 2A

Solve each proportion.

1. $\dfrac{4}{7} = \dfrac{3}{w}$

2. $\dfrac{t+4}{t-2} = \dfrac{1}{4}$

1. _____

2. _____

3. There are 142 carats in one ounce. In 1905, a rough diamond weighing 3106 carats was discovered. To the nearest ounce, how much did the diamond weigh?

3. _____

4. The state tax on a $30,000 income is $750. At this rate, what is the state tax on a $50,000 income?

4. _____

Triangles XYZ and ABC are similar. Use this information for exercises 5 and 6.

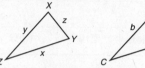

5. If $b = 15$, $x = 16$, $y = 20$, and $z = 10$, find a and c.

5. _____

6. If $a = 2\dfrac{1}{2}$, $b = 3$, $z = 5\dfrac{1}{2}$, and $y = 7$, find x and c.

6. _____

7. Triangle ABC is similar to triangle EDC. Find the distance across the lake from point A to point B.

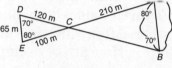

7. _____

Use the triangle at the right for exercises 8 and 9.

8. If $a = 9$ and $b = 19$, find the measure of $\angle A$ to the nearest degree.

8. _____

9. If $a = 12$, $b = 13$, and $c = 5$, find $\tan C$.

9. _____

10. A 20-inch diagonal of a rectangle makes an angle of 35° with a side of the rectangle. Find the length and width of the rectangle to the nearest tenth.

10. _____

Solve.

11. Thirty-one is what percent of 124?

11. _____

12. Seventy-two is 80% of what number?

12. _____

13. The rate of sales tax is 5.5%. What is the amount of tax charged on a pair of shoes that costs $28.00?

13. _____

14. The price of a winter coat was decreased from $89.95 to $71.96. What was the percent of decrease?

14. _____

15. Nancy bought a pair of shoes for $67.50. This price included an 8% sales tax. What did the shoes cost without tax?

15. _____

16. Lisa's salary of $31,500 was increased by 7%. What is her new salary?

16. _____

17. In a state lottery game, ping-pong balls numbered 0–49   **17.** _____
are used to select winning numbers. Balls with the numbers
0, 8, 7, and 1 have already been selected in the weekly
drawing. What is the probability that the number on the
fifth ball selected in the drawing will also be less than 10?

18. The probability of rain is 0.30. Find the odds that it will   **18.** _____
not rain.

19. The table at the right   **19.** _____
shows how registered
voters voted on
Proposition 2 in the
third district. If a
woman is chosen at
random, what is the
probability that she voted yes?

	Voted Yes	Voted No	Did Not Vote
Men	185	207	152
Women	219	138	173

20. Two airplanes leave the Atlanta airport at the same   **20.** _____
time, traveling in opposite directions. One plane travels
30 mi/h faster than the other. After 3 hours, the planes
are 3150 miles apart. What is the rate of each plane?

21. Warner bought 8 movie tickets for $40.00. Adult tickets   **21.** _____
sold for $5.50 and student tickets sold for $3.50. How
many student tickets did he buy?

22. Mrs. Lambert invested a portion of her $15,000 at 10%   **22.** _____
annual interest and the rest at 6% annual interest. If
her investments earned $1260 for the year, how much
did she invest at 10%?

23. If y varies directly as x and $y = 12$ when $x = 8$, find   **23.** _____
y when $x = -4$.

24. If y varies inversely as x and $y = -5$ when $x = 12.5$,   **24.** _____
find x when $y = 15$.

25. The volume of a gas is 40 ft³ at a pressure of 15 pounds   **25.** _____
per square inch (p.s.i.). What is the volume of the gas if
the pressure is increased to 36 p.s.i.? Assume that volume
varies inversely as pressure.

Bonus z varies directly as x and inversely as y. What   **Bonus** _____
happens to z in each case?
  a. x is doubled and y stays the same.
  b. y is doubled and x stays the same.
  c. x is doubled and y is doubled.
  d. x is doubled and y is halved.
  e. x is halved and y is doubled.

4

Chapter 4 Test, Form 2B

Solve each proportion.

1. $\dfrac{x}{6} = \dfrac{2}{9}$

2. $\dfrac{c+2}{5} = \dfrac{3}{7}$

3. If 500 sheets of paper weigh 7 pounds, how much do 2 sheets weigh?

4. Kathy can type 13 business letters in 2 hours. At that same rate, how many letters can she type in 8 hours?

Triangles MET and CUB are similar. Use this information for exercises 5 and 6.

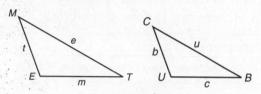

5. If $t = 3$, $m = 7$, $e = 9$, and $b = 2$, find c and u.

6. If $m = 10$, $c = 7$, $b = 4$, and $e = 15$, find t and u.

7. Find the height of the tree.

Use the triangle below for exercises 8 and 9.

8. If $r = 16$ and $s = 23$, find the measure of $\angle R$ to the nearest degree.

9. If $s = 5$, $r = 12$, and $t = 13$, find cos S.

10. Find the height of a kite to the nearest yard if the length of the string is 140 yards and the angle of elevation to the kite is 54 degrees. Assume the string is straight.

11. What number is 23% of 86?

12. Fifty-five is what percent of 220?

13. Of those children adopted in the United States, 6.5% were over 10 years old. If 8400 were adopted, how many were over 10 years old?

14. Johnny paid $24.36 including 5% sales tax for a pair of pants. What was the price of the pants without sales tax?

15. A price increased from $145 to $156.60. What was the percent of increase?

1. _____

2. _____

3. _____

4. _____

5. _____

6. _____

7. _____

8. _____

9. _____

10. _____

11. _____

12. _____

13. _____

14. _____

15. _____

Algebra 1

16. A television normally selling for $423.00 is discounted 22%. Find the sale price.

16. _____

17. If the probability in favor of an event is $\frac{5}{12}$, what are the odds of that event occurring?

17. _____

18. A computer randomly selects a letter of the alphabet. What is the probability that the letter is one of the letters in the word "probability"?

18. _____

19. The results of a survey of 284 randomly chosen students is shown below. What is the probability that a student chosen at random favors strawberry?

19. _____

Preference for Frozen Yogurt Flavors			
Students	Strawberry	Chocolate	No Preference
Male	25	87	20
Female	96	34	22

20. Joe and Janna leave home at the same time, traveling in opposite directions. Joe drives 45 mi/h and Janna drives 40 mi/h. In how many hours will they be 510 miles apart?

20. _____

21. A factory has an order for 23,500 paper clips. Machine A can make 1500 paper clips per hour while Machine B can make 2500 paper clips per hour. Machine A starts at 8:00 A.M. and Machine B starts at 1:00 P.M. At what time will the two machines complete the job?

21. _____

22. A chemist has 20 liters of a 10% acid solution. How many liters of pure acid must be added to produce a 25% acid solution?

22. _____

23. If y varies directly as x and $y = 25$ when $x = 10$, find y when $x = 4$.

23. _____

24. If y varies inversely as x and $y = 9$ when $x = 5$, find y when $x = 6$.

24. _____

25. Suppose that in a certain restaurant the number of hamburgers sold varies inversely as the price. If 70 burgers are sold at $1.50 each, how many burgers would be sold at $1.25 each?

25. _____

Bonus The intensity of illumination, I, on a movie screen varies inversely as the square of its distance from the projector. If the distance between the projector and the screen is changed from 200 feet to 100 feet, by what factor is the intensity of illumination changed?

Bonus _____

Solve each proportion.

1. $\dfrac{x}{4} = \dfrac{3}{2}$

2. $\dfrac{a-1}{3} = \dfrac{5}{1}$

1. _____

2. _____

3. A pitcher has given up 60 runs in 200 innings. How many runs is this per 9 innings?

3. _____

4. Nita can deliver 28 newspapers in 40 minutes. How many papers can she deliver in 90 minutes?

4. _____

Triangles ABC and XYZ are similar. Use this information for exercises 5 and 6.

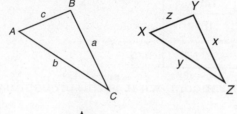

5. If $c = 8$, $b = 16$, $x = 9$, and $z = 6$, find y and a.

5. _____

6. If $a = 15$, $b = 19$, $z = 11$, and $y = 19$, find c and x.

6. _____

7. Find the height of the lamppost.

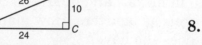

5 ft

|← 18 ft →|← 9 ft →|

7. _____

Use the triangle at the right for exercises 8 and 9.

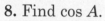

8. Find cos A.

9. Find the measure of $\angle B$ to the nearest degree.

8. _____

9. _____

10. The world's steepest standard-sized railroad track is on the Chamonix line in France. The train rises 1 meter for every 11 meters it moves along the track. Find the angle of elevation of the track to the nearest degree.

10. _____

11. Four is what percent of 40?

11. _____

12. What is 35% of 70?

12. _____

13. At the Piccolo in Germany, the smallest theater in the world, 21 people were in attendance. This represented 70% of the theater's total number of seats. Find the total number of seats.

13. _____

14. A price increased from $35 to $36.40. What was the percent of increase?

14. _____

15. During the day, the price of a stock dropped 5% to close at $36.29. What was the price at the beginning of the day?

15. _____

16. Ray's salary of $30,000 was increased by 8%. What was Ray's new salary?

16. _____

17. Suppose that you are tossing a die. What is the probability that you will get an even number?

17. _____

18. The probability that a certain event will occur is $\frac{5}{9}$. What are the odds that the event will occur?

18. _____

19. The table shows how 100 residents voted on a certain proposition.

Vote	Yes	No
Men	32	18
Women	26	24

19. _____

If a woman is chosen at random, what is the probability that she voted yes?

20. How many pounds of candy worth $3.60 per pound must be added to 10 pounds of chocolate worth $2.40 per pound to form a mixture worth $3.30 per pound?

20. _____

21. Carmen has $2.80 in nickels and quarters. She has twice as many nickels as quarters. How many of each kind of coin does she have?

21. _____

22. Two runners leave the same point, running in opposite directions. One runner runs 2 mi/h faster than the other. After running for 2 hours, the runners are 28 miles apart. How fast does the faster person run?

22. _____

23. If y varies directly as x and $y = 9$ when $x = 6$, find x when $y = 15$.

23. _____

24. If y varies inversely as x and $y = 12$ when $x = 3$, find y when $x = 6$.

24. _____

25. At a certain restaurant, the number of hamburgers sold varies inversely as the price. At $2.00 each, 90 hamburgers are sold. How many hamburgers would be sold if the price was lowered to $1.50 each?

25. _____

Bonus The area of a circle varies directly as the square of the radius. If the radius is tripled, by what factor will the area be increased?

Bonus _____

NAME_____ DATE _____

Chapter 4 Calculator-Based Test

Solve each proportion.

1. $\dfrac{4.6}{1.9} = \dfrac{23}{x}$　　　　2. $\dfrac{a}{11.75} = \dfrac{13}{15}$

3. A basketball player has made 47 out of 55 free throws. At this rate, how many free throws would the player make in the next 125 free throws?

4. Triangles ABC and DEF are similar. If $c = 17$, $a = 21$, $f = 12.75$, and $e = 22.5$, find b and d.

5. A radio station's transmitting tower is about 150 feet tall. At a certain point during the day, the tower casts a shadow 400 feet long. If a $5\frac{1}{2}$-foot-tall person stands next to the tower at this point, how long would the person's shadow be?

6. In right triangle ABC, $\angle C$ is a right angle, $a = 8$, and the measure of $\angle A$ is 34°. Find b.

Find the value of each trigonometric ratio to the nearest ten thousandth.

7. tan 33°

8. sin 62

Find the measure of each angle to the nearest degree.

9. $\cos A = 0.6429$

10. $\tan J = 0.2679$

11. What is 2.2% of 95.5%?

12. Last season, a punter averaged 39.6 yards per punt. This season, the punter is averaging 41.3 yards per kick. To the nearest tenth of a percent, by what percent has the punter improved?

13. Find the probability that you will *not* select a dime if you select a coin at random from a container with 127 pennies, 42 nickels, 34 dimes, and 25 quarters.

14. Filipe had $7480 to invest. He deposited some of the money in an account that paid 6.7% annual interest, and the rest in an account that paid 5.75% annual interest. If Filipe earned a total of $470.57 in interest, how much did he invest at 6.7%?

15. Wilma starts walking from home at 3.7 miles per hour. Fred leaves to follow Wilma 48 minutes later, walking at 4.1 miles per hour. How long will it take Fred to catch up to Wilma?

16. If y varies directly as x and $y = 123.9$ when $x = 65.3$, find y, to the nearest tenth, when $x = 81.2$.

1. _____

2. _____

3. _____

4. _____

5. _____

6. _____

7. _____

8. _____

9. _____

10. _____

11. _____

12. _____

13. _____

14. _____

15. _____

16. _____

Chapter 4 Performance Assessment

Instructions: *Demonstrate your knowledge by giving a clear, concise solution to each problem. Be sure to include all relevant drawings and justify your answers. You may show your solution in more than one way or investigate beyond the requirements of the problem.*

1. The following questions are related to the formula $d = rt$, where d represents distance, r represents rate, and t represents time.

   a. Write what is meant by direct variation.

   b. Write what is meant by inverse variation.

   c. Every day at lunchtime Kelli walks 30 minutes before returning to work. On cooler days she walks more briskly than on warm days. Does the distance she walks vary directly or inversely with her rate of walk? Justify your answer.

   d. At the Indianapolis 500 auto race, each car finishing the race travels 500 miles. Does the average speed of the cars finishing the race vary directly or inversely with the time taken to complete the race? Justify your answer.

2. A landscaper wishes to make a scale drawing of a rectangular garden. She makes the measurements indicated.

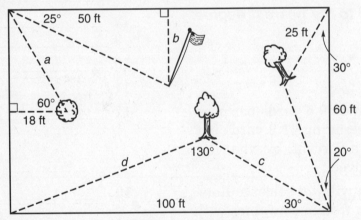

   a. Find the measurements labeled a, b, c, and d. Show your work and explain each step.

   b. Make a scale drawing based on the length of the garden being represented by 10 inches on your drawing. Show your work in determining each length in your drawing.

3. Explain how to find the sale price when you know the original price and the percent of discount.

4. Explain how to find the odds that an event will occur if you know the probability that it will occur.

4

Chapter 4 Mid-Chapter Test (Lessons 4-1 through 4-4)

Solve each proportion.

1. $\dfrac{3}{5} = \dfrac{12}{y}$ 2. $\dfrac{2r}{8} = \dfrac{3}{4}$ 3. $\dfrac{6}{5} = \dfrac{x + 2}{3}$

1. _____

2. _____

3. _____

4. A store charges $30 for a case of motor oil (24 cans). At this rate, how much would you be charged for 5 cans?

4. _____

Triangles XYZ and ABC are similar. Use this information for exercises 5–8.

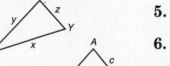

5. If $x = 9$, $a = 6$, and $z = 6$, find c.

5. _____

6. If $y = 12$, $b = 10$, and $a = 6$, find x.

6. _____

7. If $x = 12$ and $z = 3c$, find a.

7. _____

8. If $x = 8$, $c = 5$, and $y = b$, find z and a.

8. _____

Use the triangle below for exercises 9 and 10.

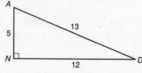

9. Find $\sin A$.

9. _____

10. Find $\tan D$.

10. _____

11. If $\cos F = 0.9511$, find the measure of $\angle F$ to the nearest degree.

11. _____

12. At a point 150 feet from the base of a radio tower, the measure of the angle of elevation is 68°. Find the height of the radio tower.

12. _____

Solve.

13. Six is what percent of 15?

13. _____

14. Seventy-two is 40% of what number?

14. _____

15. Geoff has $5000 to invest. He wants to earn $568 in interest in one year. He will invest part of the money at 12% and the other part at 10%. How will he invest to earn $568?

15. _____

16. Gina paid $161.46 for a jacket. This included an 8% sales tax. What was the price before the sales tax?

16. _____

Bonus   Find the value of x.

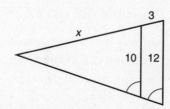

Bonus _____

Chapter 4, Quiz A (Lessons 4-1 and 4-2)

1. Solve $\frac{3}{4} = \frac{n}{20}$.

1. _____

2. Lana used 5 gallons of gas to travel 115 miles. How many miles can she travel on 18 gallons?

2. _____

Triangles ABC and XYZ are similar. For each set of measures given, find the measures of the remaining sides.

3. $y = 3$, $a = 6$, $b = 8$, $c = 10$

3. _____

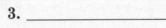

4. $x = 4$, $y = 9$, $c = 14$, $a = 10$

4. _____

5. A tree that is 25 feet tall casts a shadow 14 feet long. At exactly the same time of day, a tower near the tree casts a 23-foot shadow. How tall is the tower?

5. _____

Chapter 4, Quiz B (Lessons 4-3 and 4-4)

For triangle ABC, express each trigonometric ratio as a fraction in simplest form. Then write the fraction as a decimal to the nearest thousandth.

1. $\cos A$

1. _____

2. $\tan B$

2. _____

3. $\sin A$

3. _____

Find the measure of each angle to the nearest degree.

4. $\sin X = 0.9336$

4. _____

5. $\tan W = 0.4040$

5. _____

6. Alex is standing 80 feet from the base of a TV tower. From this point, the measure of the angle of the elevation is 32°. How tall is the TV tower?

6. _____

Use an equation to solve each problem.

7. Find 9% of 36.

7. _____

8. Thirty-six is what percent of 180?

8. _____

9. The population of a city is 280,000. 15% of the population is over 65. How many people are over 65?

9. _____

10. A computer company wants to reduce its workforce by 5%. To do this, the company will lay off 1800 workers next year. How many workers does the company currently have?

10. _____

Chapter 4, Quiz C (Lessons 4-5 and 4-6)

Solve each problem.

1. A price decreased from $48 to $36. Find the percent of decrease.

1. _____

2. Sales tax of 6% is added to a purchase price of $18. Find the total price.

2. _____

3. The odds that a candidate will win an election are 4 : 3. What is the probability that the candidate will lose the election?

3. _____

Suppose you toss a die. Find the probability of tossing each of the following.

4. a 2

4. _____

5. a number greater than 4

5. _____

NAME_____ DATE _____

Chapter 4, Quiz D (Lessons 4-7 and 4-8)

Solve each problem.

1. Claudine had twice as many dimes as quarters and six more dimes than nickels. In all, she had $5.20. How many quarters did she have?

1. _____

2. How many liters of pure acid must be added to 6 liters of a 15% acid solution to obtain a 40% acid solution?

2. _____

3. If y varies inversely as x and $y = -4$ when $x = 5$, find y when $x = 2$.

3. _____

4. Chris's wages vary directly as the time she works. If her wages for 20 hours are $90, what are her wages for 42 hours?

4. _____

5. At a given temperature, the volume of a gas is inversely proportional to its pressure. The volume of a gas is 85 cubic feet under 16 pounds per square inch (p.s.i.) of pressure. What is the volume when the pressure is 68 p.s.i.?

5. _____

4

Chapter 4 Standardized Test Practice

Choose the best answer. Write A, B, C, or D.

1. The value of $-7y - 10$ is greatest when $y =$
   A. -10.   B. -3.   C. 4.   D. 8.

   1. _____

2. 0.05% is the ratio of 5 to
   A. $\dfrac{1}{10,000}$.   B. 100.   C. 1000.   D. 10,000.

   2. _____

3. What part of 2 days is 3 minutes?
   A. $\dfrac{2}{3}$ B. $\dfrac{1}{16}$ C. $\dfrac{1}{480}$ D. $\dfrac{1}{960}$

   3. _____

4. The sum of three consecutive even integers is always divisible by
   A. 5.   B. 6.   C. 7.   D. 10.

   4. _____

5. If $a > b$ and $b < 0$, then which of the following must be true?
   A. $a < 0$ B. $a > 0$ C. $a = 0$ D. none of these

   5. _____

6. Twelve-thirteenths times two-thirds is equal to what number times four-ninths?
   A. $1\dfrac{5}{13}$ B. $\dfrac{13}{18}$ C. $\dfrac{32}{117}$ D. $3\dfrac{21}{32}$

   6. _____

7. A cookie recipe that makes 3 dozen cookies calls for $1\dfrac{1}{2}$ cups of sugar. How many cups of sugar would be needed to make 1 dozen cookies?
   A. $\dfrac{1}{3}$ B. $\dfrac{2}{3}$ C. $\dfrac{1}{6}$ D. $\dfrac{1}{2}$

   7. _____

8. A bag contains 80 white, blue, and yellow marbles. If 20% are yellow and there are the same number of white and blue marbles, what percent are blue?
   A. 10   B. 35   C. 40   D. 80

   8. _____

9. There are 15 boys in a class of 32 students. If 3 girls were absent yesterday, what part of the class were girls who were present?
   A. $\dfrac{1}{16}$ B. $\dfrac{3}{32}$ C. $\dfrac{3}{8}$ D. $\dfrac{7}{16}$

   9. _____

10. The circumferences of two circles are 18 and 10. The difference between the areas of these circles is
    A. 14.   B. 56.   C. $\dfrac{56}{\pi}$.   D. $56\pi^3$.

    10. _____

NAME_____ DATE _____

Chapter 4 Cumulative Review

1. Write a mathematical expression for twice the cube of a number. (Lesson 1-1)

1. _____

2. Write the expression $x \cdot y \cdot x \cdot x \cdot y$ using exponents. (Lesson 1-1)

2. _____

3. Evaluate $5ab^2$ if $a = 3$ and $b = 4$. (Lesson 1-3)

3. _____

4. Solve $6(2 + 6) = k$. (Lesson 1-5)

4. _____

5. What number is the multiplicative identity element? (Lesson 1-6)

5. _____

6. Simplify $5m + 8n - 3m + n$. (Lesson 1-8)

6. _____

Find each sum or difference. (Lessons 2-3 and 2-5)

7. $-43 + 26$

7. _____

8. $-3.4 + 10$

8. _____

9. $|4 - (-7)|$

9. _____

10. $\begin{bmatrix} -1 & 0 \\ 2 & 3 \end{bmatrix} + \begin{bmatrix} -2 & 5 \\ 4 & -1 \end{bmatrix}$

10. _____

Solve. (Lesson 3-1)

11. $m + 5 = -23$

11. _____

12. $-4 = 8 - k$

12. _____

13. Define a variable, write an equation, and solve. (Lesson 3-1)
The temperature at noon was 16°C. By dusk, the temperature had dropped 20°. What was the temperature at dusk?

13. _____

_____

_____

Simplify. (Lessons 2-6 and 2-7)

14. $-9(4 - 7)$

14. _____

15. $\frac{16b}{4}$

15. _____

Find the measure of the third angle of each triangle in which the measures of two angles of the triangle are given. (Lesson 3-4)

16. 38°, 75°

16. _____

17. 114°, 27°

17. _____

Find each square root. Round to the nearest hundredth if the result is not a whole number. (Lesson 2-8)

18. $\sqrt{576}$

18._____

19. $-\sqrt{60}$

19._____

Solve each question. (Lessons 3-2, 3-3, and 3-5)

20. $\frac{5}{6}b = -5$

20._____

21. $-7x + 23 = 37$

21._____

22. $8(x - 5) = 48x$

22._____

23. Find two consecutive odd integers whose sum is 56. (Lesson 3-3)

23._____

24. Solve the proportion $\frac{n}{500} = \frac{2}{40}$. (Lesson 4-1)

24._____

25. 93 is what percent of 300? (Lesson 4-4)

25._____

26. If y varies directly as x and $y = 8$ when $x = 3$, find y when $x = 5$. (Lesson 4-8)

26._____

27. If y varies inversely as x and $y = 15$ when $x = 3$, find y when $x = 5$. (Lesson 4-8)

27._____

28. How heavy is an 800-foot reel of cable if a piece 6 feet long weighs 5 pounds? (Lesson 4-8)

28._____

29. A price of $180 was increased to $207. Find the percent of increase. (Lesson 4-5)

29._____

30. A stereo normally selling for $320 is discounted 18%. Find the sale price. (Lesson 4-5)

30._____

A single die is rolled. (Lesson 4-6)

31. Find P (at least 5).

31._____

32. What are the odds of rolling a number less than 5?

32._____

33. A five-foot-tall person casts a shadow 18 feet long. At the same time, a tree casts a shadow 45 feet long. How tall is the tree? (Lesson 4-2)

33._____

Chapter 4 Answer Key

Page 85	**Page 86**
1. __C__	12. __A__
2. __A__	13. __D__
3. __D__	14. __D__
4. __D__	15. __D__
5. __D__	16. __C__
6. __B__	17. __B__
7. __D__	18. __C__
8. __D__	19. __B__
9. __B__	20. __D__
10. __A__	
11. __B__	Bonus __9:46 P.M.__

Page 87	**Page 88**
1. __C__	12. __C__
2. __D__	13. __A__
3. __B__	14. __D__
4. __A__	15. __D__
5. __C__	16. __D__
6. __C__	17. __C__
7. __B__	18. __D__
8. __A__	19. __C__
9. __B__	20. __D__
10. __C__	
11. __D__	Bonus __252 figurines__

Chapter 4 Answer Key

1. __B__

2. __A__

3. __A__

4. __C__

5. __A__

6. __C__

7. __C__

8. __D__

9. __C__

10. __B__

11. __B__

12. __C__

13. __D__

14. __B__

15. __C__

16. __C__

17. __A__

18. __B__

19. __B__

20. __A__

Bonus __10__

1. $5\frac{1}{4}$

2. -6

3. 22 oz

4. $1250

5. $a = 12$; $c = 7.5$

6. $x = 5\frac{5}{6}$; $c = 2\frac{5}{14}$

7. $AB = 136.5$ m

8. $28°$

9. $\frac{5}{12}$

10. about 11.5 in. and 16.4 in.

11. 25%

12. 90

13. $1.54

14. 20%

15. $62.50

16. $33,705

17. $\frac{2}{15}$

18. 7 : 3

19. $\frac{219}{530}$

20. 510 mi/h; 540 m/h

21. 2 student tickets

22. $9000

23. -6

24. $-4\frac{1}{6}$

25. $16\frac{2}{3}$ ft³

Bonus
a: doubled;
b: halved;
c: same;
d: 4 times as great;
e: $\frac{1}{4}$ as great

Chapter 4 Answer Key

Form 2B

1. $1\frac{1}{3}$

2. $\frac{1}{7}$

3. 0.028 lb

4. 52 letters

5. $c = \frac{14}{3}$; $u = 6$

6. $t = \frac{40}{7}$; $u = 10\frac{1}{2}$

7. $40\frac{1}{2}$ ft

8. 35°

9. $\frac{12}{13}$

10. about 113 yd

11. 19.78

12. 25%

13. 546 children

14. $23.20

15. 8%

16. $329.94

17. 5 : 7

18. $\frac{9}{26}$

19. $\frac{121}{284}$

20. 6 h

21. 5 P.M.

22. 4 liters

23. 10

24. $\frac{15}{2}$, or $7\frac{1}{2}$

25. 84 burgers

Bonus   4

Chapter 4 Answer Key

Form 2C

Page 95

1. 6
2. 16
3. 2.7 runs
4. 63 newspapers
5. $y = 12; a = 12$
6. $c = 11; x = 15$
7. 15 ft
8. $\frac{12}{13}$
9. 67°
10. 5°
11. 10%
12. 24.5
13. 30 seats
14. 4%
15. $38.20
16. $32,400

Page 96

17. $\frac{1}{2}$
18. 5 : 4
19. $\frac{13}{25}$, or 0.52
20. 30 lb
21. 8 quarters; 16 nickels
22. 8 mi/h
23. 10
24. 6
25. 120 hamburgers

Bonus 9

Calculator-Based

Page 97

1. 9.5
2. 10.18333333
3. about 107
4. $b = 30; d = 15.75$
5. $14\frac{2}{3}$ feet
6. 11.86048775
7. 0.6494
8. 0.8829
9. 50°
10. 15°
11. 2.101
12. 4.3%
13. $\frac{97}{114}$
14. $4260
15. 7.4 hours
16. 154.1

Scoring Guide
Chapter 4
Performance Assessment

Level	Specific Criteria
3 Superior	• Shows thorough understanding of the concepts of *proportion; direct and inverse variation; similar triangles; sine, cosine, and tangent; percent of change;* and *probability*. • Uses appropriate strategies to solve problems. • Computations are correct. • Written explanations are exemplary. • Diagrams are accurate and appropriate. • Goes beyond requirements of some or all problems.
2 Satisfactory, with Minor Flaws	• Shows understanding of the concepts of *proportion; direct and inverse variation; similar triangles; sine, cosine, and tangent; percent of change;* and *probability*. • Uses appropriate strategies to solve problems. • Computations are mostly correct. • Written explanations are effective. • Diagrams are mostly accurate and appropriate. • Satisfies all requirements of problems.
1 Nearly Satisfactory, with Serious Flaws	• Shows understanding of most of the concepts of *proportion; direct and inverse variation; similar triangles; sine, cosine, and tangent; percent of change;* and *probability*. • May not use appropriate strategies to solve problems. • Computations are mostly correct. • Written explanations are satisfactory. • Diagrams are mostly accurate and appropriate. • Satisfies most requirements of problems.
0 Unsatisfactory	• Shows little or no understanding of the concepts of *proportion; direct and inverse variation; similar triangles; sine, cosine, and tangent; percent of change;* and *probability*. • May not use appropriate strategies to solve problems. • Computations are incorrect. • Written explanations are not satisfactory. • Diagrams are not accurate or appropriate. • Does not satisfy requirements of problems.

Chapter 4 Answer Key
Performance Assessment

Page 98

1. **a.** As one variable increases or decreases, the other variable increases or decreases in a proportional amount.

   b. As one variable increases or decreases, the other variable decreases or increases (the opposite) in a proportional amount.

   c. directly, because $d = rt$ where t is a constant

   d. inversely, because $r = \dfrac{d}{t}$ where d is a constant

2. **a.** $a = \dfrac{18}{\cos 60°} = 36$ feet

   $b = 50 \tan 25°$, or 23.3, feet

   $\dfrac{c}{100} = \dfrac{25}{60}$, $c = 41.7$ feet

   $\dfrac{d}{100} = \dfrac{40}{60}$, $d = 66.7$ feet

   b. The scale should be 1 inch = 10 feet.

3. Change the percent discount to a decimal. Multiply the original price by the decimal to find the discount. Subtract the discount from the original price.

4. Subtract the number of ways the event can occur from the total number of outcomes; this gives the number of ways the event cannot occur. Write a ratio that compares successes to failures.

Chapter 4 Answer Key

Mid-Chapter Test
Page 99

1. 20

2. 3

3. $\frac{8}{5}$, or $1\frac{3}{5}$

4. $6.25

5. 4

6. $\frac{36}{5}$, or $7\frac{1}{5}$

7. 4

8. $z = 5$, $a = 8$

9. $\frac{12}{13}$

10. $\frac{5}{12}$

11. 18°

12. about 371 ft

13. 40%

14. 180

15. $3400 at 12%; $1600 at 10%

16. $149.50

Bonus 15

Quiz A
Page 100

1. 15

2. 414 mi

3. $x = 2\frac{1}{4}$; $z = 3\frac{3}{4}$

4. $z = 5\frac{3}{5}$; $b = 22\frac{1}{2}$

5. about 41 ft

Quiz B
Page 100

1. $\frac{33}{65}$; 0.508

2. $\frac{33}{56}$; 0.589

3. $\frac{56}{65}$; 0.862

4. 69°

5. 22°

6. about 50 ft

7. 3.24

8. 20%

9. 42,000

10. 36,000

Quiz C
Page 101

1. 25%

2. $19.08

3. $\frac{3}{7}$

4. 0.17

5. 0.51

Quiz D
Page 101

1. 10

2. $2\frac{1}{2}$ liters

3. −10

4. $189

5. 20 ft³

Chapter 4 Answer Key

Standardized Test Practice Page 102	Cumulative Review Page 103	Page 104
1. **A**	1. $2n^3$	18. **24**
	2. x^3y^2	19. **−7.75**
2. **D**	3. **240**	20. **−6**
	4. **48**	21. **−2**
3. **D**	5. **1**	22. **−1**
	6. $2m + 9n$	23. **27, 29**
4. **B**	7. **−17**	24. **25**
	8. **6.6**	25. **31%**
5. **D**	9. **11**	26. $13\frac{1}{3}$
6. **A**	10. $\begin{bmatrix} -3 & 5 \\ 6 & 2 \end{bmatrix}$	27. **9**
	11. **−28**	28. $666\frac{2}{3}$ **pounds**
7. **D**	12. **12**	29. **15%**
8. **C**	13. x = temp at dusk; $16 - 20 = x; -4°C$	30. **$262.40**
9. **D**	14. **27**	31. $\frac{1}{3}$
	15. $4b$	32. **2:1**
	16. **67°**	33. **12.5 feet**
10. **C**	17. **39°**	

5

Chapter 5 Test, Form 1A

Write the letter for the correct answer in the blank at the right of each problem.

Use the graph to answer questions 1–3.

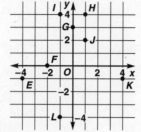

1. What is the ordered pair for point I?
   A. $(1, -4)$ B. $(-1, 4)$
   C. $(-4, 1)$ D. $(4, -1)$

   1._____

2. Name the quadrant in which the point K is located.
   A. I   B. II   C. III   D. IV

   2._____

3. What is the domain of the relation graphed?
   A. $\{-4, -1, 0, 2, 3, 4\}$ B. $\{-4, -2, -1, 0, 1, 2, 3, 4\}$
   C. $\{-4, -2, -1, 0, 1, 4\}$ D. {all the integers}

   3._____

4. Which relation is the inverse of $\{(3, -1), (2, 5), (-3, 4)\}$?
   A. $\{(-3, 1), (-2, -5), (3, -4)\}$ B. $\{(-3, 4), (2, 5), (3, -1)\}$
   C. $\{(-1, 3), (5, 2), (4, -3)\}$ D. $\{(2, 5), (-3, 4), (3, -1)\}$

   4._____

5. What are the domain and range of the relation shown in the table?
   A. domain: $\{-2, 5\}$; range: $\{6, 7\}$
   B. domain: $\{6, 7\}$; range: $\{-2, 5\}$
   C. domain: $\{-2, 6\}$; range: $\{5, 7\}$ D. domain: $\{5, 7\}$; range: $\{-2, 6\}$

x	y
-2	6
5	7

   5._____

6. The x-coordinate of each point on the y-axis is
   A. the same as the y-coordinate.   B. always positive.
   C. always zero.   D. any number.

   6._____

7. To plot the point $(-7, 4)$, you start at the origin and go
   A. down 4 and left 7.   B. down 7 and left 4.
   C. left 7 and up 4.   D. left 4 and up 7.

   7._____

8. When $2x - 3y = 6$ is solved for y, which equation results?
   A. $-3y = 6 - 2x$ B. $y = \dfrac{2x - 6}{3}$

   C. $y = \dfrac{6 + 2x}{3}$ D. $y = \dfrac{6 - 2x}{3}$

   8._____

9. Which set of ordered pairs shows the relation in the mapping?
   A. $\{(-2, 5), (0, -1), (-1, 4), (-1, 5)\}$
   B. $\{(-2, -1), (0, 4), (-1, 5)\}$
   C. $\{(-1, 0), (4, -1), (5, -1), (5, -2)\}$
   D. $\{(-1, -2), (4, 0), (5, -1)\}$

   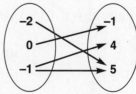

   9._____

10. What is the solution set of the equation $n = 2w + 1$ if the domain is $\{-3, 5, 9\}$?
    A. $\{(-3, -2), (5, 2), (9, 4)\}$ B. $\{(-2, -3), (2, 5), (4, 9)\}$
    C. $\{(-3, -5), (5, 11), (9, 19)\}$ D. $\{(-5, -3), (11, 5), (19, 9)\}$

    10._____

11. Which equation is not a linear equation?   11._____
    A. $-4v + 2w = 7$ **B.** $\frac{x}{4} = y$ **C.** $x = -5$ **D.** $\frac{2}{x} + \frac{3}{y} = 6$

12. The graph of $x - 2y = 4$ is which line?   12._____
    A. ℓ **B.** m **C.** p **D.** q

13. Which equation has a graph   13._____
    that is a vertical line?
    A. $y - 5 = 0$
    B. $y = x$
    C. $2x + 4 = 0$
    D. $x + y = 0$

14. The graph of $y = 0$ is   14._____
    A. the origin.   **B.** the x-axis.
    C. the y-axis.   **D.** not possible to draw.

15. Determine which relation is not a function.   15._____

    A. 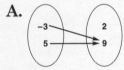   **B.** 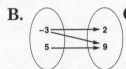   **C.** 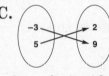   **D.** more than
                                                                      one of
                                                                      these

16. If $g(x) = 3x^2 - 4x + 1$, what is the value of $g(-2)$?   16._____
    A. 21   **B.** 29   **C.** 45   **D.** 5

17. When an equation for the relation shown in the   17._____
    chart is solved for y, the coefficient of x is

x	1	3	5	7
y	6	14	22	30

    A. 2.   **B.** 4.   **C.** 6.   **D.** 8.

18. Find the interquartile range for the data listed below.   18._____
    379, 307, 332, 386, 502, 593, 622, 676
    A. 315   **B.** 290   **C.** 288   **D.** 252

19. Find the lower quartile for the data   19._____
    represented in the stem-and-leaf plot
    at the right, where 3|5 represents 35.

Stem	Leaf
3	1 3 5
4	2
5	0 0 6 7
6	8

    A. 33   **B.** 34
    C. 35   **D.** 50

20. Which value would change if 6|8 is changed to 6|9 in   20._____
    question 19?
    A. lower quartile   **B.** upper quartile
    C. range   **D.** median

Bonus   Name at least two points that complete a parallelogram   **Bonus** _____
            formed by $(-1, 7)$, $(5, 7)$, $(2, -1)$. Then find the area of each
            parallelogram. Which has the greater area?   _____

Write the letter for the correct answer in the blank at the right of each problem.

Use the graph to answer questions 1–3.

1. What is the ordered pair for point L?
   A. $(1, -4)$ **B.** $(-4, 1)$
   C. $(-1, -4)$ **D.** $(-4, -1)$

   1. _____

2. Name the quadrant in which the point E is located.
   A. I   **B.** II
   C. III   **D.** IV

   2. _____

3. What is the range of the relation graphed?
   A. $\{-4, -1, 0, 2, 3, 4\}$ **B.** $\{-4, -2, -1, 0, 1, 2, 3, 4\}$
   C. $\{-4, -2, -1, 0, 1, 4\}$ **D.** {all the integers}

   3. _____

4. Which relation is the inverse of $\{(-2, -1), (2, 1), (-2, 4)\}$?
   A. $\{(-1, 2), (-2, -1), (-2, -4)\}$ **B.** $\{(2, 1), (-2, -1), (2, -4)\}$
   C. $\{(-2, 4,), (2, 1), (-2, -1)\}$ **D.** $\{(-1, -2), (1, 2), (4, -2)\}$

   4. _____

5. What are the domain and range of the relation shown in the table?
   A. domain: $\{-3, 4\}$; range: $\{0, 6\}$
   B. domain: $\{4, 6\}$; range: $\{-3, 0\}$
   C. domain: $\{0, 6\}$; range: $\{-3, 4\}$
   D. domain: $\{-3, 0\}$; range: $(4, 6\}$

   5. _____

x	y
-3	4
0	6

6. The y-coordinate of each point on the x-axis is
   A. the same as the x-coordinate. **B.** always positive.
   C. always zero.   **D.** any number.

   6. _____

7. To plot the point $(-5, 2)$, you start at the origin and go
   A. down 5 and right 2.   **B.** up 2 and left 5.
   C. left 5 and down 2.   **D.** right 2 and up 5.

   7. _____

8. When $3x - 5y = 12$ is solved for y, which equation results?
   A. $y = 7 - 3x$ **B.** $-5y = 12 - 3x$
   C. $y = \dfrac{3x - 12}{5}$ **D.** $y = \dfrac{12 - 3x}{5}$

   8. _____

9. Which set of ordered pairs shows the relation in the mapping?
   A. $\{(-3, 5), (1, -1), (1, 6), (8, 2)\}$
   B. $\{(5, 3), (2, 1), (-1, 1), (6, 8)\}$
   C. $\{(5, 3), (2, 8), (-1, 1), (6, 1)\}$
   D. $\{(3, 5), (1, 2), (1, -1), (8, 6)\}$

   9. _____

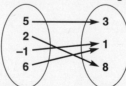

10. What is the solution set of the equation $2r + s = 8$ if the domain is $\{-2, 0, 4\}$?
    A. $\{(-2, 12), (0, 8), (4, 0)\}$ **B.** $\{(12, -2), (8, 0), (0, 4)\}$
    C. $\{(-2, 6), (0, 4), (4, 2)\}$ **D.** $\{(6, -2), (4, 0), (2, 4)\}$

    10. _____

11. Which equation is a linear equation?   11._____
    A. $2x^2 + 5y = 3$ **B.** $y = -10$ **C.** $5 = 3xy$ **D.** $y = \frac{1}{x} + 4$

12. The graph of $\frac{1}{2}x + \frac{2}{3}y = 1$ is   12._____
    which line?
    A. r **B.** s
    C. t **D.** v

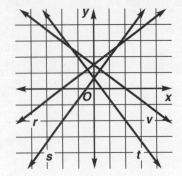

13. The graph of $x = 0$ is   13._____
    A. the origin.
    B. the x-axis.
    C. the y-axis.
    D. not possible to draw.

14. Which equation has a graph that is a horizontal line?   14._____
    A. $x - 7 = 0$ **B.** $x = y$ **C.** $2y + 3 = 4$ **D.** $x + y = 0$

15. Determine which relation is a function.   15._____
    A. $\{(2, 8), (-1, 3), (2, -2)\}$ **B.** $y^2 = 3x + 2$
    C. $3x - 11 = 0$ **D.** $y = x^2 + 5x + 1$

16. Which is the graph of a function?   16._____

    A. 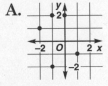 **B.** **C.** **D.** none
                                                        of these

17. If $f(x) = 7 - x$, which of the following is true?   17._____
    A. $f(-1) = (-1, 8)$ **B.** $2[f(3)] = f(6)$
    C. $f(0) = 0$ **D.** $f(7 - w) = w$

18. When an equation for the relation shown in the   18._____
    chart is solved for y, the constant term is

x	3	4	5
y	-10	-8	-6

    A. -16. **B.** -4. **C.** 0. **D.** 4.

19. If the lower quartile = 38 and the upper quartile = 54 for a set of   19._____
    data, find the least value above 54 that could be an outlier.
    A. 55.5 **B.** 70 **C.** 109 **D.** 78

20. Find the upper quartile for the data   20._____
    represented in the stem-and-leaf plot
    at the right. 9|7 represents 97.

Stem	Leaf
8	4 5 6 7
9	7 9
10	2 2 3 4 9

    A. 102 **B.** 86
    C. 23 **D.** 103

Bonus Graph all ordered pairs (x, y) that make   **Bonus**
    $2x^2 - 5x - 3 = 0$ true.

Chapter 5 Test, Form 1C

Write the letter for the correct answer in the blank to the right of each problem.

Use the graph to answer questions 1–3.

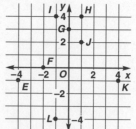

1. What is the ordered pair for point H?
   A. $(1, -4)$ B. $(4, 1)$
   C. $(1, 4)$ D. $(4, -1)$

   1. _____

2. Name the quadrant in which point E is located.
   A. I   B. II   C. III   D. IV

   2. _____

3. What is the domain of the relation graphed?
   A. $\{-4, -2, -1, 0, 1, 4\}$ B. $\{-1, 0, 4, -4, 3, 2, 4\}$
   C. $\{-4, -1, 0, 1, 2, 3, 4\}$ D. $\{-4, -3, -2, -1, 0, 1, 2, 3, 4\}$

   3. _____

4. Which relation is the inverse of $\{(0, 1), (1, 0), (3, -4), (3, 3)\}$?
   A. $\{(0, 0), (1, 1), (3, -4), (3, 3)\}$ B. $\{(0, 1), (1, 0), (3, -4), (3, 3)\}$
   C. $\{(1, 0), (0, 1), (-4, 3), (-3, -3)\}$ D. $\{(1, 0), (0, 1), (-4, 3), (3, 3)\}$

   4. _____

5. What are the domain and range of the relation shown in the table?
   A. domain: $\{1, -3\}$; range: $\{-4, 5\}$
   B. domain: $\{1, -4\}$; range: $\{-3, 5\}$
   C. domain: $\{-3, 5\}$; range: $\{1, -4\}$
   D. domain: $\{5, -4\}$; range: $\{-3, 1\}$

x	y
1	-3
-4	5

   5. _____

6. What is the graph of the set of ordered pairs $(0, a)$, where a is any number?
   A. the x-axis   B. the y-axis
   C. any line on the graph   D. cannot be determined

   6. _____

7. To plot the point $(5, -2)$, you start at the origin and go
   A. down 2 and left 5.   B. down 5 and left 2.
   C. up 5 and left 2.   D. right 5 and down 2.

   7. _____

8. The equation $4x - 3y = 9$ can be rewritten as which equation?
   A. $y = \frac{4}{3}x - 3$ B. $y = \frac{3}{4}x - 3$ C. $y = \frac{3}{4}x + 3$ D. $y = \frac{4}{3}x + 3$

   8. _____

9. What is the domain of the relation shown in the mapping?
   A. $\{-1, 4, 0, -3\}$ B. $\{-4, -3, 0, 2\}$
   C. $\{-1, 0, 1, 2\}$ D. $\{1, 0, -1, -2\}$

   9. _____

10. What is the range of the solution set of the equation $2a + 3b = 6$ if the domain is $\{-3, 0, 3\}$?
    A. $\{12, 6, 0\}$ B. $\{4, 2, 0\}$ C. $\{0, 2, 0\}$ D. $\{7.5, 3, 1.5\}$

    10. _____

11. Which equation is a linear equation?
    A. $4m^2 = 6$ B. $3a + 5b = -3$
    C. $\frac{2}{3}xy - \frac{3}{4}y + 3 = 0$ D. $x^2 + y^2 = 0$

    11. _____

Use the graph to answer questions 12 and 13.

12. The graph of $y = 2x + 4$ is which line?
    A. l B. m
    C. p D. q

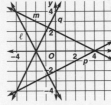

12. _____

13. The coordinates of the point where
    line m intersects line p are
    A. $(-2, 0)$.   B. $(4, 0)$.   C. $(-4, 4)$.   D. $(-4, -4)$.

13. _____

14. Determine which relation is a function.
    A.
    $$x \quad 2 \to 1 \quad 4 \to 3 \quad -2 \to 5 \quad y$$

    B.
x	y
3	−1
4	2
4	3
5	6

    C. $2r + 3q + 7 = 3$ D. $\{(3, 0), (-2, -2), (7, -2), (-2, 0)\}$

14. _____

15. If $h(r) = \dfrac{2}{3}r - 6$, what is the value of $h(-9)$?

    A. 12   B. 0   C. −12   D. $-6\dfrac{2}{3}$

15. _____

16. Which of the following represents a function?
    A.
x	y
3	−1
0	−4
3	1

    B. x $-3 \to 2$ $5 \to 9$ y

    C. (graph)

    D. (graph)

16. _____

17. Which equation represents
    the function?

x	−2	0	1	4
y	−3	−1	0	3

    A. $-x + y = 1$ B. $x - y = 1$ C. $x + y = 1$ D. $x + y = -1$

17. _____

**Use the stem-and-leaf plot at the right for
questions 18–20. 2|4 represents 24.**

Stem	Leaf
1	1 5 6 7 7 8
2	0 2 4 5 7 9 9
3	3 3 3 9

18. Find the range of the set of data.
    A. 28   B. 9
    C. 13   D. 11

18. _____

19. Find the interquartile range of the data.
    A. 1   B. 2   C. 7   D. 14

19. _____

20. Find the outlier in the data.
    A. 11   B. 39   C. 33   D. none

20. _____

Bonus   Graph the equations $3x - 2y = 12$ and $y = 3$ on the same
graph. Find the coordinates of the point where the graphs
intersect.

Bonus _____

5

Chapter 5 Test, Form 2A

1. Name the quadrant in which each point is located.
   $A(-3, -8)$ $B(-6, 2)$ $C(0, -7)$

   1. _____

2. Graph these points on the coordinate plane provided.
   $A(4, 1)$ $B(2, -4)$
   $C(-2, 0)$ $D(0, 4)$

   2.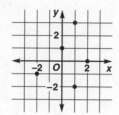

Use the graph to answer questions 3 and 4.

3. Write the relation as a set of ordered pairs.

   3. _____

4. State the domain, range, and inverse of the relation.

   4. _____

5. Draw a mapping for the relation $\{(4, -1), (6, -2), (3, -1)\}$.

   5.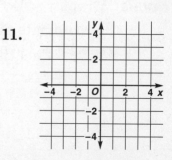

6. Write the relation in the table as a set of ordered pairs.

x	y
-4	3
5	2

   6. _____

7. Solve $9 - 6t = 10d$ for t.

   7. _____

8. Solve $6m - 5n = -14$ for m.

   8. _____

9. Solve the equation $m + 2w = -5$ if the domain is $\{-3, 0, 4\}$.

   9. _____

10. Which of the following equations are linear equations? Write the letter for each linear equation in the answer blank.
    a. $x - 6y = 8$ **b.** $y = -1$ **c.** $y = x^2 + 4$
    d. $\frac{x}{2} + \frac{y}{3} = 5$ **e.** $\frac{5}{x} + \frac{3}{y} = 8$

    10. _____

11. Graph $y = 2x - 1$. Use the coordinate plane provided.

    11.

Algebra 1

12. Graph $y = -1$. Use the coordinate plane provided.

12.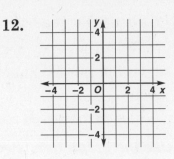

13. Determine whether each relation is a function. Then write the letter for each function in the answer blank.

13. _____

a.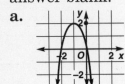

b. $\{(-6, -2), (5, 8), (5, 4)\}$
c. $\{(4, 9), (2, -1), (5, 9)\}$
d. $3x = 11$
e. $y - 6 = -3$

14. Given $f(x) = -3x + 5$, find $f(4)$.

14. _____

15. Given $g(x) = 2x^2 - 3$, find $g(-4)$.

15. _____

16. Find the range and interquartile range for the data listed below.
397, 372, 421, 557, 591, 572, 545

16. _____

Write an equation for the relation given in each chart.

17.

x	1	2	3	4	5
y	7	10	13	16	19

18.

x	-2	0	2	4
y	9	5	1	-3

17. _____

18. _____

19. In a set of data, the lower quartile is 83 and the upper quartile is 97. Find the greatest number below 83 that can be an outlier.

19. _____

20. Find the median, lower quartile, upper quartile, and interquartile range of the data listed below. Determine whether there are any outliers.
3, 10, 16, 19, 27, 31, 35, 64

20. _____

Bonus Graph $y = \frac{1}{2}x$, $2y + 3x = 8$, and $y = -2$ on the coordinate plane provided. Name the geometric figure formed. Then state the coordinates at each vertex.

Bonus _____

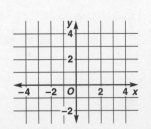

5

Chapter 5 Test, Form 2B

Use the table to answer questions 1 and 2.

1. Write the relation as a set of ordered pairs.

x	y
6	−2
−3	4
0	5

1. _____

2. State the domain, range, and inverse of the relation.

2. _____
_____
_____

3. Graph these points on the coordinate plane provided.
   A(3, 2)   B(−3, 0)   C(0, −2)   D(3, −4)

3.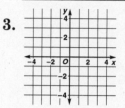

4. Name the quadrant in which each point is located.
   A(−5, 7)   B(2, −4)   C(6, 0)

4. _____

5. Draw a mapping for the relation {(1, 4), (−5, 0), (7, 4)}.

5.

Use the graph to answer questions 6 and 7.

6. Write the relation in the graph as a set of ordered pairs.

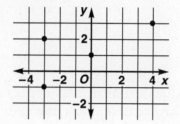

6. _____

7. State the domain, range, and inverse of the relation.

7. _____
_____
_____

8. Solve $3x + y = 6$ for y.

8. _____

9. Solve the equation $m - 2n = 9$ if the domain is {−1, 0, 5}.

9. _____

10. Which of the following equations are linear equations? Write the letter for each linear equation in the answer blank.
    a. $xy = 6$ b. $y = 0$ c. $4x = 2y$
    d. $x - y = 0$ e. $y^2 - 4x = 0$

10. _____

11. Graph $x - 4y = 2$. Use the coordinate plane provided.

11.

12. Graph $2x = -3y$. Use the coordinate plane provided.

12.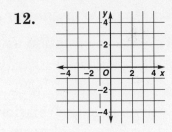

13. Determine whether each relation is a function. Then write the letter for each function in the answer blank.
    a. $\{(5, 3), (2, -1), (-1, 3)\}$ e.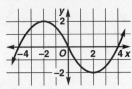
    b. $\{(2, 1), (2, -4), (-3, 0)\}$
    c. $x - 8 = 0$
    d. $4y = 9x$

13. _____

14. Given $f(x) = x^2 + 3x - 2$, find $f(2)$.

14. _____

15. Given $h(x) = 4x + 8$, find $4\left[h\left(-\dfrac{3}{4}\right)\right]$.

15. _____

Write an equation for the relation given in each chart.

16.
x	1	2	3	4	5
y	5	7	9	11	13

16. _____

17.
x	-2	0	2	4
y	10	2	-6	-14

17. _____

18. Li Teng is ordering graduation announcements for the senior class. If 100 announcements are ordered, the cost is $225. The cost for 175 announcements is $375, and 200 announcements cost $425. Write an equation to describe this relationship and use it to find the cost of 250 announcements.

18. _____

19. Find the median and upper and lower quartiles for this set of data: 200, 250, 230, 180, 160, 140.

19. _____

20. Find the interquartile range for the data in question 19.

20. _____

Bonus Graph $x = 3$, $y = -1$, and $2x - 2y = 0$ on the coordinate plane provided. Name the geometric figure formed. Then state the coordinates of each vertex.

Bonus _____

5 Chapter 5 Test, Form 2C

1. Name the quadrant in which each point is located.
   $A(1, -3)$ $B(-2, -4)$ $C(0, 0)$

1. _____

2. Graph the points on the coordinate plane provided.
   $A(-3, 0)$ $B(2, -2)$ $C(1, 5)$ $D(-2, -4)$

2.

Use the table at the right for questions 3–5.

3. State the domain, range, and inverse of the relation.

x	y
8	7
4	-5
0	-2
-2	0

3. _____
_____
_____
_____

4. Write the relation as a set of ordered pairs.

4. _____

5. Draw a mapping for the relation.

5.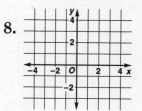

6. Solve $4s - 6t = 12$ for t.

6. _____

7. Find the domain of the equation $2x = 3y$ if the range is $\{0, 2, 4, 5\}$.

7. _____

8. Graph the equation in question 7 on the coordinate plane provided.

8.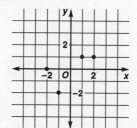

9. Given $g(x) = 3x - 7$, find $2[g(\frac{5}{6})]$.

9. _____

Use the graph to answer questions 10 and 11.

10. Write the relation in the graph as a set of ordered pairs.

10. _____

11. State the inverse of the relation.

11. _____

12. Which of the following equations are linear equations? Write the letter for each linear equation in the answer blank.
    a. $2x^2 - 3y^2 = 36$ b. $2r + 3q + 7 = 3$
    c. $xy + 3y = -2$ d. $\frac{1}{x} + \frac{1}{y} = \frac{2}{3}$

12. _____

13. Graph $m + 4n - 3 = 0$. Use the coordinate plane provided.

13.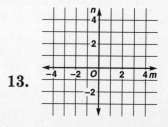

14. Determine whether each relation is a function. Then write the letter for each function in the answer blank.

14. _____

   a.

x	3	2	0	5
y	0	1	-1	2

   b. $\{(1, 3), (-1, 3), (3, 0), (1, 5)\}$

   c.

   d.

   e.

15. The weights of each of the players on a football team are given below. Find the range, the upper quartile, and the lower quartile for the data.
175, 189, 198, 198, 228, 245, 248, 287, 293, 319, 347, 399

15. _____

Write an equation for the relation given in each chart.

16.

x	-1	0	1	2
y	3	1	-1	-3

16. _____

17.

x	-1	0	1	2
y	-6	-3	0	3

17. _____

18. Marika is ordering box lunches for a class picnic. A caterer tells her that 15 lunches will cost $52.50, 20 lunches will cost $70.00, and 25 lunches will cost $87.50. Write an equation to describe this relationship and use it to find the cost of 30 lunches.

18. _____

19. Find the interquartile range for the data in the stem-and-leaf plot. 3|8 represents 38.

Stem	Leaf
1	4 7 8 8 9
2	4 5 9
3	0 0 2 5 8
4	1 1 9

19. _____

20. State the outlier for the data in problem 15, if there is one. If there is no outlier, write *none* on the answer blank.

20. _____

Bonus Graph the points $(4, -2)$, $(4, 3)$, $(-2, 3)$. Find a fourth point that completes a rectangle with the given three points. Use the coordinate plane provided.

Bonus _____

5

Chapter 5 Calculator-Based Test

Plot each set of points. Then, if possible, on your graphing calculator, connect the points. Tell what shape is formed.

1. $\{(2, 5), (6, -17), (-1, -17), (-5, 5)\}$

2. $\{(3, 1), (3, -5), (-3, -5), (-3, 1)\}$

1. _____

2. _____

Graph each relation. State the quadrants in which the graph lies.

3. $y = 3x + 7$

4. $y = \frac{2}{3}x$

5. $3x + 4y = 12$

6. $2x - 5y = 25$

7. $6.4x + 2.5y = 0$

8. $1.7x + 0.7y = -3$

3. _____

4. _____

5. _____

6. _____

7. _____

8. _____

Determine whether the linear equations in each pair are equivalent.

9. $2x + 4.5y = 12$
    $4x + 9y = 24$

10. $7.2x - 3.6y = 7$
     $1.5y = 5.1x + 3$

9. _____

10. _____

Graph each relation. Tell whether it is a function or not a function.

11. $y = \frac{4}{5}x - 2$

12. $y = x^2 + 2x - 3$

13. $y = x^3 - 3x + 1$

11. _____

12. _____

13. _____

The average points per game scored by the 11 players on a basketball team are shown below.

   0.7   12.2   15.1   8.6   5.5   3.2   11.0   21.3   8.8   1.8   2.2

14. Find the range of the data.

14. _____

15. Find the median and the upper and lower quartiles.

15. _____

16. Find the interquartile range.

16. _____

5 Chapter 5 Performance Assessment

Instructions: *Demonstrate your knowledge by giving a clear, concise solution to each problem. Be sure to include all relevant drawings and justify your answers. You may show your solution in more than one way or investigate beyond the requirements of the problem.*

1. The members of sets X and Y are shown at the right.

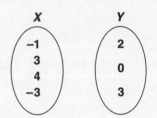

a. Draw a mapping of X to Y that shows a function. Tell how you know it is a function.

b. Draw a mapping of X to Y that represents a relation but not a function. Tell how you know it is a relation. Tell how you know it is not a function.

c. Graph the relation $\{(-1, 3), (3, 5), (3, -2), (4, 0), (-3, 2)\}$. Use the vertical line test to determine if the relation is a function. Write a sentence to explain your reasoning.

d. Express the relation shown in the mapping for part a as a set of ordered pairs. Then write the inverse of the relation. Is the inverse a function? Tell why or why not.

2. a. Complete the pattern in the chart.

x	-2	-1	0	1	2	3		
y	-9	-5	-1	3	7			

b. Write an equation for the relation shown in the chart.

c. Is the equation in part b a linear equation? Explain your answer.

d. Graph the equation in part b.

e. Is the inverse of the relation a linear function? Explain your answer.

3. The opening day scores in a local golf tournament are 78, 83, 70, 84, 89, 67, 84, 92, 78, 91, 85, 77, 68, 80, 71, 78, 99, 81, 75, 88, 90, 71, 73.

a. Find the range and interquartile range of the scores. Tell in your own words the purpose of finding the range or interquartile range.

b. Is the range or the interquartile range more affected by outliers?

c. Display the results in a stem-and-leaf plot.

NAME_____ DATE _____

Chapter 5 Mid-Chapter Test (Lessons 5-1 through 5-4)

1. Graph these points on the coordinate system provided.

   $A(-3, 0)$ $B(1, -2)$ $C(0, 2)$ $D(-2, -1)$

1.

2. Name the quadrant in which each point above is located.

2. _____

Write each relation as a set of ordered pairs.

3.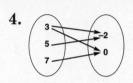

4.

5.

x	y
-2	3
5	0
7	-1
3	9

3. _____

4. _____

5. _____

Given the relation {(−1, 2), (3, −4), (0, 5)}, state each of the following.

6. the domain   7. the range   8. the inverse

6. _____

7. _____

8. _____

Solve each equation for the variable indicated.

9. $-5x + y = -10$ for y 10. $4m = 5 - 2t$ for t

9. _____

10. _____

Solve each equation if the domain is {−1, 0, 4}.

11. $y = 2x - 7$ 12. $x - y = 10$ 13. $3y - x = 6$

11. _____

12. _____

13. _____

Determine whether each equation is a linear equation.

14. $xy = 24$ 15. $x - 9 = 0$

16. $3x = 8y$ 17. $y^2 = x - 6$

14. _____

15. _____

16. _____

17. _____

18. Graph $2x - 3y = 6$.

18.

A video rental costs \$1.25 plus \$.75 for each day. The total charge t, in dollars, for a video rental of d days is given by the equation $t = 0.75d + 1.25$.

19. Draw the graph of this equation.

19.

20. Use the graph to estimate the number of days you can rent a videotape for \$5.00.

20. _____

Bonus Find the domain of $y = x^2$ if the range is {4, 9}.

Bonus _____

5

Chapter 5, Quiz A (Lessons 5-1 and 5-2)

1. Graph the relation {(4, 3), (3, 2), (−5, −3)}. Use the coordinate plane at the right.

1.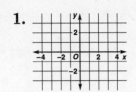

2. State the domain, range, and inverse of the relation {(4, 3), (3, 2), (−5, −3)}.

2. _____
_____
_____

3. Write the relation shown in the graph as a set of ordered pairs.

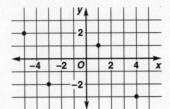

3. _____

4. Draw a mapping for the relation {(3, 5), (−4, 6), (3, 8)}.

4.

5. Name the quadrant in which the point $P(8, −5)$ is located.

5. _____

5

Chapter 5, Quiz B (Lessons 5-3 and 5-4)

1. Solve for w: $6y + w = −8$.

1. _____

2. Solve $y = 4x − 3$ if the domain is {−3, 0, 2}.

2. _____

Determine whether each equation is a linear equation.

3. $y = 2x − 1$ 4. $3x + y^2 = 7$

3. _____

4. _____

5. Graph $3x − y = 3$. Use the coordinate plane at the right.

5.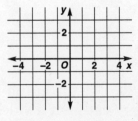

NAME_____ DATE _____

Chapter 5, Quiz C (Lessons 5-5 and 5-6)

Determine whether each relation is a function.

1. $\{(-2, 3), (-1, 2), (0, 1), (1, 0)\}$ 1. _____

2. $\{(1, -1), (-1, 1), (2, -2), (2, 3)\}$ 2. _____

3. $x^2 = y + 1$ 4. $x = 4$ 3. _____

4. _____

Given $g(x) = x^2 - 3x + 2$, determine the value for each function.

5. $g(-4)$ 6. $g(2a)$ 7. $g\left(\dfrac{1}{3}\right)$ 8. $g(0.1)$ 5. _____

6. _____

7. _____

8. _____

Write an equation for the relation given in each chart.

9.
x	1	2	3	4
y	7	17	27	37

10.
m	2	3	4	5
n	4	7	10	13

9. _____

10. _____

NAME_____ DATE _____

Chapter 5, Quiz D (Lesson 5-7)

The average number of miles per gallon for cars manufactured by a certain company in each year of a recent ten-year period are given below.
16.3, 13.9, 14.2, 15.3, 17.1, 16.8, 15.7, 14.3, 13.7, 14.5

1. Find the median for the data.   1. _____

2. Find the range for the data.   2. _____

3. State the upper and lower quartiles for the data.   3. _____

4. State the interquartile range.   4. _____

5. State the outlier or outliers for the data. If there is none, write *none* in the answer blank.   5. _____

Choose the best answer. Write A, B, C, or D.

1. Find $\frac{a}{c}$ if a is $\frac{2}{3}$ of b and b is $\frac{5}{7}$ of c.
   A. $\frac{10}{21}$ B. $\frac{14}{15}$ C. $\frac{7}{10}$ D. $\frac{9}{8}$

   1._____

2. The ratio of Coretta's weight to Justin's weight is 3:4. If Coretta gains 5 pounds, the ratio of their weights will be 4:5. How many pounds does Justin weigh?
   A. 25   B. 75   C. 80   D. 100

   2._____

3. How much more is $x - 12$ than -12?
   A. $12 - x$ B. -12 C. x D. 12

   3._____

4. The price of an item was reduced by 20%, then later reduced by 15%. The two reductions are equivalent to a single deduction of
   A. 32%.   B. 35%.   C. 65%.   D. 68%.

   4._____

5. If $m > 1$ and $n < 0$, then
   A. $m > n$.   B. $n > m$.   C. $m = n$.   D. none of these

   5._____

6. If Amy earns d dollars in h hours, how many dollars will she earn in 40 hours?
   A. $40dh$ B. $40d$ C. $\frac{40h}{d}$ D. $\frac{40d}{h}$

   6._____

7. For the relation $\{(-1, 0), (3, -3), (5, -2), (4, 3), (3, 1)\}$, $\{0, -3, -2, 3, 1\}$ is the
   A. domain.
   C. upper quartile.
   B. range.
   D. interquartile range.

   7._____

8. Which of the following is the greatest?
   A. the number of which 12 is 30%   B. the number of which 12 is 10%
   C. the number of which 12 is 60%   D. the number of which 12 is 100%

   8._____

9. If $24 \cdot 24 = 8 \cdot 8 \cdot y$, then $y =$
   A. 3.   B. 6.   C. 8.   D. 9.

   9._____

10. If $4y - 1$ is an odd integer, what is the next consecutive odd integer?
    A. $4y$ B. $4y - 3$ C. $4y + 1$ D. $4y + 3$

    10._____

5

Chapter 5 Cumulative Review

1. Evaluate $[9(7 - 5) + 8 \cdot 2^2] \div 2 + 8$. (Lesson 1-3)

1. _____

2. State the property shown in the following statement: If $3 + 2 = 5$, then $5 = 3 + 2$. (Lesson 1-6)

2. _____

3. Graph the solution set of $x < 6$ on the number line. (Lesson 2-1)

3. ⟵+┼┼┼┼┼┼┼┼+⟶
   −1 0 1 2 3 4 5 6 7

Simplify. (Lessons 2-6 and 2-7)

4. _____

4. $(-3)(-5)(6)$

5. $\dfrac{-27}{-\frac{1}{3}}$

5. _____

Solve each equation. (Lessons 1-3, 3-3, and 3-5)

6. _____

6. $x + (-7) = 16$

7. $12 = m - (-6)$

7. _____

8. $\dfrac{a}{2} + 9 = 30$

9. $\dfrac{3}{4}n - 8 = \dfrac{2}{3}n + 5$

8. _____

Find the next two items in each pattern or sequence. (Lesson 1-2)

9. _____

10. 1, 3, 2, 6, 5, 15

10. _____

11.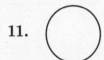

11. _____

Use the stem-and-leaf plot for exercises 12–17. (Lessons 1-4, 2-2, 3-7, and 4-6)

Test Scores

Stem	Leaf
6	0 4 8
7	0 3 3 5 8
8	1 1 5 6 9 9 9
9	0 1 3 5 7

$7|5 = 75$

12. Make a line plot of the data.

12. _____

13. Find the mode of the data.

13. _____

14. Find the median of the data.

14. _____

15. Find the mean of the data.

15. _____

16. What is the probability that a student chosen at random had a score in the 70s?

16. _____

17. What are the odds that a student chosen at random had a score in the 90s?

17. _____

18. Graph the solution set of $r \neq -6$ on the number line. (Lesson 2-1)

18. ⟵+┼┼┼┼┼┼┼┼+⟶
   −8 −7 −6 −5 −4 −3 −2 −1 0 1

Algebra 1

19. If tan $D = 1.4213$, find the measure of $\angle D$ to the nearest degree. (Lesson 4-3)

19._____

20. The length of the side opposite the 30° angle in a 30°-60° right triangle is 5.5 cm. Find the length of the hypotenuse. (Lesson 4-3)

20._____

21. Solve right triangle ABC if $\angle C$ is the right angle, the measure of $\angle A = 36°$, and $a = 7$. (Lesson 4-3)

21._____

Solve each problem.

22. Phyllis invested $12,000, part at 14% annual interest and the remainder at 10%. Last year she earned $1632 in interest. How much money did she invest at each rate? (Lesson 4-7)

22._____

23. Paul and Charlene are 420 miles apart. They start toward each other with Paul driving 16 mi/h faster than Charlene. They meet in 5 hours. Find Charlene's speed. (Lesson 4-7)

23._____

24. Tosha has 7 more nickels than quarters. In all, she has $1.25. How many nickels does she have? (Lesson 4-7)

24._____

25. If y varies directly as x and $y = 5$ when $x = -4$, find y when $x = 7$. (Lesson 4-8)

25._____

26. A price of $48 was reduced by $12. Find the percent of decrease. (Lesson 4-5)

26._____

27. A pair of running shoes cost $64. There is a 4.5% sales tax. Find the total price. (Lesson 4-5)

27._____

28. State the quadrant in which the point with coordinates $(-1, 5)$ is located. (Lesson 5-1)

28._____

29. Express the relation at the right as a set of ordered pairs. Then state the domain and range. (Lesson 5-2)

29._____

30. State whether the relation in exercise 29 is a function. (Lesson 5-5)

30._____

31. Write an equation for the relationship between the variables in the chart at the right. (Lesson 5-6)

x	1	2	3	4
y	8	10	12	14

31._____

32. Solve $4x = 5 + y$ if the domain is $\{-3, -1, 1, 5\}$. (Lesson 5-3)

32._____

33. Given $f(x) = 12x^2 - 5x - 3$, find $f(-2)$. (Lesson 5-5)

33._____

Chapter 5 Answer Key

1. **B**

11. **D**

2. **D**

12. **C**

13. **C**

3. **C**

4. **C**

14. **B**

5. **A**

15. **B**

6. **C**

16. **A**

7. **C**

17. **B**

8. **B**

18. **D**

19. **B**

20. **C**

9. **A**

Bonus **Some possible points are $(-4, -1)$, $(7, -1)$, and $(2, 15)$. The area of all the parallelograms is the same.**

10. **C**

1. **C**

11. **B**

12. **D**

2. **C**

13. **C**

3. **A**

4. **D**

14. **C**

5. **D**

15. **D**

16. **C**

6. **C**

7. **B**

17. **D**

8. **C**

18. **A**

19. **D**

9. **C**

20. **D**

Bonus

10. **A**

Chapter 5 Answer Key

Form 1C		Form 2A	
Page 117	**Page 118**	**Page 119**	**Page 120**

Form 1C

Page 117

1. __C__

2. __C__

3. __A__

4. __D__

5. __B__

6. __B__

7. __D__

8. __A__

9. __C__

10. __B__

11. __B__

Page 118

12. __D__

13. __B__

14. __C__

15. __C__

16. __C__

17. __B__

18. __A__

19. __D__

20. __B__

Bonus __(6, 3)__

Form 2A

Page 119

1. __III; II; none__

2.

3. $\{(-2, -1), (0, 1), (1, 3), (1, -2,), (2, 0)\}$

4. D: $\{-2, 0, 1, 2\}$; R: $\{-2, -1, 0, 1, 3\}$; I: $\{(-1, -2), (1, 0), (3, 1), (-2, 1), (0, 2)\}$

5.

6. $\{(-4, 3), (5, 2)\}$

7. $t = \dfrac{9 - 10d}{6}$

8. $m = \dfrac{5n - 14}{6}$

9. $\{(-3, -1), \left(0, -\dfrac{5}{2}\right), \left(4, -\dfrac{9}{2}\right)\}$

10. __a, b, d__

11.

Page 120

12.

13. __a, c, e__

14. __−7__

15. __29__

16. range: 219; interq. range: 175

17. $y = 3x + 4$

18. $y = -2x + 5$

19. __62__

20. median: 23; LQ: 13; UQ: 33; interq. range: 20; 64 is an outlier

Bonus __triangle; (2, 1), (4, −2), (−4, −2)__

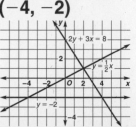

Chapter 5 Answer Key

Form 2B

Page 121

1. {(6, −2), (−3, 4), (0, 5)}

2. D: {6, −3, 0};
   R: {−2, 4, 5};
   I: {(−2, 6), (4, −3), (5, 0)}

3.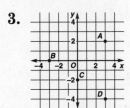

4. II; IV; none

5.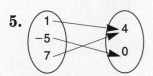

6. {(−3, 2), (−3, −1), (0, 1), (4, 3)}

7. D: {−3, 0, 4};
   R: {−1, 1, 2, 3};
   I: {(−1, −3), (1, 0), (2, −3), (3, 4)}

8. $y = 6 − 3x$

9. {(−1, −5), $\left(0, -\dfrac{9}{2}\right)$, (5, −2)}

10. b, c, d

11.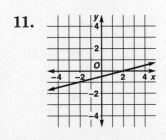

Page 122

12.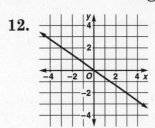

13. a, d, e

14. 8

15. 20

16. $y = 2x + 3$

17. $y = −4x + 2$

18. $c = 25 + 2a$; $525

19. median: 190; UQ: 230; LQ: 160

20. interq. range: 70

Bonus   triangle; (3, 3), (3, −1), (−1, −1)

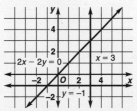

Chapter 5 Answer Key

Page 123	Page 124	Calculator-Based Page 125

1. *A*: IV; *B*: III; *C*: none

2.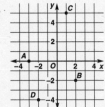

3. D: {8, 4, 0, −2};
R: {7, −5, −2, 0};
I: {(7, 8), (−5, 4),
(−2, 0), (0, −2)}

4. {(8, 7), (4, −5),
(0, −2), (−2, 0)}

5. *x*
8 → 7
4 → −5
0 → −2
−2 → 0
y

6. $t = \dfrac{2s - 6}{3}$

7. {0, 3, 6, 7.5}

8. (graph)

9. −9

10. {(−2, 0), (−1, −2),
(1, 1), (2, 1)}

11. {(0, −2), (−2, −1),
(1, 1), (1, 2)}

12. b

13. (graph)

14. a, d

15. R: 224; UQ: 306;
LQ: 198

16. $y = -2x + 1$

17. $y = 3x - 3$

18. $y = 3.50x$; $105.00

19. 18

20. none

Bonus   (−2, −2)

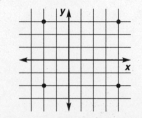

Calculator-Based Page 125

1. parallelogram

2. square

3. I, II, III

4. I, III

5. I, II, IV

6. I, III, IV

7. II, IV

8. II, III, IV

9. equivalent

10. not equivalent

11. function

12. function

13. function

14. 20.6

15. median: 8.6; UQ:
12.2; LQ: 2.2

16. 10

Scoring Guide
Chapter 5
Performance Assessment

Level	Specific Criteria
3 Superior	• Shows thorough understanding of the concepts of *relation, function, inverse function, domain, range, linear equation,* and *measures of variation.* • Computations are correct. • Written explanations are exemplary. • Graphs and diagrams are accurate and appropriate. • Goes beyond requirements of some or all problems.
2 Satisfactory, with Minor Flaws	• Shows understanding of the concepts of *relation, function, inverse function, domain, range, linear equation,* and *measures of variation.* • Computations are mostly correct. • Written explanations are effective. • Graphs and diagrams are accurate and appropriate. • Satisfies all requirements of problems.
1 Nearly Satisfactory, with Serious Flaws	• Shows understanding of most of the concepts of *relation, function, inverse function, domain, range, linear equation,* and *measures of variation.* • Computations are mostly correct. • Written explanations are satisfactory. • Graphs and diagrams are mostly accurate and appropriate. • Satisfies most requirements of problems.
0 Unsatisfactory	• Shows little or no understanding of the concepts of *relation, function, inverse function, domain, range, linear equation,* and *measures of variation.* • May not use appropriate strategies to solve problems. • Computations are incorrect. • Written explanations are not satisfactory. • Graphs and diagrams are not accurate or appropriate. • Does not satisfy requirements of problems.

Chapter 5 Answer Key
Performance Assessment

Page 126

1. a.

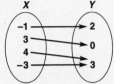

It is a function because each element in X, the domain, is paired with only one element in Y, the range.

b.

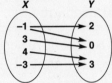

It is a relation because it represents a set of ordered pairs, but it is not a function because -1 in the domain is paired with two values in the range.

c.

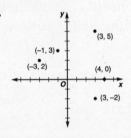

It is not a function because you can draw a vertical line that passes through two points on the graph of the relation.

d. Answers based on answers to part a. relation: $\{(-1, 2), (3, 0), (4, 3), (-3, 3)\}$; inverse: $\{(2, -1), (0, 3), (3, 4), (3, -3)\}$. It is not a function because an element in the domain is paired with two elements in the range.

2. a.

x	-2	-1	0	1	2	3	4	5
y	-9	-5	-1	3	7	11	15	19

b. $y = 4x - 1$

c. yes, because it can be written as $4x - y = 1$, which is in linear form

d.

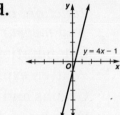

e. yes, because $y = \dfrac{x + 1}{4}$, the inverse relation, is a linear function

3. a. Range is $99 - 67 = 32$. Interquartile range is $88 - 73 = 15$.

b. range

c.

Stem	Leaf
6	7 8
7	0 1 1 3 5 7 8 8 8
8	0 1 3 4 4 5 8 9
9	0 1 2 9

Chapter 5 Answer Key

Mid-Chapter Test Page 127	Quiz A Page 128	Quiz C Page 129

Mid-Chapter Test
Page 127

1. [graph]

2. *A*: none; *B*: IV;
   C: none; *D*: III

3. $\{(-3, -2), (-1, 0),$
   $(2, 2), (3, -1)\}$

4. $\{(3, -2), (3, 0),$
   $(5, -2), (7, 0)\}$

5. $\{(-2, 3), (5, 0),$
   $(7, -1), (3, 9)\}$

6. $\{-1, 3, 0\}$

7. $\{2, \quad 4, 5\}$

8. $\{(2, -1), (-4, 3),$
   $(5, 0)\}$

9. $y = 5x - 10$

10. $t = \dfrac{5 - 4m}{2}$

11. $\{(-1, -9), (0, -7),$
    $(4, 1)\}$

12. $\{(-1, -11), (0, -10),$
    $(4, -6)\}$

13. $\left\{\left(-1, 1\dfrac{2}{3}\right), (0, 2),\right.$
    $\left.\left(4, 3\dfrac{1}{3}\right)\right\}$

14. no

15. yes

16. yes

17. no

18. [graph]

19. [graph]

20. 5 days

Bonus $\{\pm 2, \pm 3\}$

Quiz A
Page 128

1. [graph]

2. D: $\{4, 3, -5\}$;
   R: $\{3, 2, -3\}$;
   I: $\{(3, 4), (2, 3),$
   $(-3, -5)\}$

3. $\{(-5, 2), (-3, -2),$
   $(1, 1), (4, -3)\}$

4.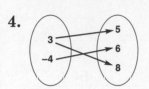

5. IV

Quiz B
Page 128

1. $w = -6y - 8$

2. $\{(-3, -15), (0, -3),$
   $(2, 5)\}$

3. yes

4. no

5. [graph]

Quiz C
Page 129

1. yes

2. no

3. yes

4. no

5. 30

6. $4a^2 - 6a + 2$

7. $1\dfrac{1}{9}$

8. 1.71

9. $y = 10x - 3$

10. $n = 3m - 2$

Quiz D
Page 129

1. 14.9

2. 3.4

3. 16.3; 14.2

4. 2.1

5. none

Algebra 1

Chapter 5 Answer Key

Standardized Test Practice
Page 130

1. __A__

2. __D__

3. __C__

4. __A__

5. __A__

6. __D__

7. __B__

8. __B__

9. __D__

10. __C__

Cumulative Review

Page 131

1. __33__

2. __symmetric__

3.

4. __90__

5. __81__

6. __23__

7. __6__

8. __42__

9. __156__

10. __14, 42__

11.

12.

13. __89__

14. __83__

15. __81.35__

16. $\frac{1}{4}$, or __0.25__

17. __1:3__

18.

Page 132

19. __55°__

20. __11 cm__

21. $\angle B = 54°$; $b = 9.6$; $c = 11.9$

22. __$10,800 at 14%; $1200 at 10%__

23. __34 mi/h__

24. __10 nickels__

25. __−8.75__

26. __25%__

27. __$66.88__

28. __II__

29. {(−2, 3), (−1, 2), (0, 2), (1, 1), (2, 0), (2, −1); D: {−2, −1, 0, 1, 2}; R: {−1, 0, 1, 2, 3}

30. __no__

31. $y = 2x + 6$

32. {(−3, −17), (−1, −9), (1, −1), (5, 15)}

33. __55__

6

Chapter 6 Test, Form 1A

Write the letter for the correct answer in the blank at the right of each problem.

1. What is the slope of the line passing through (1, 9) and (−3, 16)?   1. _____
   A. $-\frac{7}{4}$ B. $-\frac{4}{7}$ C. $-\frac{25}{2}$ D. $-\frac{2}{25}$

2. Find the value of r so that the line through (8, r) and (4, 5) has a   2. _____
   slope of −4.
   A. 11   B. −11   C. 4   D. −4

3. What is the slope of the line passing through (−4, 3) and (5, 3)?   3. _____

   A. 0   B. no slope   C. 9   D. 1

4. Find an equation of the line through (6, −3) with slope $\frac{2}{3}$.   4. _____
   A. $-2x + 3y = 24$ B. $-2x + 3y = -21$
   C. $3x - 2y = 24$ D. $3x - 2y = -21$

5. Find an equation of the line through (4, −5) and (6, −9).   5. _____
   A. $x + 2y = -6$ B. $x + 2y = -12$
   C. $2x + y = 3$ D. $14x + 10y = 6$

6. Which equation is graphed at the right?   6. _____
   A. $2y - x = 10$
   B. $2x + y = -5$
   C. $2x - y = 5$
   D. $2y + x = -5$

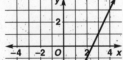
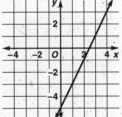

7. Which is the scatter plot for (1970, 45.3),   7. _____
   (1980, 31.2), (1986, 24.5)?
   A.   B.   C.   D.

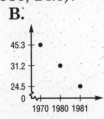
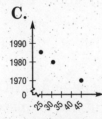
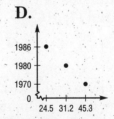

8. If a scatter plot of y versus x has a positive correlation, then   8. _____
   A. as y decreases, x increases.   B. as y decreases, x decreases.
   C. as y increases, x decreases.   D. both A and C are true.

9. Find an equation of the line containing (2, −5) and (6, 3).   9. _____
   A. $y = \frac{1}{2}x - 6$ B. $y = \frac{1}{2}x$

   C. $y = 2x + 12$ D. $y = 2x - 9$

10. What is the equation of the line whose graph passes through   10. _____
    the origin and has a slope of $\frac{1}{4}$?

    A. $y = 4x$ B. $y = \frac{1}{4}x$ C. $y = x + \frac{1}{4}$ D. $y + \frac{1}{4} = x$

11. What is the x-intercept of the graph of the equation $3x - 4y = 20$?   11. _____
    A. 3   B. $\frac{3}{4}$ C. −5   D. $\frac{20}{3}$

12. What is the slope of the graph of $4x + 5y = 10$?

    A. $-\dfrac{4}{5}$ **B.** 2   **C.** 4   **D.** -4

12._____

13. Which line is the graph of the equation $y = -3x + 1$?

    A. p **B.** q
    C. r **D.** s

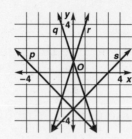

13._____

14. If line m has a slope of $-\dfrac{3}{8}$, then what is the slope of a line perpendicular to m?

    A. $-\dfrac{3}{8}$ **B.** $\dfrac{3}{8}$ **C.** $\dfrac{8}{3}$ **D.** $-\dfrac{8}{3}$

14._____

15. Find an equation of the line parallel to the graph of $4x + 2y = 8$ and containing $(-1, 5)$.

    A. $y = -2x + 9$ **B.** $y = 2x - 9$ **C.** $y = 2x + 7$ **D.** $y = -2x + 3$

15._____

16. What is the y-intercept of the line containing $(2, 7)$ and perpendicular to a line with slope $-\dfrac{3}{2}$?

    A. $-\dfrac{8}{3}$ **B.** $\dfrac{17}{3}$ **C.** $6\dfrac{1}{3}$ **D.** $5\dfrac{1}{2}$

16._____

17. What are the coordinates of the midpoint of the line segment with endpoints $(-6, 2)$ and $(7, 10)$?

    A. $(8, 13)$ **B.** $\left(\dfrac{13}{2}, 4\right)$ **C.** $\left(\dfrac{1}{2}, 6\right)$ **D.** $\left(-2, \dfrac{17}{2}\right)$

17._____

18. The center of a circle is $(-4, 7)$ and one endpoint of a diameter is $(2, -1)$. What is the other endpoint of the diameter?

    A. $(6, 15)$ **B.** $(-10, 16)$ **C.** $(-6, 13)$ **D.** $(-10, 15)$

18._____

19. What point is one-fourth the distance from A to B along segment AB for $A(-5, 3)$ and $B(7, -5)$?

    A. $P(1, -1)$ **B.** $P(-2, 1)$ **C.** $P\left(\dfrac{1}{2}, -\dfrac{1}{2}\right)$ **D.** $P(3, -2)$

19._____

20. To calculate the charge for a load of bricks, including delivery, the Redstone Brick Co. uses the equation $c = 0.42b + 25$, where c is the charge and b is the number of bricks. What is the delivery charge per load?

    A. \$42   **B.** \$67   **C.** \$25   **D.** \$17

20._____

Bonus For what value of k does $kx + 7y = 10$ have a slope of 3?

Bonus _____

6

Chapter 6 Test, Form 1B

Write the letter for the correct answer in the blank at the right of each problem.

1. What is the slope of the line passing through $(2, -8)$ and $(4, 1)$?
   A. $\frac{2}{9}$
   B. $-\frac{6}{7}$
   C. $-\frac{7}{6}$
   D. $\frac{9}{2}$

   1. _____

2. What is the slope of the line passing through $(-4, -6)$ and $(9, -6)$?
   A. $-\frac{12}{5}$
   B. $-\frac{5}{12}$
   C. 0
   D. no slope

   2. _____

3. Find an equation of the line through $(0, -3)$ with slope $\frac{2}{5}$.
   A. $-5x + 2y = 15$
   B. $-5x - 2y = -15$
   C. $2x - 5y = 15$
   D. $-2x + 5y = 15$

   3. _____

4. Find an equation of the line through $(-1, 7)$ and $(-4, 9)$.
   A. $-2x + 3y = 23$
   B. $-3x + 2y = 17$
   C. $2x + 3y = 19$
   D. $3x + 2y = 11$

   4. _____

5. Find an equation of the line through $(-2, -3)$ with no slope.
   A. $x = -2$
   B. $y = -3$
   C. $-2x - 3y = 0$
   D. $-3x + 2y = 0$

   5. _____

6. Which set of data is correctly displayed by the scatter plot at the right?
   A. 1980, 5.5; 1982, 6.1; 1989, 7.6
   B. 1980, 5.5; 1985, 6.1; 1989, 7.6
   C. 1980, 5.5; 1985, 6.6; 1990, 8.0
   D. 1980, 5.5; 1982, 6.6; 1990, 8.0

   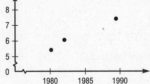

   6. _____

7. Based on the scatter plot in exercise 6, where would you expect the y-values to be in the year 1995?
   A. between 7 and 8
   B. higher than 8
   C. between 5 and 7
   D. impossible to tell

   7. _____

8. Which of the following r values indicates a strong negative correlation for a regression line?
   A. -1
   B. 0
   C. -2
   D. 1

   8. _____

9. Which is the slope of the line graphed at the right?
   A. $\frac{1}{2}$
   B. 2
   C. $-\frac{1}{2}$
   D. -2

   9. _____

10. Which line at the right has a slope of zero and contains $(-2, 1)$?
    A. e
    B. g
    C. h
    D. t

    10. _____

Algebra 1

11. What is the equation in slope-intercept form of the line whose graph has a slope of 5 and y-intercept of -8?
    A. $y = -8x + 5$ **B.** $y = 8x - 5$ **C.** $5x - y = -8$ **D.** $y = 5x - 8$

    11._____

12. Find an equation in slope-intercept form of the line that passes through $(-4, -9)$ and the origin.
    A. $y = \frac{9}{4}x$ **B.** $9x + 4y = 0$ **C.** $y = -9$ **D.** $y + 9 = x$

    12._____

13. A baby blue whale weighs 3 tons at birth. In 10 days, it weighs 4 tons. Assume that the growth can be represented by a straight line. Which equation shows the weight, w, when the whale is d days old?
    A. $w = 10d + 3$ **B.** $w = 10d + 4$
    C. $w = \frac{1}{10}d + 3$ **D.** $w = d + 10$

    13._____

14. What is the slope of the graph of $6x - 2y = 24$?
    A. -12 **B.** 3   **C.** -6 **D.** 6

    14._____

15. What is the x-intercept of the graph of $9x - y = 18$?
    A. 2   **B.** -2 **C.** 18   **D.** -18

    15._____

16. The lines $2x + y = 7$ and $2y = 9 - 4x$ are
    A. parallel.   **B.** perpendicular.
    C. the same line.   **D.** none of these.

    16._____

17. Find the equation of the line parallel to the graph of $12x - 3y = 10$ and passing through $(-5, 3)$.
    A. $y = -4x - 17$ **B.** $y = 4x - 13$
    C. $y = -4x + 13$ **D.** $y = 4x + 23$

    17._____

18. Find an equation of the line perpendicular to the graph of $y = 2x - 3$ and passing through $(2, -5)$.
    A. $x + 2y = -8$ **B.** $x - 2y = 12$
    C. $2x - y = 9$ **D.** $2x - y = -12$

    18._____

19. What are the coordinates of the midpoint of the segment whose endpoints are $(8, -5)$ and $(-6, 11)$?
    A. $(3, 1)$ **B.** $(7, 8)$ **C.** $(1, 3)$ **D.** $(7, -8)$

    19._____

20. P is the midpoint of line segment AB. If A has coordinates $(7, 1)$ and P has coordinates $(-3, -9)$, what are the coordinates of B?
    A. $(2, -4)$ **B.** $(-13, -19)$ **C.** $(17, 11)$ **D.** none of these

    20._____

Bonus Find the equation in slope-intercept form of the line with x-intercept -5 and y-intercept 8.

     Bonus _____

Write the letter for the correct answer in the blank at the right of each problem.

1. What is the slope of the line passing through (3, 7) and (−1, 4)?   1. _____
   A. $\frac{4}{3}$ B. $\frac{3}{4}$ C. $\frac{11}{2}$ D. $\frac{2}{11}$

2. What is the slope of the line passing through (−3, 2) and (6, 2)?   2. _____
   A. $\frac{4}{9}$ B. $\frac{4}{3}$ C. 0   D. no slope

3. What is the slope of the line at the right?   3. _____
   A. $\frac{2}{3}$ B. $\frac{3}{2}$
   C. $-\frac{3}{2}$ D. $-\frac{2}{3}$

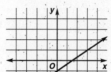

4. Find an equation of the line through (4, −2) with slope $\frac{1}{2}$.   4. _____

   A. $x + 2y = 0$ B. $x − 2y = 8$ C. $2x − y = 10$ D. $4x − 2y = 0$

5. Find an equation of the line through (−1, 1) and (2, 3).   5. _____
   A. $4x − 3y = −7$ B. $3x − 4y = −7$
   C. $3x − 2y = −5$ D. $2x − 3y = −5$

6. Find an equation of the line through (2, 4) with slope 0.   6. _____
   A. $x = 2$ B. $y = 2$ C. $x = 4$ D. $y = 4$

7. Which is the scatter plot for the data set (1970, 4), (1980, 5.5), (1990, 7)?   7. _____
   A.   B.   C.   D.

8. Based on the scatter plot below, where would you expect the   8. _____
   y-value to be in the year 2000?
   A. between 70 and 80   B. between 65 and 70
   C. between 55 and 65   D. below 55

9. Based on the scatter plot in exercise 8, how   9. _____
   would you best describe the relationship
   between the x- and y-values?
   A. strong negative correlation
   B. weak negative correlation
   C. weak positive correlation
   D. strong positive correlation

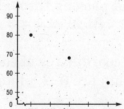

10. What is the equation of the line whose graph has a slope of 2   10. _____
    and a y-intercept of −5?
    A. $y = −5x + 2$ B. $y = 5x + 2$ C. $y = 2x + 5$ D. $y = 2x − 5$

11. What is the equation of the line that passes through (3, −4) and (0, 0)?   11. _____
    A. $y = −\frac{3}{4}x$ B. $y = −\frac{4}{3}x$ C. $y = 3x − 4$ D. $y = \frac{3}{4}x$

12. Which of the following is an equation of the line shown below?   12._____

    A. $y = 2x + 4$

    B. $y = -2x + 4$

    C. $y = \frac{1}{2}x + 4$

    D. $y = -\frac{1}{2}x + 4$

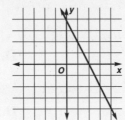

13. What is the x-intercept of the graph of $2x + 5y = 10$?   13._____

    A. 5   **B.** −5   **C.** 2   **D.** −2

14. What is the slope of the graph of $3x + 5y = 15$?   14._____

    A. 5   **B.** 3   **C.** $-\frac{3}{5}$ **D.** $-\frac{5}{3}$

15. Which of the following is the graph of $x - 2y = 4$?   15._____

    A. 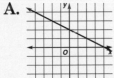   **B.**   **C.**   **D.**

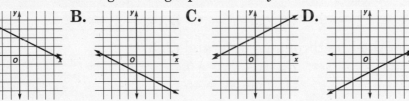

16. If line m has a slope of $\frac{4}{7}$, what is the slope of a line   16._____
perpendicular to m?

    A. $\frac{4}{7}$ **B.** $-\frac{4}{7}$ **C.** $\frac{7}{4}$ **D.** $-\frac{7}{4}$

17. Find the equation of the line parallel to the graph of $y = 2x - 3$ 17._____
and passing through $(-1, 2)$.

    A. $y = 2x + 4$ **B.** $y = -\frac{1}{2}x + 4$

    C. $y = 2x - 3$ **D.** $y = -\frac{1}{2} - 3$

18. Find the equation of the line perpendicular to the graph of   18._____
$x - 3y = 5$ and passing through $(0, 6)$.

    A. $x - 3y = 6$ **B.** $3x + y = 6$ **C.** $3y - x = 6$ **D.** $3x - y = 6$

19. What are the coordinates of the midpoint of the line segment   19._____
whose endpoints are $(-2, 5)$ and $(6, -7)$?

    A. $(4, -1)$ **B.** $(4, -2)$ **C.** $(2, -1)$ **D.** $(2, -2)$

20. One endpoint of a line segment is $(-3, -4)$. If the midpoint of the seg-   20._____
ment is at the origin, what are the coordinates of the other endpoint?

    A. $(3, 4)$ **B.** $(4, 3)$ **C.** $(-1.5, -2)$ **D.** $(-6, -8)$

Bonus   Find an equation in slope-intercept form of the line with   **Bonus** _____
x-intercept -3 and y-intercept 6.

Chapter 6 Test, Form 2A

Determine the slope of the line that passes through each pair of points. If the slope is undefined, write "no slope."

1. $(-8, 7)$ and $(5, -2)$

2. $(5, 9)$ and $(5, -3)$

Write an equation in standard form of the line satisfying the given conditions.

3. has a slope $-\frac{3}{5}$ and passes through $(2, 1)$

4. passes through $(2, -3)$ and $(-3, 7)$

5. Write $y + 4 = -\frac{2}{3}(x - 9)$ in standard form.

6. Make a scatter plot of the data listed in the table below. Plot the percent spent on entertainment on the vertical axis and the age on the horizontal axis.

Age	30	40	50	60	70	80
Percent Spent on Entertainment	6.1	6.0	5.4	5.0	4.7	3.4

7. Does the scatter plot in exercise 9 show a positive or negative correlation? What does that show about the relationship between age and the percent spent on entertainment?

8. Graph the line with x-intercept -3 and y-intercept -2. Use the coordinate plane at the right.

9. Graph the line with y-intercept -1 and slope $-\frac{2}{3}$. Use the coordinate plane at the right.

10. Graph the equation $y = 3x - 4$. Use the coordinate plane at the right.

1. _____

2. _____

3. _____

4. _____

5. _____

6.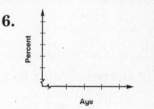

7. _____

8.

9.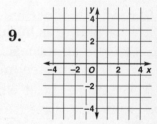

10.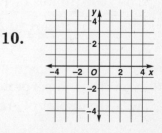

Write an equation in slope-intercept form of the line satisfying the given conditions.

11. has y-intercept -8 and slope 3

11. _____

12. has slope $\frac{5}{2}$ and passes through $(4, -1)$

12. _____

13. passes through $(-3, 7)$ and $(2, 4)$

13. _____

14. parallel to the graph of $3x - 5y = 7$ and passes through $(0, -6)$

14. _____

15. perpendicular to $y = \frac{3}{4}x - 2$ and passes through $(-12, 7)$

15. _____

16. perpendicular to the y-axis and passes through $(-2, 5)$

16. _____

17. Find the coordinates of the midpoint of the line segment with endpoints $(-3, 6)$ and $(-1, -9)$.

17. _____

18. P is the midpoint of the line segment AB. The coordinates of P are $(5, -6)$. The coordinates of A are $(-1, 10)$. Find the coordinates of B.

18. _____

19. A carpenter is building a stairway. The depth of each tread is 10 inches. The height of each riser is 8 inches. What is the steepness (slope) of the stairway?

19. _____

20. The endpoints of $\overline{AB}$ are $A(-4, 8)$ and $B(12, -4)$. Find the coordinates of P if P lies on $\overline{AB}$ and is $\frac{3}{8}$ the distance from A to B.

20. _____

Bonus Find the equation in slope-intercept form of the line that is perpendicular to $\overline{AB}$ and passes through the midpoint of $\overline{AB}$. Let $A = (-6, 2)$ and $B = (4, -10)$.

Bonus _____

Chapter 6 Test, Form 2B

Determine the slope of the line passing through each pair of points. If the slope is undefined, write "no slope."

1. $(6, -4)$ and $(-3, 7)$

1. _____

2. $(-2, -6)$ and $(7, -6)$

2. _____

3. Determine the value of r so that the line through $(-4, 8)$ and $(r, -6)$ has a slope of $\frac{2}{3}$.

3. _____

Write an equation in standard form of the line satisfying the given conditions.

4. has no slope and passes through $(-6, 4)$

4. _____

5. passes through $(1, -4)$ and $(-6, 8)$

5. _____

6. passes through $(7, -3)$ and has a y-intercept of 2

6. _____

The average SAT math and verbal scores for selected years from 1967 to 1985 are listed in the table below. Use the data for problems 7–9.

Year	Verbal Score	Math Score
1967	466	492
1970	460	488
1975	434	472
1980	424	466
1985	431	475

7. Make a scatter plot of the data with the verbal score on the horizontal axis and the math score on the vertical axis.

7.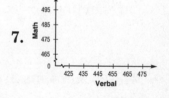

8. Is the correlation positive or negative?

8. _____

9. Predict the mathematics score corresponding to a verbal score of 445.

9. _____

10. Graph the line with x-intercept -3 and y-intercept 2. Use the coordinate plane at the right.

10.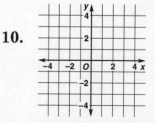

11. Graph the line with y-intercept 3 and slope $-\dfrac{3}{4}$. Use the coordinate plane at the right.

11.

12. Graph the equation $4x - 3y = -9$. Use the coordinate plane at the right.

12.

Write an equation in slope-intercept form of the line satisfying the given conditions.

13. passes through $(5, 4)$ and $(6, -1)$

13. _____

14. slope $\dfrac{1}{3}$ and passes through $(-2, 8)$

14. _____

15. passes through $(10, -3)$ and has a y-intercept of 2

15. _____

16. parallel to the graph of $9x + 3y = 6$ and passes through $(5, 3)$

16. _____

17. perpendicular to the graph of $4x - y = 12$ and passes through $(8, 2)$

17. _____

18. parallel to the x-axis and passes through $(4, 2)$

18. _____

19. Find the coordinates of the midpoint of the segment whose endpoints are $(-2, 14)$ and $(3, -9)$.

19. _____

20. The center of a circle is $M(-3, 0)$. If $\overline{AB}$ is a diameter, and $A(-7, 3)$ is one endpoint on the circle, find the coordinates of B.

20. _____

Bonus In a certain lake, a 1-year-old bluegill fish is 3 inches long, while a 4-year-old bluegill is 6.6 inches long. Assuming the growth rate can be approximated by a linear equation, write an equation in slope-intercept form for the length of a bluegill fish in inches (y) after x years. Use this equation to estimate the length of a 10-year-old bluegill. About how old is a 9-inch-long bluegill?

Bonus _____

Chapter 6 Test, Form 2C

Determine the slope of the line that passes through each pair of points. If the slope is undefined, write "no slope."

1. $(-2, 1)$ and $(3, -2)$

1. _____

2. $(-1, 3)$ and $(6, 3)$

2. _____

3. Determine the value of r so that the line through $(4, 5)$ and $(r, 3)$ has a slope of $\frac{2}{3}$.

3. _____

Write an equation in standard form of the line satisfying the given conditions.

4. has slope 3 and passes through $(4, 2)$

4. _____

5. passes through $(-5, 3)$ and $(1, -1)$

5. _____

6. has no slope and passes through $(5, -3)$

6. _____

7. Make a scatter plot of the data shown in the table. Plot the minutes spent studying on the horizontal axis and the percent score on the vertical axis.

Time Spent Studying (min)	10	20	30	40	50
Score	53	67	78	87	95

7.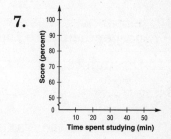

8. Is the correlation positive or negative?

8. _____

9. Predict a student's score if the student spent 35 minutes studying.

9. _____

10. Graph the line with x-intercept 3 and y-intercept -2. Use the coordinate plane at the right.

10.

11. Graph the line with y-intercept 2 and slope $-\frac{1}{2}$. Use the coordinate plane at the right.

11.

12. Graph the equation $y = 2x - 1$. Use the coordinate plane at the right.

12.

Write an equation in slope-intercept form of the line satisfying the given conditions.

13. has y-intercept -3 and slope 4

13. _____

14. passes through $(-1, -2)$ and $(3, 4)$

14. _____

15. has slope $\frac{4}{3}$ and passes through $(3, 0)$

15. _____

16. parallel to the graph of $2x + y = 5$ and passes through $(0, 1)$

16. _____

17. perpendicular to the graph of $y = -\frac{3}{2}x - 7$ and passes through $(3, -2)$

17. _____

18. parallel to the x-axis and passes through $(2, 3)$

18. _____

19. Segment RS contains endpoint $R(2, 5)$ and midpoint $M(3, 8)$. Find the coordinates of endpoint S.

19. _____

20. Find the coordinates of the midpoint of the line segment whose endpoints are $(-1, -3)$ and $(7, 11)$.

20. _____

Bonus   The center of a circle is $M(2, 0)$. If $\overline{AB}$ is a diameter, and $A(-1, 4)$ is one endpoint on the circle, find the coordinates of B.

Bonus _____

Chapter 6 Calculator-Based Test

Find the slope of the line that passes through each pair of points.

1. $(-458, 922)$ and $(240, -125)$

1. _____

2. $(3.07, 0.26)$ and $(2.94, -0.39)$

2. _____

3. $(12.7, -5.9)$ and $(-2.4, -7.2)$

3. _____

4. $(1954, 6546)$ and $(1995, 117{,}902)$

4. _____

Use the data in the table below for questions 5 and 6. Round numbers to the nearest hundredth.

Study Time (min)	15	25	21	50	55	30	36	42	28	18	23	47	53	39	37
Test Score	80	72	65	93	84	80	77	81	75	68	70	88	90	70	73

5. Use a graphing calculator to make a scatter plot of the data. Then describe the pattern of the points in the scatter plot.

5. _____

6. Write a sentence that generally describes the relationship between a student's test score and the amount of time he or she spent studying.

6. _____

Graph each group of equations on the same screen. Then describe the similarities and differences of the graphs.

7. $13y + 52x = 91$
$y = -4x - 1$
$8x + 2y = 10$

8. $y - 2 = 3(x - 2)$
$y = -\dfrac{1}{3}x - 4$
$2x - 3y = 12$

7. _____

8. _____

Determine whether the lines are parallel, perpendicular, or neither.

9. $4.813x + 1.745y = 10$ and $1.745x - 4.813y = -5$

9. _____

10. $12.73x - 4.924y = 15$ and $6.365x - 2.462y = 7$

10. _____

Write the equation of the line in standard form satisfying the given conditions.

11. passes through $(6.34, -3.12)$ and $(-1.66, 2.38)$

11. _____

12. has slope $-\dfrac{12}{19}$ and passes through $\left(3\dfrac{4}{7}, 6\dfrac{5}{11}\right)$

12. _____

13. passes through $(4.75, 0)$ and is parallel to the graph of $8x + 125y = 20$

13. _____

14. passes through $(-4.16, -1.35)$ and is perpendicular to the graph of $1.6x - 2.56y = 23.5$

14. _____

Let P be the midpoint of the segment AB.

15. If the endpoints are $A(-12.63, 8.92)$ and $B(4.84, -0.65)$, find the coordinates of P.

15. _____

16. If $A(-2.91, -3.4)$ and $P(1.56, 7.24)$ are known, find the coordinates of B.

16. _____

Chapter 6 Performance Assessment

6

Instructions: *Demonstrate your knowledge by giving a clear, concise solution to each problem. Be sure to include all relevant drawings and justify your answers. You may show your solution in more than one way or investigate beyond the requirements of the problem.*

1. **a.** Write a linear equation in standard form. Tell how you know the equation is linear.

   b. Use the coefficients and constant term to name the slope and y-intercept of the graph. Then write the equation in slope-intercept form.

   c. Use the y-intercept and slope to graph the equation. Explain how you graphed the equation.

   d. Write an equation whose graph is parallel to the graph in part c. Tell how you know they are parallel.

   e. Write an equation of a line perpendicular to the graph in part c. Tell how you know they are perpendicular.

2. **a.** Describe the pattern of the points in the scatter plot at the right.

   b. Give at least two examples of real-life situations that, if graphed, would result in a correlation like the one shown in this scatter plot.

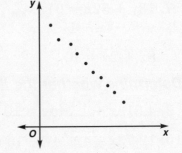

3. The graphs of each group of equations have at least one characteristic in common. Name the characteristic(s) and then graph each group of equations on the same axes to verify your answer.

   a. $y = x$, $y = 3x$, $y = 5x$

   b. $y = 2x$, $y = 2x + 1$, $y = 2x - 3$

   c. $y = \frac{1}{2}x$, $y = \frac{1}{3}x$, $y = \frac{2}{5}x$

   d. $2y = 6x$, $4y - 12x = 0$, $3x - y = 0$

   e. $2x - 4y = 12$, $3y + 2x = -2$, $x + y = 0$

Chapter 6 Mid-Chapter Test (Lessons 6-1 through 6-4)

Determine the slope of the line passing through each pair of points.

1. $(2, 5)$, $(3, 6)$

2. $(3, -5)$, $(4, 3)$

3. $(1, 10)$, $(-3, -4)$

4. $(4, 1)$, $(-4, 1)$

1. _____

2. _____

3. _____

4. _____

Write the standard form of the equation of the line passing through the given point and having the given slope.

5. $(3, 1)$, $\frac{1}{4}$

6. $(0, 9)$, 2

7. $(-6, -2)$, $-\frac{1}{3}$

8. $(1, -3)$, -1

5. _____

6. _____

7. _____

8. _____

Write the standard form of the equation of the line passing through each pair of points.

9. $(-1, -7)$ and $(1, 3)$

10. $(5, 3)$ and $(-4, 3)$

9. _____

10. _____

11. Make a scatter plot of the data with the number of hours driven on the horizontal axis.

Hours Driven	1	2	2.5	4
Miles	50	85	120	180

11.

12. Is the correlation positive or negative?

12. _____

13. Predict the number of miles driven after driving for 3 hours.

13. _____

Write an equation in slope-intercept form of the line satisfying the given conditions.

14. has y-intercept 5 and slope $-\frac{3}{4}$

14. _____

15. passes through $(4, 2)$ and $(0, -2)$

15. _____

16. has slope -3 and passes through $(2, -4)$

16. _____

Bonus Write an equation in slope-intercept form of the line with y-intercept -6 and slope the same as the line whose equation is $5x + 6y - 13 = 0$.

Bonus _____

Chapter 6, Quiz A (Lessons 6-1 and 6-2)

Determine the slope of the line passing through each pair of points. If the slope is undefined, write "no slope."

1. $(-4, 6)$, $(5, 8)$ 2. $(9, 4)$, $(3, 6)$ 1. _____

2. _____

3. $(-3, 6)$, $(-3, 10)$ 4. $(-4, -5)$, $(9, -2)$ 3. _____

4. _____

Write the standard form of an equation of the line passing through the given point and having the given slope.

5. $(1, 1)$, $\frac{1}{4}$ 6. $(6, 0)$, $-\frac{1}{3}$ 5. _____

6. _____

Write the standard form of the equation of the line passing through each pair of points.

7. $(9, 2)$, $(-2, 6)$ 8. $(6, 1)$, $(-2, 9)$ 7. _____

8. _____

9. $(0, 5)$, $(-2, 4)$ 9. _____

10. Determine the value of r so that the line passing   10. _____
    through $(6, 3)$ and $(r, 2)$ has a slope of $\frac{1}{2}$.

Chapter 6, Quiz B (Lessons 6-3 and 6-4)

The median incomes for a group of people ages 26–30 are listed in the table at the right.

Ages	Median Income
26	$16,800
27	$19,100
28	$23,300
29	$25,800
30	$33,900

1.

1. Make a scatter plot of the data with the ages on the horizontal axis.

2. Is there a positive, negative, or no correlation? What does this tell you about the people's income?   2. _____

3. Determine the slope and y-intercept of the graph of $3x + 6y = 12$.   3. _____

4. Write an equation in slope-intercept form of the line with a slope of $-\frac{1}{4}$ and a y-intercept of 5.   4. _____

5. Write an equation in standard form for a line that passes through $(4, 2)$ and $(-3, 1)$.   5. _____

6

Chapter 6, Quiz C (Lessons 6-5 and 6-6)

1. Determine the slope and *y*-intercept of the graph of $2y - 8x = 7$.

1. _____

2. Graph $4x + 3y = 12$ using the *x*- and *y*-intercepts. Use the coordinate plane at the right.

2. _____

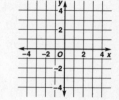

3. Find the slopes of the lines parallel and perpendicular to the graph of $3x - 8y = 11$.

3. _____

4. Write an equation in standard form of the line that passes through (5, 3) and is parallel to $x + 3y = 6$.

4. _____

5. Write an equation in slope-intercept form of the line that passes through (0, 3) and is perpendicular to the graph of $9x - 4y = -8$.

5. _____

6

Chapter 6, Quiz D (Lesson 6-7)

Find the coordinates of the midpoint of $\overline{AB}$.

1. $A(4, 5)$, $B(6, -1)$ 2. $A(-12, 2)$, $B(3, 7)$

1. _____

2. _____

3. *P* is the midpoint of $\overline{AB}$. The coordinates of *P* are $(-2, -1)$. The coordinates of *A* are $(-3, -5)$. Find the coordinates of *B*.

3. _____

4. The endpoints of a diameter of a circle are $A(5, -4)$ and $B(-7, 6)$. Find the coordinates of the center of the circle.

4. _____

5. The center of a circle is the origin $(0,0)$. If $\overline{AB}$ is a diameter, and $A(-3, 4)$ is one endpoint on the circle, find the coordinates of *B*.

5. _____

Chapter 6 Standardized Test Practice

Choose the best answer. Write A, B, C, or D.

1. If $(2m - 1)(6m + 2) = 12m^2 - 2m - 2$, then $(2m + 1)(6m - 2) =$
      A. $12m^2 - 2m + 2$.
      B. $12m^2 + 2m - 2$.
      C. $12m^2 + 2m + 2$.
      D. $12m^2 + 10m + 2$.

   1. _____

2. If $4f - g = 10$ and $4f + g = 12$, then $16f^2 - g^2 =$
      A. -2.   **B.** 2.   **C.** 22.   **D.** 120.

   2. _____

3. 16% of 980 is 9.8% of
      A. 1.6.   **B.** 16.   **C.** 160.   **D.** 1600.

   3. _____

4. Which number is closest to $\frac{2}{5}$?

      A. $\frac{1}{2}$ **B.** $\frac{2}{3}$ **C.** $\frac{3}{7}$ **D.** $\frac{5}{9}$

   4. _____

5. If $3y + 3 \neq 6y$, then
      A. $y = 1$.   **B.** $y > 1$.   **C.** $y < 1$.   **D.** $y \neq 1$.

   5. _____

6. For what value(s) of r is $3r - 6$ equal to $7 + 3r$?
      A. all positive integers   **B.** all numbers
      C. all negative integers   **D.** no values of r

   6. _____

7. If $-|a| = a$, then
      A. $a = 0$.   **B.** $a \leq 0$.   **C.** $a \geq 0$.   **D.** $a < 0$.

   7. _____

8. $\dfrac{195 + 195 + 195 + 195}{4} =$

      A. 23.75 **B.** 195 **C.** 390 **D.** 780

   8. _____

9. If $xyz = 10$ and $y = z$, then $x =$
      A. z^2.   **B.** $\frac{1}{y^2}$.   **C.** $\frac{10}{y^2}$.   **D.** $\frac{1}{10y^2}$.

   9. _____

10. Two-thirds of a number added to itself is 20. What is the number?
       A. 12 **B.** $13\frac{1}{3}$ **C.** 30 **D.** $33\frac{1}{3}$

    10. _____

11. If $a:b = c:d$, then
       A. $ad = bc$.   **B.** $ac = bd$.   **C.** $ab = cd$.   **D.** $ad > bc$.

    11. _____

Chapter 6 Cumulative Review

6

1. Write the expression $2 \cdot r \cdot r \cdot s \cdot s$ using exponents. (Lesson 1-1)

1._____

2. Evaluate $2xy - y^2$ if $x = 6$ and $y = 12$. (Lesson 1-3)

2._____

Simplify. (Lessons 2-5, 2-6, and 2-7)

3. $4\frac{7}{8} - 2\frac{5}{8}$

3._____

4. $\frac{3}{8} \times 2\frac{7}{18}$

4._____

5. $-\frac{2}{3} + \frac{3}{4}$

5._____

6. $-3.9 + (-2.5) + (-8.7)$

6._____

7. $4(2y + y) - 6(4y + 3y)$

7._____

8. $\frac{12a - 18b}{-6}$

8._____

Solve each equation. (Lessons 3-1 and 3-2)

9. $13 - m = 21$

9._____

10. $\frac{3}{4}x = \frac{2}{3}$

10._____

11. Find three consecutive even integers whose sum is 132. (Lesson 3-3)

11._____

12. Which is a better buy: a liter of milk for 59¢ or 1.5 liters for 81¢?

12._____

13. Six is what percent of 80?

13._____

Find the final price of each item. When there is a discount and sales tax, compute the discount price first.

14. calculator: $90
   sales tax: 8%

14._____

15. magazine: $3.95
   discount: 10%
   sales tax: 6.5%

15._____

16. A can contains two different kinds of nuts, weighs
    5 pounds, and costs $16. One type of nut costs $3.50
    a pound. The other type costs $2.75 a pound. How
    many pounds of $2.75 nuts are there? (Lesson 4-1)

16. _____

17. Solve $x - 2y = 12$ if the domain is $\{-3, -1, 0, 2, 5\}$.
    (Lesson 5-3)

17. _____

18. Graph $3x - y = 1$. Use the coordinate plane provided.
    (Lesson 5-4)

18.

19. State whether the following relation is a function.
    (Lesson 5-5)
    $\{(1, 4), (2, 6), (3, 7), (4, 4)\}$

19. _____

20. Write an equation for the
    relationship between the
    variables in the chart at
    the right. (Lesson 5-6)

x	0	2	4	6
y	2	5	8	11

20. _____

21. Determine the slope of the line passing through
    $(2, 7)$ and $(-5, 2)$. (Lesson 6-1)

21. _____

22. Write an equation in standard form for the line
    passing through $(2, 6)$ and having a slope of -3.
    (Lesson 6-2)

22. _____

23. Write an equation in slope-intercept form for the line
    in exercise 22. (Lesson 6-4)

23. _____

24. Write an equation for the line that is parallel to the
    graph of $5x - 3y = 1$ and passes through $(0, -4)$.
    (Lesson 6-6)

24. _____

25. Graph $y = 2x - 3$. Use the coordinate plane at the
    right. (Lesson 6-5)

25.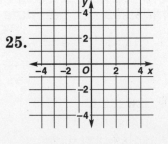

Chapter 6 Answer Key

Form 1A

Page 141

1. A
2. B
3. A
4. B
5. C
6. C
7. A
8. B
9. D
10. B
11. D

Page 142

12. A
13. B
14. C
15. D
16. B
17. C
18. D
19. B
20. C

Bonus   −21

Form 1B

Page 143

1. D
2. C
3. C
4. C
5. A
6. A
7. B
8. A
9. B
10. A

Page 144

11. D
12. A
13. C
14. B
15. A
16. A
17. D
18. A
19. C
20. B

Bonus $y = \dfrac{8}{5}x + 8$

Algebra 1

Chapter 6 Answer Key

Form 1C

Page 145

1. __B__

2. __C__

3. __A__

4. __B__

5. __D__

6. __D__

7. __C__

8. __D__

9. __A__

10. __D__

11. __B__

Page 146

12. __B__

13. __A__

14. __C__

15. __D__

16. __D__

17 __A__

18. __B__

19. __C__

20. __A__

Bonus $y = 2x + 6$

Form 2A

Page 147

1. $-\dfrac{9}{13}$

2. __no slope__

3. $3x + 5y = 11$

4. $2x + y = 1$

5. $2x + 3y = 6$

6.

7. negative; percent decreases with age

8.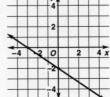

9.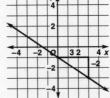

10.

Page 148

11. $y = 3x - 8$

12. $y = \dfrac{5}{2}x - 11$

13. $y = -\dfrac{3}{5}x + \dfrac{26}{5}$

14. $y = \dfrac{3}{5}x - 6$

15. $y = -\dfrac{4}{3}x - 9$

16. $y = 5$

17. $\left(-2, -1\dfrac{1}{2}\right)$

18. $(11, -22)$

19. $\dfrac{4}{5}$

20. $\left(2, 3\dfrac{1}{2}\right)$

Bonus $y = \dfrac{5}{6}x - \dfrac{19}{6}$

Algebra 1

Chapter 6 Answer Key

Form 2B

1. $-\dfrac{11}{9}$

2. 0

3. -25

4. $x = -6$

5. $12x + 7y = -16$

6. $5x + 7y = 14$

7.
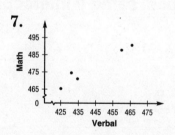

8. positive

9. about 478

10.
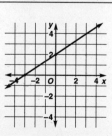

11.
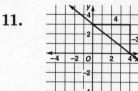

12.

13. $y = -5x + 29$

14. $y = \dfrac{1}{3}x + \dfrac{26}{3}$

15. $y = -\dfrac{1}{2}x + 2$

16. $y = -3x + 18$

17. $y = -\dfrac{1}{4}x + 4$

18. $y = 2$

19. $\left(\dfrac{1}{2}, 2\dfrac{1}{2}\right)$

20. $(1, -3)$

Bonus $y = 1.2x + 1.8$; 13.8 in.; 6 yr

          Algebra 1

Chapter 6 Answer Key

Page 151

1. $-\dfrac{3}{5}$

2. 0

3. 1

4. $3x - y = 10$

5. $2x + 3y = -1$

6. $x = 5$

7.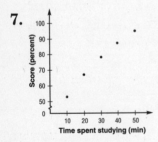

8. positive

9. about 83

10.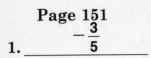

Page 152

11.

12.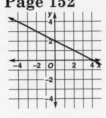

13. $y = 4x - 3$

14. $y = \dfrac{3}{2}x - \dfrac{1}{2}$

15. $y = \dfrac{4}{3}x - 4$

16. $y = -2x + 1$

17. $y = \dfrac{2}{3}x - 4$

18. $y = 3$

19. $S(4, 11)$

20. $(3, 4)$

Bonus $(5, -4)$

Page 153

1. -1.5

2. 5

3. 0.086092715

4. 2716

5. Sample: The points seem to be positively correlated.

6. Sample: The higher the test score, the more time was spent studying.

7. same slope, different y-intercepts

8. different slopes, same y-intercept

9. perpendicular

10. parallel

11. $550x + 800y = 991$

12. $924x + 1463y = 12{,}743$

13. $8x + 125y = 38$

14. $800x + 500y = -4003$

15. $(-3.895, 4.135)$

16. $(6.03, 17.88)$

Scoring Guide
Chapter 6
Performance Assessment

Level	Specific Criteria
3 Superior	• Shows thorough understanding of the concepts of *standard form, linear equation, slope, y-intercept, slope-intercept form, parallel and perpendicular lines, scatter plot,* and *correlation.* • Uses appropriate strategies to solve problems. • Computations are correct. • Written explanations are exemplary. • Real-life examples concerning negative linear correlation are appropriate and make sense. • Graphs are accurate and appropriate. • Goes beyond requirements of some or all problems.
2 Satisfactory, with Minor Flaws	• Shows understanding of the concepts of *standard form, linear equation, slope, y-intercept, slope-intercept form, parallel and perpendicular lines, scatter plot,* and *correlation.* • Uses appropriate strategies to solve problems. • Computations are mostly correct. • Written explanations are effective. • Real-life examples concerning negative linear correlation are appropriate and make sense. • Graphs are mostly accurate and appropriate. • Satisfies all requirements of problems.
1 Nearly Satisfactory, with Serious Flaws	• Shows understanding of most of the concepts of *standard form, linear equation, slope, y-intercept, slope-intercept form, parallel and perpendicular lines, scatter plot,* and *correlation.* • May not use appropriate strategies to solve problems. • Computations are mostly correct. • Written explanations are satisfactory. • Real-life examples concerning negative linear correlation are appropriate and sensible. • Graphs are mostly accurate and appropriate. • Satisfies most requirements of problems.
0 Unsatisfactory	• Shows little or no understanding of the concepts of *standard form, linear equation, slope, y-intercept, slope-intercept form, parallel and perpendicular lines, scatter plot,* and *correlation.* • May not use appropriate strategies to solve problems. • Computations are incorrect. • Written explanations are not satisfactory. • Real-life examples concerning negative linear correlation are not appropriate or sensible. • Graphs are not accurate or appropriate. • Does not satisfy requirements of problems.

Chapter 6 Answer Key
Performance Assessment

Page 154

1. a. $2x - y = 6$; it is linear because it is in the standard form of a linear equation, $Ax + By = C$.

b. slope $= -\dfrac{A}{B} = \dfrac{-2}{-1}$, or 2;

y-intercept $= \dfrac{C}{B} = \dfrac{6}{-1}$, or -6; $y = 2x - 6$

c.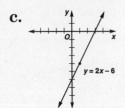

First, graph $(0, -6)$. Then move up two and to the right one because the slope is 2. Draw the graph through the points $(0, -6)$ and $(1, -4)$.

d. $y = 2x - 1$; the graph of the equation will be parallel to the graph in part c because it has the same slope.

e. $y = -\dfrac{1}{2}x - 1$; the graph of the equation is perpendicular to the graph in part c because $-\dfrac{1}{2}(2) = -1$.

2. a. In this graph, x and y have a very strong negative correlation.

b. sample answer: the value of a car and its age; the volume of water in a leaky bucket and the time since the bucket was filled

3. a. All pass through $(0, 0)$.

b. parallel lines

c. All pass through $(0, 0)$.

d. They are the same line.

e. All pass through $(2, -2)$.

Chapter 6 Answer Key

Mid-Chapter Test
Page 155

1. 1
2. 8
3. $\dfrac{7}{2}$
4. 0
5. $x - 4y = -1$
6. $2x - y = -9$
7. $x + 3y = -12$
8. $x + y = -2$
9. $5x - y = 2$
10. $y = 3$
11.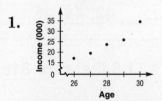
12. positive
13. about 140 miles
14. $y = -\dfrac{3}{4}x + 5$
15. $y = x - 2$
16. $y = -3x + 2$

Bonus $y = -\dfrac{5}{6}x - 6$

Quiz A
Page 156

1. $\dfrac{2}{9}$
2. $-\dfrac{1}{3}$
3. no slope
4. $\dfrac{3}{13}$
5. $x - 4y = -3$
6. $x + 3y = 6$
7. $4x + 11y = 58$
8. $x + y = 7$
9. $x - 2y = -10$
10. 4

Quiz B
Page 156

1.

2. positive; increases with age
3. $-\dfrac{1}{2}; 2$
4. $y = -\dfrac{1}{4}x + 5$
5. $x - 7y = -10$

Quiz C
Page 157

1. $4; 3\dfrac{1}{2}$
2.
3. $\dfrac{3}{8}; -\dfrac{8}{3}$
4. $x + 3y = 14$
5. $y = -\dfrac{4}{9}x + 3$

Quiz D
Page 157

1. $(5, 2)$
2. $\left(-\dfrac{9}{2}, \dfrac{9}{2}\right)$
3. $(-1, 3)$
4. $(-1, 1)$
5. $(3, -4)$

Chapter 6 Answer Key

1. __B__

2. __D__

3. __D__

4. __C__

5. __D__

6. __D__

7. __B__

8. __B__

9. __C__

10. __A__

11. __A__

1. $2r^2s^2$

2. 0

3. $2\frac{1}{4}$

4. $\frac{43}{48}$

5. $\frac{1}{12}$

6. -15.1

7. $-30y$

8. $-2a + 3b$

9. -8

10. $\frac{8}{9}$

11. $42, 44, 46$

12. 1.5 liters for 81¢

13. 7.5%

14. $97.20

15. $3.79

16. 2 pounds at $2.75

17. $\{(-3, -7.5),\ (-1, -6.5),\ (0, -6),\ (2, -5),\ (5, -3.5)\}$

18.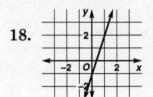

19. yes

20. $y = \frac{3}{2}x + 2$

21. $\frac{5}{7}$

22. $3x + y = 12$

23. $y = -3x + 12$

24. $y = \frac{5}{3}x - 4$

25.

Chapter 7 Test, Form 1A

Write the letter for the correct answer in the blank at the right of each problem.

1. Solve $-51 \leq x - (-38)$.
   A. $\{x \mid x \leq -13\}$ B. $\{x \mid x \leq 89\}$ C. $\{x \mid x \geq -89\}$ D. $\{x \mid x \geq -13\}$

   1. _____

2. Solve $m - \frac{3}{8} > \frac{1}{2}$.
   A. $\left\{m \mid m > \frac{7}{8}\right\}$ B. $\left\{m \mid m < \frac{7}{8}\right\}$ C. $\left\{m \mid m < \frac{1}{8}\right\}$ D. $\left\{m \mid m > \frac{1}{8}\right\}$

   2. _____

3. Solve $6n \geq 5n + 19$.
   A. $\{n \mid n \geq -19\}$ B. $\{n \mid n \geq 19\}$ C. $\{n \mid n \leq 19\}$ D. $\left\{n \mid n \leq \frac{11}{19}\right\}$

   3. _____

4. Solve $\frac{5}{14} > -\frac{2}{7}d$.
   A. $\left\{d \mid d < \frac{5}{4}\right\}$ B. $\left\{d \mid d > \frac{5}{4}\right\}$ C. $\left\{d \mid d < -\frac{5}{4}\right\}$ D. $\left\{d \mid d > -\frac{5}{4}\right\}$

   4. _____

5. Solve $-3.5z < 42$.
   A. $\{z \mid z > 12\}$ B. $\{z \mid z < 12\}$ C. $\{z \mid z < -12\}$ D. $\{z \mid z > -12\}$

   5. _____

6. Solve $4w - 6 > 6w - 20$.
   A. $\{w \mid w < 7\}$ B. $\{w \mid w < 2\}$ C. $\{w \mid w < -7\}$ D. $\{w \mid w < -2\}$

   6. _____

7. Solve $-14 > 5(2m - 3) - m$.
   A. $\{m \mid m < 1\}$ B. $\left\{m \mid m < \frac{1}{9}\right\}$ C. $\{m \mid m > 1\}$ D. $\left\{m \mid m > \frac{1}{9}\right\}$

   7. _____

8. Solve $8r - (5r + 4) \geq -31$.
   A. $\{r \mid r \leq -9\}$ B. $\{r \mid r \geq -9\}$ C. $\{r \mid r \geq 9\}$ D. $\{r \mid r \leq 9\}$

   8. _____

9. The sum of two consecutive positive odd integers is at most 7. What is the lesser integer?
   A. 4 B. 3 C. 2 D. 1

   9. _____

10. A student guesses the answers to all five questions on a true-false quiz. What is the probability that he answers all five questions correctly?
    A. $\frac{1}{32}$ B. $\frac{1}{16}$ C. $\frac{5}{32}$ D. $\frac{32}{5}$

    10. _____

11. If 2 six-sided dice are tossed, what is the probability that the sum of the numbers will be greater than 10?
    A. $\frac{7}{36}$ B. $\frac{1}{5}$ C. $\frac{29}{36}$ D. $\frac{5}{6}$

    11. _____

12. There are 20 possible combinations of background color and text color on Robin's World Wide Web home page. If the page has 5 background colors, how many text colors does it have?
    A. 4 B. 5 C. 15 D. 25

    12. _____

13. What percent of the data shown in the box-and-whisker plot below is located between 80 and 100?

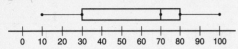

   A. 20   **B.** 25   **C.** 50   **D.** 80

13. _____

14. Larry earns $23,500 in salary and an 8% commission on his sales. How much must he sell to have an income of over $28,800 but not over $34,100?
   A. $66,250 or more   **B.** $66,250 or less
   C. less than $132,500   **D.** between $66,250 and $132,500

14. _____

15. Which of the following is the graph of the solution set of $y < -3$ or $y < 1$?
   A. ◄─┼─┼─⊕─┼─┼─┼─⊕─┼─┼─┼─►   -5-4-3-2-1 0 1 2 3 4 5
   B. ◄─┼─┼─┼─┼─┼─┼─┼─⊕─┼─┼─┼─►   -5-4-3-2-1 0 1 2 3 4 5
   C. ◄─┼─┼─⊕━━━━⊕─┼─┼─┼─►   -5-4-3-2-1 0 1 2 3 4 5
   D. ◄─┼─┼─⊕━━━━━━━━━━►   -5-4-3-2-1 0 1 2 3 4 5

15. _____

16. What compound inequality is graphed?
   A. $-1 < n < 2$ **B.** $-1 \leq n < 2$
   C. $n \geq -1$ or $n < 2$ **D.** $-1 < y \leq 2$

16. _____

17. Which of the following is the graph of the solution set of $-4 < 3t + 5 \leq 20$?
   A. ◄─┼─┼─⊕━━━━━━━━●─►   -5-4-3-2-1 0 1 2 3 4 5
   B. ◄─┼─┼─⊕─┼─┼─┼─┼─┼─┼─►   -5-4-3-2-1 0 1 2 3 4 5
   C. ◄━━━━━━━━━━━━━━━━►   -5-4-3-2-1 0 1 2 3 4 5
   D. ◄─┼─┼─⊕─┼─┼─┼─┼━━●─►   -5-4-3-2-1 0 1 2 3 4 5

17. _____

18. Which of the following is the solution set of $|x + 4| = 2$?
   A. {2, 6}   **B.** {-6, -2}   **C.** {-6}   **D.** {6}

18. _____

19. Which of the following is a graph of the solution set of $|w - 5| \leq 3$?
   A. ◄─●━━━━━━━━━●─┼─►   -2-1 0 1 2 3 4 5 6 7 8
   B. ◄─┼─┼─┼─┼─┼─┼─┼─┼─●─►   -2-1 0 1 2 3 4 5 6 7 8
   C. ◄─┼─┼─●━━━━━●─┼─►   -2-1 0 1 2 3 4 5 6 7 8
   D. ◄─┼─┼─┼─┼─┼─┼─┼━━━━►   -2-1 0 1 2 3 4 5 6 7 8

19. _____

20. Which ordered pair is a solution of the inequality $5 - y \leq -3x$?
   A. $(2, -1)$ **B.** $(-2, -1)$ **C.** $(-3, -5)$ **D.** $(3, -5)$

20. _____

Bonus   Solve $6(|n| - 3) - 4|n| + 5 = 11$.

Bonus _____

7

Chapter 7 Test, Form 1B

Write the letter for the correct answer in the blank at the right of each problem.

1. Solve $2x - 7 \geq 3x$.

   A. $\left\{x \mid x \leq \dfrac{5}{7}\right\}$ **B.** $\{x \mid x \leq -7\}$ **C.** $\{x \mid x \geq 7\}$ **D.** $\{x \mid x \geq -7\}$

   1. _____

2. Solve $-13 > w - (-12)$.

   A. $\{w \mid w < -25\}$ **B.** $\{w \mid w > -25\}$ **C.** $\{w \mid w > -1\}$ **D.** $\{w \mid w < -1\}$

   2. _____

3. Solve $\dfrac{m}{5} < -3$.

   A. $\{m \mid m > -15\}$ **B.** $\{m \mid m < -15\}$ **C.** $\{m \mid m < 15\}$ **D.** $\{m \mid m > 15\}$

   3. _____

4. Solve $-\dfrac{2}{3} s > 6$.

   A. $\{s \mid s > -9\}$ **B.** $\{s \mid s > 9\}$ **C.** $\{s \mid s < 9\}$ **D.** $\{s \mid s < -9\}$

   4. _____

5. Solve $-1.1t \leq 4.62$.

   A. $\{t \mid t \leq -5.06\}$ **B.** $\{t \mid t \geq -5.06\}$ **C.** $\{t \mid t \leq -4.2\}$ **D.** $\{t \mid t \geq -4.2\}$

   5. _____

6. Solve $6d + 10 < 46$.

   A. $\{d \mid d < 6\}$ **B.** $\{d \mid d > 6\}$ **C.** $\{d \mid d < -6\}$ **D.** $\{d \mid d > -6\}$

   6. _____

7. Solve $5z - 4 > 2z + 8$.

   A. $\{z \mid z > 4\}$ **B.** $\{z \mid z < 1\}$ **C.** $\{z \mid z < 4\}$ **D.** $\{z \mid z > 1\}$

   7. _____

8. Solve $5w - (w - 8) > 9 + 3(2w - 3)$.

   A. $\left\{w \mid w < \dfrac{11}{5}\right\}$ **B.** $\left\{w \mid w < -\dfrac{11}{5}\right\}$ **C.** $\{w \mid w < -4\}$ **D.** $\{w \mid w < 4\}$

   8. _____

9. Solve $(0.5)(r + 1) \leq (0.6)(r - 2)$.

   A. $\{r \mid r \leq 30\}$ **B.** $\{r \mid r \geq 17\}$ **C.** $\{r \mid r \geq 30\}$ **D.** $\{r \mid r \leq 17\}$

   9. _____

10. The sum of two consecutive positive integers is at most 3. What is the greater integer?

    A. 5   **B.** 1   **C.** 3   **D.** 2

    10. _____

11. If one coin and one die are tossed, what is P(one head and one 5)?

    A. $\dfrac{1}{24}$ **B.** $\dfrac{1}{2}$ **C.** $\dfrac{1}{12}$ **D.** $\dfrac{1}{6}$

    11. _____

12. Renata's World Wide Web home page has 9 possible background colors and 3 possible text colors. How many combinations of background color and text color does the page have?

    A. 27   **B.** 12   **C.** 6   **D.** 30

    12. _____

13. If 2 six-sided dice are tossed, what is the probability of getting two different numbers?

    A. $\dfrac{1}{12}$ **B.** $\dfrac{1}{6}$ **C.** $\dfrac{1}{2}$ **D.** $\dfrac{5}{6}$

    13. _____

14. What percent of the data shown
in the box-and-whisker plot at
right is located between 30 and 70?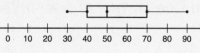
    A. 25   B. 40   C. 50   D. 75

14. _____

15. What compound sentence is graphed below?

    A. $-2 < y < 3$ B. $-2 < y \leq 3$ C. $y \geq -2$ or $y < 3$ D. $-2 \leq y < 3$

15. _____

16. Which of the following is a graph of the solution set of the
compound sentence $x > 0$ or $x < -4$?

    A.    B.

    C.   D.

16. _____

17. Which of the following is the graph of the solution set of
$-3 < 2x + 7 \leq 13$?

    A.    B.

    C.   D.

17. _____

18. Which of the following is the solution set of $|x - 3| = 6$?
    A. $\{9\}$ B. $\{-3\}$ C. $\{-3, 9\}$ D. $\{-9, 3\}$

18. _____

19. Which inequality is graphed at the right?
    A. $2x - 4y \leq -6$
    B. $2x - 4y < -6$
    C. $2x - 4y \geq -6$
    D. $2x - 4y > -6$

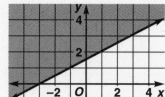

19. _____

20. Which of the following is a graph of the solution
set of $|4x - 8| \leq 16$?

    A.

    B.

    C.

    D.

20. _____

Bonus

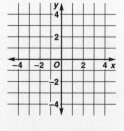

Bonus   Graph $y = \begin{cases} 3 \text{ if } x \geq 1 \\ 2 \text{ if } x < 1 \end{cases}$. Use the coordinate
plane provided.

7

Chapter 7 Test, Form 1C

Write the letter for the correct answer in the blank to the right of each problem.

1. Solve $w - 4 < 23$.
   A. $\{w \mid w < 27\}$ B. $\{w \mid w > 27\}$ C. $\{w \mid w < 19\}$ D. $\{w \mid w > 19\}$

   1. _____

2. Solve $-11 \leq m - 3$.
   A. $\{m \mid m \leq -14\}$ B. $\{m \mid m \geq -8\}$ C. $\{m \mid m \geq 8\}$ D. $\{m \mid m \leq 14\}$

   2. _____

3. Solve $5s < -25$.
   A. $\{s \mid s < 125\}$ B. $\{s \mid s < -125\}$ C. $\{s \mid s > -5\}$ D. $\{s \mid s < -5\}$

   3. _____

4. Solve $-36 \leq 3t$.
   A. $\{t \mid t \geq -12\}$ B. $\{t \mid t \leq 12\}$ C. $\{t \mid t \geq 12\}$ D. $\{t \mid t \leq -12\}$

   4. _____

5. Solve $-\frac{3}{4}b > \frac{2}{3}$.

   A. $\left\{b \mid b > -\frac{1}{2}\right\}$ B. $\left\{b \mid b < -\frac{1}{2}\right\}$ C. $\left\{b \mid b > -\frac{8}{9}\right\}$ D. $\left\{b \mid b < -\frac{8}{9}\right\}$

   5. _____

6. Solve $-28.8 < -2.4x$.
   A. $\{x \mid x < 1.2\}$ B. $\{x \mid x < 12\}$ C. $\{x \mid x < -1.2\}$ D. $\{x \mid x < -12\}$

   6. _____

7. Solve $4 \geq 3m + 7$.
   A. $\left\{m \mid m \geq \frac{11}{3}\right\}$ B. $\left\{m \mid m \leq -1\right\}$ C. $\left\{m \mid m \leq 9\right\}$ D. $\left\{m \mid m \leq -9\right\}$

   7. _____

8. Solve $6y - 8 > 4y + 26$.
   A. $\{y \mid y > -12\}$ B. $\{y \mid y > -17\}$ C. $\{y \mid y > 12\}$ D. $\{y \mid y > 17\}$

   8. _____

9. Solve $3(2d - 1) \geq 4(2d - 3) - 3$.
   A. $\{d \mid d \geq -9\}$ B. $\{d \mid d \leq -6\}$ C. $\{d \mid d \geq 3\}$ D. $\{d \mid d \leq 6\}$

   9. _____

10. The sum of two consecutive positive even integers is at most 6. What is the greater integer?
    A. 5   B. 4   C. 6   D. 2

    10. _____

11. Visitors to Thomas's home page on the World Wide Web are equally likely to get a yellow, green, or blue background. The text visitors see is equally likely to be black or red. What is the probability that a visitor will see red text on a green background?
    A. $\frac{1}{3}$ B. $\frac{1}{6}$ C. $\frac{1}{12}$ D. $\frac{1}{2}$

    11. _____

12. If a coin is tossed three times, what is the probability of getting three tails?
    A. $\frac{1}{2}$ B. $\frac{1}{4}$ C. $\frac{1}{8}$ D. $\frac{3}{4}$

    12. _____

13. If 2 six-sided dice are tossed, what is the probability of getting 2 ones?
    A. 1   B. $\frac{1}{2}$ C. $\frac{1}{36}$ D. $\frac{1}{12}$

    13. _____

14. Kim is planning to buy a new coat and new shoes. She has
saved $122. Which of the following describes the amount of
money Kim can spend for a coat if her shoes cost $47.95?
A. not more than $122   B. not more than $47.95
C. not more than $74.05   D. not more than $75.05

14. _____

15. Which of the following is the graph of the solution set of
$m > -1$ and $m \le 1$?

15. _____

A.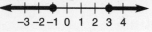
   −2 −1 0 1 2 3

B. ←+⊕—⊕+—+→
   −2 −1 0 1 2 3

C. ←+⊕—●+—+→
   −2 −1 0 1 2 3

D. ←+—⊕+●—+→
   −2 −1 0 1 2 3

16. Which of the following is the solution set of $|s - 6| = 12$?

16. _____

A. {6, −18}   B. {−6}   C. {18}   D. {−6, 18}

17. What compound sentence is graphed below?

17. _____

←+—+●—+—+—+●—+→
 −3 −2 −1 0 1 2 3 4

A. $x \le -1$ or $x > 3$ B. $x > -1$ or $x \ge 3$
C. $x > -1$ or $x < 3$ D. $x \le -1$ or $x \ge 3$

18. Which of the following is a graph of the solution set of
$2s + 1 < 9$ and $s > -1$?

18. _____

A. ←+⊕—+—+—+⊕+→
   −2 −1 0 1 2 3 4 5

B. ←+●—+—+—+●—+→
   −2 −1 0 1 2 3 4 5

C. ←+⊕—+—+—+⊕—+→
   −2 −1 0 1 2 3 4 5

D. ←+—+—+—+●—+●→
   −2 −1 0 1 2 3 4 5

19. Which box-and-whisker
plot has the greatest
interquartile range?

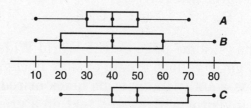

19. _____

A. A   B. B
C. C   D. They all have the same interquartile range.

20. Which inequality has a graph that includes its boundary?
A. $12y < 2x - 6$ B. $2(3x - 40) - 3 > 24y$
C. $3x > 4y$ D. $2x - 5 \le 3y$

20. _____

Bonus Find the perimeter of the
triangle if x is > 4.

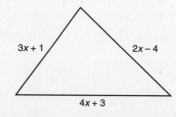

Bonus _____

Chapter 7 Test, Form 2A

Solve each inequality.

1. $m - (-3.4) \geq 12.7$

2. $3m - \frac{1}{5} \leq 2m + \frac{1}{2}$

3. $-2.6 \geq \frac{w}{4}$

4. $-11t < -9$

5. $5x - 3(x - 6) < 0$

6. $5(4s - 12) \geq 2(s - 30)$

7. Write an inequality and solve: Negative three sevenths of a number is at least 102.

1. _____

2. _____

3. _____

4. _____

5. _____

6. _____

7. _____

Define a variable, write an inequality, and solve each problem.

8. Raul plans to spend $78.00 on two shirts and a pair of jeans. He bought the two shirts for $19.89 each. How much can he spend on the jeans?

9. The sum of two consecutive positive even integers is at most 15. What are the possible pairs of integers?

10. Susan makes 10% commission on her sales. She also receives a salary of $25,600. How much must she sell to receive a total income between $32,500 and $41,900?

8. _____

9. _____

10. _____

Solve each open sentence and graph the solution set on the number lines provided.

11. $6 - 4m < 10$ and $m < 2$

12. $-4 < x + 2 \leq 10$

13. $-\frac{n}{2} < 3$ or $2n - 3 > 12$

14. $|5x - 3| = 17$

15. $|4x + 8| \geq 16$

11. ⟵+++++++++++⟶
   $-5\,-4\,-3\,-2\,-1\ 0\ 1\ 2\ 3\ 4\ 5$

12. ⟵+++++++++++⟶
   $-8\,-6\,-4\,-2\ 0\ 2\ 4\ 6\ 8\ 10$

13. ⟵+++++++++++⟶
   $-8\,-6\,-4\,-2\ 0\ 2\ 4\ 6\ 8\ 10$

14. ⟵+++++++++++⟶
   $-5\,-4\,-3\,-2\,-1\ 0\ 1\ 2\ 3\ 4\ 5$

15. ⟵+++++++++++⟶
   $-5\,-4\,-3\,-2\,-1\ 0\ 1\ 2\ 3\ 4\ 5$

16. Graph $-y \leq 3x$. Use the coordinate plane provided.

16.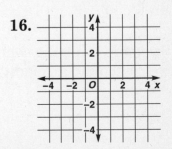

17. What percent of the data shown in the box-and-whisker plot below is between 10 and 20?

17._____

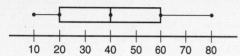

18. From the four aces in a 52-card deck, one card is drawn at random. From the remaining three cards, a second card is drawn at random. Find the probability that both cards are red.

18._____

19. Draw a tree diagram to represent the outcomes of tossing a coin followed by rolling a single die. What is the probability of tossing heads and then rolling a 2?

19._____

20. A jar contains 3 red marbles and 2 blue marbles. One marble is drawn at random and replaced. Then a second marble is drawn at random. What is the probability of drawing 2 red marbles?

20._____

21. The speedometer of a car can be off by as much as 5%. Write an inequality involving absolute value to express what a car's actual speed might be if the speedometer reads 40 mph.

21._____

Use the following daily high temperatures (in degrees Fahrenheit) for exercises 22 and 23.

    60, 60, 61, 61, 62, 62, 62, 64, 65, 66, 66, 67, 67, 68

22. Find the median.

22._____

23. Find the interquartile range.

23._____

Which ordered pairs from the given set are part of the solution set for each inequality?

24. $x > 5y$ {(−5, −2), (−5, −1), (2, 0), (0, 0), (5, 1), (5, 2)}

24._____

25. $x − 3y − x < 10$ {(−2, −3), (−2, −2), (0, 0), (0, 2), (2, −2), (2, −4)}

25._____

Bonus Graph the solution set of the compound inequality $3 < |x − 4| < 7$.

Bonus ←|—|—|—|—|—|—|—|—|—|—|→
                −6 −4 −2 0 2 4 6 8 10 12 14

Chapter 7 Test, Form 2B

Solve each inequality.

1. $-14 \le n + 5$

2. $3a < 6 + 4a$

3. $\dfrac{3y}{8} > -\dfrac{2}{5}$

4. $-\dfrac{t}{6} \ge 14$

5. $-19.8 \ge 3.6y$

6. $4x - 5 < 2x + 11$

7. $1.3(c - 4) \le 2.6 + 0.7c$

8. Write an inequality and solve: Forty less three times a number is no less than the number increased by 15.

Define a variable, write an inequality, and solve.

9. Ray had scores of 75, 82, 94, and 77 on his first four science tests. What must he score on the next test to have an average of at least 85?

10. Felicita's bank charges $2.25 a month plus $0.10 per check. How many checks does she write if her bank charges are always between $3.50 and $5.00?

Solve each open sentence and graph the solution set on the number lines provided.

11. $3w < 6$ and $-5 < w$

12. $-4 \le n$ or $3n + 1 < -2$

13. $-2 \le x + 1 < 4$

14. $|1 - y| = 2$

15. $|3 - 2x| \ge 1$

16. $|3w + 1| > -8$

1. _____

2. _____

3. _____

4. _____

5. _____

6. _____

7. _____

8. _____

9. _____

10. _____

11. _____
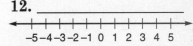

12. _____
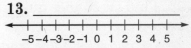

13. _____
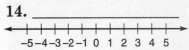

14. _____
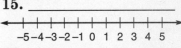

15. _____
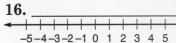

16. _____

17. Graph $2y - 4x < 8$. Use the coordinate plane provided.

17.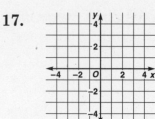

18. What percent of the data shown in the box-and-whisker plot below are between 20 and 70?

18. _____

Bob, Ted, and Al each have to make a presentation in Mrs. Small's speech class. Mrs. Small chooses students for the three presentations at random. Each student speaks exactly once.

19. Draw a tree diagram to show the possible outcomes.

19. _____

20. What is the probability that Al speaks third?

20. _____

21. One spinner is divided into 4 sections labeled 0–3. A second spinner is divided into 3 sections labeled 0, 1, and 5. Customers at a department store spin both spinners to determine the amount they will save on large purchases; the first spinner gives the tens digit and the second spinner gives the ones digit of the discount. What is the probability that a customer will save at least $10?

21. _____

Use the following math quiz scores for exercises 22 and 23.

3, 3, 4, 5, 5, 6, 6, 6, 6, 7, 7, 7, 8, 8, 9, 10

22. Find the median.

22. _____

23. Find the upper quartile.

23. _____

Which ordered pairs from the given set are part of the solution set for each inequality?

24. $y > \frac{x}{2}$ {(−4, −2), (−6, −2), (0, 2), (0, 0), (6, 4), (6, 3)}

24. _____

25. $2y - x > 5$ {(−1, 2), (−2, 4), (0, 2), (0, 3), (1, 3), (1, 4)}

25. _____

Bonus Graph the solution set of the compound inequality

$\frac{n+4}{5} < 3$ and $\frac{n}{5} + 4 > 3$.   **Bonus**

Solve each inequality.

1. $m + 6 < -3$

1. _____

2. $5t + 8 \leq 4t - 3$

2. _____

3. $3m < -18$

3. _____

4. $\dfrac{h}{3} \geq 9$

4. _____

5. $5.6 \geq 2.8k$

5. _____

6. $3(-w - 6) < 2(2w + 8)$

6. _____

Define a variable, write an inequality, and solve each problem.

7. Twice a number less seven is at least 17.

7. _____

8. Camille has no more than $10.00 to spend each week for lunch and bus fare. If she spends a total of $4.10 on Monday and Tuesday, how much does she have to spend during the rest of the week?

8. _____

9. The sum of two consecutive odd integers is at most 9. What are three possible pairs of integers?

9. _____

10. What percent of the data in the box-and-whisker plot below is between 20 and 70?

10. _____

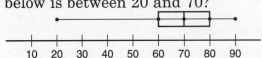

Solve each open sentence and graph the solution set on the number line provided.

11. $9 > 4 - 7w$ and $w < 3$

11.
$-5-4-3-2-1\ 0\ 1\ 2\ 3\ 4\ 5$

12. $4 < 2y + 3 \leq 11$

12. ←++++++++++++→
$-5-4-3-2-1\ 0\ 1\ 2\ 3\ 4\ 5$

13. $\dfrac{w}{3} < 1$ or $3w + 5 > 11$

13. ←++++++++++++→
$-5-4-3-2-1\ 0\ 1\ 2\ 3\ 4\ 5$

14. $|2x - 5| = 3$

14. ←++++++++++++→
$-5-4-3-2-1\ 0\ 1\ 2\ 3\ 4\ 5$

15. $|w - 1| \leq 4$

15. ←++++++++++++→
$-5-4-3-2-1\ 0\ 1\ 2\ 3\ 4\ 5$

16. Graph $x + 4y \leq -2$. Use the coordinate plane provided.

16.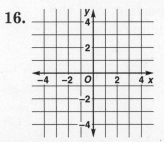

Chapter 7 Test, Form 2C (continued)

One spinner is divided into 3 sections labeled 0–2. A second spinner is divided into two sections, which are labeled 0 and 5. Customers at a department store spin both spinners to determine the amount they will save on large purchases; the first spinner gives the tens and the second spinner gives the ones digit of the discount.

17. Draw a tree diagram showing all the possible outcomes.

17. _____

18. What is the probability that a customer will save less than $15?

18. _____

19. What is the probability that a customer will save $20 or more?

19. _____

20. Define a variable, write an inequality, and solve the following. Carlo's class is selling tickets to the school carnival. The class hopes to raise at least $275 from the ticket sales. So far, the ticket sales have raised $188. What is the least amount of money the class still must raise?

20. _____

21. Write an inequality involving absolute value for the following statement: The width of an iron bar must be within 0.01 of 1 inch.

21. _____

Use the following set of test scores for exercises 22 and 23.

60, 70, 70, 75, 80, 85, 85, 90, 95, 100

22. Find the median.

22. _____

23. Find the lower quartile.

23. _____

Which ordered pairs from the given set are part of the solution set for each inequality?

24. $x < y$ {(−2, −1), (−1, −1), (−1, 0), (0, 1) (2, 1), (1, 3)}

24. _____

25. $y \geq x + 2$ {(−2, −1), (−1, −1), (−1, 0), (0, 1), (2, 1), (1, 3)}

25. _____

Bonus Find the value of x if the perimeter of the triangle must be less than 50.

Bonus _____

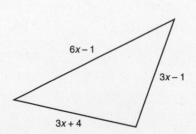

$6x - 1$

$3x - 1$

$3x + 4$

7

Chapter 7 Calculator-Based Test

Solve each inequality.

1. $2x + 5 < 5x - 1$

1. _____

2. $6x - 7 \geq 8x - 3$

2. _____

3. $5(x - 2) > 3x$

3. _____

4. $-3(x + 1) + 5 \leq 2x - (x - 6)$

4. _____

Solve each compound inequality.

5. $2x + 5 \leq 11$ and $4(x - 1) + 12 \geq 0$

5. _____

6. $5 - 2x > -3$ or $3(6 - x) < 2(x - 6)$

6. _____

7. $3x > 4 - x$ or $2(x + 3) > 5x - 3$

7. _____

Solve each open sentence.

8. $|x + 2| > 3$

8. _____

9. $|2x - 5| \leq 7$

9. _____

10. $|x - 1| \geq 4$ and $|x| \geq 3$

10. _____

Use a graphing calculator to graph each inequality. Make a sketch of the graph.

11. $y \geq 2.5x - 5$

11. _____

12. $3x + 2y < 8$

12. _____

13. $x - 2y \geq -4$ and $y \geq 0$

13. _____

14. Alicia just downloaded some software that will help her set up her own home page on the World Wide Web. Alicia can choose the background color for her page as well as the colors for plain text and highlighted text. How many color combinations are possible if Alicia can select from 276 background colors, 11 plain text colors, and 9 highlighted text colors?

14. _____

15. A contest involves tossing a six-sided die 15 times. The contest ends if a contestant tosses a 4. What is the probability of tossing the die 15 times without tossing a 4?

15. _____

16. A computer is programmed to generate a 7-digit number by randomly selecting the digits 1–9 twelve times. What is the probability that the number will be 1111111?

16. _____

NAME_____ DATE _____

Chapter 7 Performance Assessment

Instructions: *Demonstrate your knowledge by giving a clear, concise solution to each problem. Be sure to include all relevant drawings and justify your answers. You may show your solution in more than one way or investigate beyond the requirements of the problem.*

1. An architect is designing a house for the Frazier family. In the design he must consider the desires of the family and the local building codes. The rectangular lot on which the house will be built has 91 feet of frontage on a lake and is 158 feet deep.

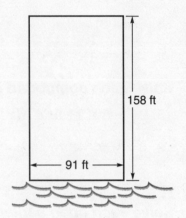

   a. The building codes state that one can build no closer than 10 feet to the lot line. Write an inequality and solve to see how long the front of the house facing the lake may be.

   b. The Fraziers requested that the house contain no less than 2800 ft² and no more than 3200 ft² of floor space. Write an inequality to represent the range of permissible widths for the house.

   c. The Fraziers have asked that the cost of the house be about $175,000 and are willing to deviate from this price no more than $20,000. Write an open sentence involving an absolute value and solve. Give the meaning of the answer.

2. a. Write a word problem involving an inequality with more than one operation.

   b. Solve and give the meaning of the answer.

3. Students on a band trip are given a soft drink and a sandwich chosen at random for lunch. They may then trade with other band members if they wish to do so. Students have an equal chance of getting root beer or orange drink and peanut butter and jelly, bologna, or ham sandwich. Use a tree diagram to find the probability of getting an orange drink and meat sandwich. Give your reasoning.

4. Describe the data set used to make this box-and-whisker plot. What can't you tell about the data by looking at the box-and-whisker plot?

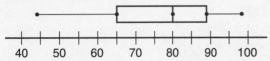

NAME_____ DATE _____

Chapter 7 Mid-Chapter Test (Lessons 7-1 through 7-4)

Solve and check each inequality.

1. $n + 5 \geq 32$

2. $x - 4 > 1$ or $x + 3 < 0$

3. $4.2 > -11 + t$

4. $-\frac{3}{10} + d < \frac{9}{10}$

5. $16w \geq 15w + (-8)$

6. $2y > 6$ and $3y < 15$

7. $-5w < 75$

8. $-\frac{3}{5}v > -\frac{4}{15}$

9. $-\frac{a}{5} < -14$

10. $7x - 5 < 9$

11. $\frac{n}{-4} + 8 \leq 1$

12. $6 > -4 - 5d$ and $8 - 3d > -7$

13. $-6(3w - 4) + w \leq -10$

14. $x > 2$ or $x - 3 > 1$

1. _____
2. _____
3. _____
4. _____
5. _____
6. _____
7. _____
8. _____
9. _____
10. _____
11. _____
12. _____
13. _____
14. _____

Define a variable, write an inequality, and solve each problem.

15. For a package to qualify for a certain postage rate, the sum of its length and girth cannot exceed 85 inches. If the girth is 63 inches, how long can the package be?

15. _____

16. The minimum daily requirement of vitamin C for 14-year-olds is 50 mg per day. An average-sized apple contains 6 mg of vitamin C. How many apples would a person have to eat each day to satisfy this requirement?

16. _____

17. Janet had scores of 75, 64, 83, 91, and 95 on 5 tests. What does her score have to be on the sixth test to have an average score of at least 80?

17. _____

18. Angus always eats twice as many dog biscuits as Ignatz. How many biscuits will Ignatz eat if the dogs eat no more than 27 biscuits?

18. _____

19. An empty book crate weighs 30 lb. What is the greatest number of books weighing 1.5 lb each that can be packed in the crate if the filled crate may weigh no more than 60 lb?

19. _____

20. The sum of $\frac{1}{2}$ a number and 6 is between 3 and 8. What is the number?

20. _____

Bonus Two couples are playing pinochle. The first couple has a score of 145 while the second couple has a score of 138. The couple with the higher score of 150 or more wins the game. Each hand dealt is worth 25 points. How many of the 25 points must the first couple take to win the game?

Bonus _____

NAME_____ DATE _____

Chapter 7, Quiz A (Lessons 7-1 and 7-2)

Solve and check each inequality.

1. $w + 9 \leq -5$

2. $\frac{1}{4} + m \geq \frac{3}{4}$

1. _____

2. _____

3. $5x - 10 \leq 6x$

4. $-8 + 9r > 10r - 23$

3. _____

4. _____

5. $-3n \leq 84$

6. $\frac{m}{13} > -6$

5. _____

6. _____

7. $-\frac{4}{9} < -\frac{5}{12}r$

8. $-3.22 \geq 1.4w$

7. _____

8. _____

9. Write an inequality and solve:
   Two times a number is at least 16; find the number.

9. _____

10. Define a variable, write an inequality, and solve:
    Rita plans to spend at most $115.00 on a skirt and two blouses.
    She bought the two blouses for $38.95 each. How much can she
    spend on the skirt?

10. _____

NAME_____ DATE _____

Chapter 7, Quiz B (Lessons 7-3 and 7-4)

Solve and check each inequality.

1. $-\frac{3r}{8} > \frac{5}{7}$

2. $-\frac{d}{5} - 12 \geq 8$

1. _____

2. _____

3. $9y - 6 > 2y + 15$

4. $0.2(x + 20) \leq 0.5(3x + 8)$

3. _____

4. _____

5. $-6 < 5y - (2y - 9)$

6. $4 + 2(5x - 6) > 14x$

5. _____

6. _____

7. Graph the solution set of $x \geq -4$ and $x < 2$
   on the number line provided.

7.
   -5 -4 -3 -2 -1 0 1 2 3 4 5

8. Solve the compound inequality $2y - 3 \leq 7$ or
   $-3y \leq -18$ and graph the solution set on the number
   line provided.

8. ←++++++++++++→
   -3 -2 -1 0 1 2 3 4 5 6 7

9. Write a compound inequality for the solution
   set that is graphed.
   -7 -6 -5 -4 -3 -2 -1 0 1 2 3 4 5

9. _____

10. Write a compound inequality and solve:
    Eight times an integer is between 16 and 40; find all
    possible values for the integer.

10. _____

NAME_____ DATE _____

Chapter 7, Quiz C (Lessons 7-5 and 7-6)

Solve each open sentence and graph the solution set on the number lines provided.

1. $|m - 5| < 3$

2. $|3x + 4| \geq 7$

3. $|6 - 2x| = 0$

4. Write an open sentence involving absolute value for this graph.

1. ⟵|—|—|—|—|—|—|—|—|—|—|—⟶
   −1 0 1 2 3 4 5 6 7 8 9

2. ⟵|—|—|—|—|—|—|—|—|—|—|—⟶
   −5−4−3−2−1 0 1 2 3 4 5

3. ⟵|—|—|—|—|—|—|—|—|—|—|—⟶
   −5−4−3−2−1 0 1 2 3 4 5

4. _____

Judy has two cards labeled 1 and 2. Mark has three cards labeled 1, 2, and 3. A card is chosen at random from each set.

5. Draw a tree diagram to show the possible outcomes.   5.

NAME_____ DATE _____

Chapter 7, Quiz D (Lessons 7-7 and 7-8)

In degrees Fahrenheit, the average daily temperatures in Jacksonville, Florida, from January to December are 52.4, 55.2, 61.1, 67.0, 73.4, 79.1, 81.6, 81.2, 78.1, 69.8, 61.9, 55.1, respectively.

1. Find the median for the data.   1. _____

2. State the upper and lower quartiles for the data.   2. _____

3. State the interquartile range.   3. _____

4. Make a box-and-whisker plot in the space provided.   4.

5. Graph $-2y + 3x \geq 4$ on the coordinate plane at the right.   5.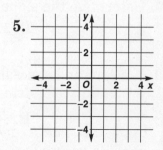

Chapter 7 Standardized Test Practice

Choose the best answer. Write A, B, C, or D.

1. If $a^2 > c^2$, then

   A. $a > c$.   **B.** $a < c$.   **C.** $|a| > |c|$.   **D.** $a = c$.

   1. _____

2. If r and s are integers and rs is a negative integer, which of the following can be true?

   A. $r < 0$ and $s < 0$ **B.** $r < 0$ and $s \geq 0$

   C. $r > 0$ and $s > 0$ **D.** $r < 0$ and $s > 0$

   2. _____

3. Which ordered pair is a solution of the equation $y = 2x - 1$?

   A. $(-1, -1)$ **B.** $(9, 5)$ **C.** $(-5, -2)$ **D.** $(2, 3)$

   3. _____

4. Which fraction is greater than $\frac{1}{8}$ but less than $\frac{1}{5}$?

   A. $\frac{1}{4}$ **B.** $\frac{2}{11}$ **C.** $\frac{5}{13}$ **D.** $\frac{1}{3}$

   4. _____

5. Which group of numbers is arranged from least to greatest?

   A. $-8, -10, \frac{1}{3}, 0.6, 1$ **B.** $1, 0.6, \frac{1}{3}, -8, -10$

   C. $-10, -8, 0.6, \frac{1}{3}, 1$ **D.** $-10, -8, \frac{1}{3}, 0.6, 1$

   5. _____

6. If $2x - 2y = 10$, then

   A. $x > y$.   **B.** $y > x$.

   C. $x > y$ and $y \geq 0$.   **D.** $y > x$ and $y \geq 0$.

   6. _____

7. What is the total length of fencing needed to enclose a square region that measures 12 feet on a side?

   A. 4 yards   **B.** 8 yards   **C.** 12 yards   **D.** 16 yards

   7. _____

8. The discount price for a \$65 item is \$58.50. What is the discount price for a \$110 item if the rate of discount is $2\frac{1}{2}$ times the rate of discount for the \$65 item?

   A. \$16.25   **B.** \$25   **C.** \$27.50   **D.** \$82.50

   8. _____

9. Determine the slope of the line passing through $(2, 5)$ and $(3, 6)$.

   A. 1   **B.** 2   **C.** $\frac{1}{2}$ **D.** -1

   9. _____

10. If a coin and a six-sided die are tossed, what is the probability of getting a tail and a 5?

    A. $\frac{1}{2}$ **B.** $\frac{1}{12}$ **C.** $\frac{1}{3}$ **D.** $\frac{5}{12}$

    10. _____

Chapter 7 Cumulative Review

1. Evaluate $(2x + 5y)^2$ if $x = 0$ and $y = -\frac{4}{3}$. (Lesson 1-3)

   1. _____

2. State the property shown in $8 \cdot 1 = 8$. (Lesson 1-6)

   2. _____

Simplify. (Lesson 1-7)

3. $7(r + 2t) - 5t$

   3. _____

4. $5(4a + b) + 3a + b$

   4. _____

Find each sum or difference. (Lessons 2-3 and 2-5)

5. $-19 + 40$

   5. _____

6. $-\frac{1}{2} + \left(-\frac{1}{6}\right) + \left(-\frac{2}{3}\right)$

   6. _____

7. $\begin{bmatrix} 3.1 & -6.3 \\ -8 & 1 \end{bmatrix} - \begin{bmatrix} 3.1 & -6.3 \\ 4 & -5 \end{bmatrix}$

   7. _____

8. Solve $\frac{a}{6} - 5 = 12$. (Lesson 3-3)

   8. _____

9. Elisabeth is 6 years older than her sister Elisa. Their mother's age is twice the sum of their ages. How old are they if their mother is 40? (Lesson 2-9)

   9. _____

10. Find the mean, median, and mode of the data represented in the stem-and-leaf plot at the right. (Lessons 1-4 and 3-7)

Stem	Leaf
4	2 7
5	1 2 4
6	0 5 5 $5|4 = 54$

    10. _____

    _____

    _____

11. Find both the complement and the supplement for an angle of 63°. (Lesson 3-4)

    11. _____

12. Find the measure of each of the two congruent angles of an isosceles triangle if the third angle is 84°. (Lesson 3-4)

    12. _____

13. How many pounds of peanuts costing $2.00 a pound should be mixed with 4 pounds of cashews costing $4.50 a pound to obtain a mixture costing $3.00 a pound? (Lesson 4-8)

    13. _____

14. Three times a number is 16 less than five times the number. Find the number. (Lesson 3-6)

    14. _____

15. Find 2.9% of 84. (Lesson 4-4)

    15. _____

16. Twenty-eight is 40% of what number? (Lesson 4-4)

    16. _____

A card is selected at random from a standard deck of 52 cards.
Then a second card is selected without replacing the first card.
(Lesson 4-6)

17. Find the probability of selecting two red cards.

17. _____

18. Find the odds in favor of selecting a black face card for the first card.

18. _____

19. If y varies inversely as x and $x = 15$ when $y = 8$, find x when $y = 12$. (Lesson 4-8)

19. _____

20. $\triangle DEF$ and $\triangle ABC$ are similar. Find a and e. (Lesson 4-2)

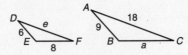

20. _____

21. Write an equation for the relationship between the variables in the chart at the right. (Lesson 5-6)

x	−3	−1	1	3
y	2	1	0	−1

21. _____

Use the stem-and-leaf plot for exercises 22–26. (Lesson 5-7)

22. What is the range?

Stem	Leaf
3	1 3 7 7 8
4	0 2 2 6 9
5	3 5 8
6	0 4

$4|2 = 42$

22. _____

23. What is the median?

23. _____

24. What is the lower quartile?

24. _____

25. What is the upper quartile?

25. _____

26. What is the interquartile range?

26. _____

27. Determine the slope of the line passing through $(3, -2)$ and $(1, 1)$. (Lesson 6-1)

27. _____

28. Graph $-4x + 2y = 2$ using the slope-intercept method. (Lesson 6-5)

28.

29. Find the coordinates of the midpoint of the line segment whose endpoints are $(8, 10)$ and $(-2, 7)$. (Lesson 6-7)

29. _____

Solve each inequality. (Lessons 7-1 and 7-2)

30. $4y + 6 \geq 6y - 4$

30. _____

31. $-13a > 68$

31. _____

32. Graph the solution set of $m > 2$ or $m < -3$. (Lesson 7-4)

32.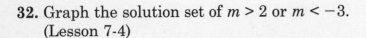

33. If twice an integer increased by 12 lies between 20 and 24, what is the integer? (Lesson 7-1)

33. _____

Chapter 7 Answer Key

Form 1A

Page 169	Page 170
1. **C**	13. **B**
2. **A**	
3. **B**	14. **D**
4. **C**	
5. **D**	15. **B**
6. **A**	
7. **B**	16. **D**
8. **B**	17. **A**
9. **D**	
10. **A**	18. **B**
11. **A**	19. **C**
12. **A**	20. **B**
	Bonus {−12, 12}

Form 1B

Page 171	Page 172
1. **B**	14. **D**
2. **A**	
3. **B**	15. **D**
4. **D**	16. **B**
5. **D**	
6. **A**	17. **A**
7. **A**	
8. **D**	18. **C**
9. **B**	19. **A**
10. **D**	
11. **C**	20. **C**
12. **A**	
13. **D**	Bonus

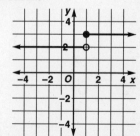

Chapter 7 Answer Key

Form 1C

Page 173

1. __A__
2. __B__
3. __D__
4. __A__
5. __D__
6. __B__
7. __B__
8. __D__
9. __D__
10. __B__
11. __B__
12. __C__
13. __C__

Page 174

14. __C__
15. __C__
16. __D__
17. __D__
18. __A__
19. __B__
20. __D__

Bonus __greater than 36 units, or $p > 36$__

Form 2A

Page 175

1. $\{m \mid m \geq 9.3\}$
2. $\left\{m \mid m \leq \dfrac{7}{10}\right\}$
3. $\{w \mid w \leq -10.4\}$
4. $\left\{t \mid t > \dfrac{9}{11}\right\}$
5. $\{x \mid x < -9\}$
6. $\{s \mid s \geq 0\}$
7. $-\dfrac{3}{7}n \geq 102$; __-238 or less__
8. j = amt. on jeans; $78 \geq 2(19.89) + j$; no more than $38.22
9. n = lesser integer; $n + (n + 2) \leq 15$; (0, 2), (2, 4), (4, 6), (6, 8)
10. s = amt. on sales; $32{,}500 \leq 25{,}600 + 0.1s \leq 41{,}900$; between $69,000 and $163,000
11. $-1 < m < 2$
12. $-6 < x \leq 8$
13. $x > -6$
14. $\{-2.8, 4\}$
15. $x \leq -6$ or $x \geq 2$
16.

Page 176

17. __25%__
18. $\dfrac{1}{6}$
19.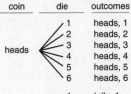
20. $\dfrac{9}{25}$
21. $|s - 40| \leq 0.05(40)$, or $|s - 40| \leq 2$
22. __63__
23. __5__
24. $\{(-5, -2), (2, 0)\}$
25. $\{(-2, -3), (-2, -2), (0, 0), (0, 2), (2, -2)\}$

Bonus $-3 < x < 1$ or $7 < x < 11$

Chapter 7 Answer Key

Form 2B

Page 177

1. $\{n \mid n \geq -19\}$

2. $\{a \mid a > -6\}$

3. $\left\{y \mid y > -\dfrac{16}{15}\right\}$

4. $\{t \mid t \leq -84\}$

5. $\{y \mid y \leq -5.5\}$

6. $\{x \mid x < 8\}$

7. $\{c \mid c \leq 13\}$

8. $40 - 3n \geq n + 15$; $n \leq 6\dfrac{1}{4}$

9. s = score needed;
$\dfrac{75 + 82 + 94 + 77 + s}{5} \geq 85$;
97 or greater

10. c = no. of checks;
$3.50 < 0.10c + 2.25 < 5.00$;
between 13 and 27

11. $-5 < w < 2$
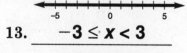

12. {all numbers}

13. $-3 \leq x < 3$

14. $\{-1, 3\}$

15. $x \leq 1$ or $x \geq 2$

16. {all numbers}

Page

17.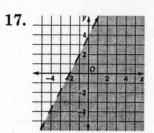

18. 75%

19.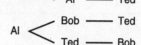

20. $\dfrac{1}{3}$

21. $\dfrac{3}{4}$

22. 6

23. 7.5

24. $\{(-6, -2), (0, 2), (6, 4)\}$

25. $\{(-2, 4), (0, 3), (1, 4)\}$

Bonus $\left\{-5 < n < 11\right\}$

Chapter 7 Answer Key

Form 2C

1. $\{m \mid m < -9\}$

2. $\{t \mid t \le -11\}$

3. $\{m \mid m < -6\}$

4. $\{h \mid h \ge 27\}$

5. $\{k \mid k \le 2\}$

6. $\left\{ w \mid w > -4\frac{6}{7} \right\}$

7. $2n - 7 \ge 17$;
   $n \ge 12$

8. $4.10 + d \le 10$;
   $d \le 5.90$

9. $n + (n + 2) \le 9$; $(-3, -1)$, $(1, 3)$, $(3, 5)$

10. 50%

11. $-\frac{5}{7} < w < 3$

    -5-4-3-2-1 0 1 2 3 4 5

12. $\frac{1}{2} < y \le 4$

    -5-4-3-2-1 0 1 2 3 4 5

13. {all numbers}

    -5-4-3-2-1 0 1 2 3 4 5

14. $x = 4$ or $x = -1$

    -5-4-3-2-1 0 1 2 3 4 5

15. $-3 \le x \le 5$

    -5-4-3-2-1 0 1 2 3 4 5

16.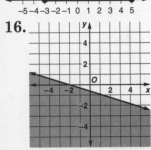

Page 180

1st spinner	2nd spinner	Savings
0	0	$0
	5	$5
1	0	$10
	5	$15
2	0	$20
	5	$25

17.

18. $\dfrac{1}{2}$

19. $\dfrac{1}{3}$

20. $m =$ money to be raised;
    $188 + m \ge 275$;
    $m \ge \$87$

21. $|w - 1| \le 0.01$

22. 82.5

23. 70

24. $\{(-2, -1), (-1, 0), (0, 1), (1, 3)\}$

25. $\{(1, 3)\}$

Bonus $x < 4$

Calculator-Based

1. $\{x \mid x > 2\}$

2. $\{x \mid x \le -2\}$

3. $\{x \mid x > 5\}$

4. $\{x \mid x \ge -1\}$

5. $-2 \le x \le 3$

6. $x < 4$ or $x > 6$

7. x is a real number.

8. $x < -5$ or $x > 1$

9. $-1 \le x \le 6$

10. $x \le -3$ or $x \ge 5$

11.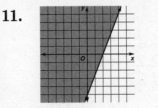

12.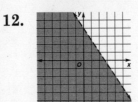

13.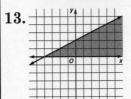

14. 27,324 combinations

15. 0.06

16. 2.1×10^{-7}

Scoring Guide
Chapter 7
Performance Assessment

Level	Specific Criteria
3 Superior	• Shows thorough understanding of the concepts of *inequality, compound inequality, absolute value, solving inequalities, compound events,* and *box-and-whisker plot.* • Uses appropriate strategies to solve problems. • Computations are correct. • Written explanations are exemplary. • Word problem concerning inequality with more than one operation is appropriate and makes sense. • Goes beyond requirements of some or all problems.
2 Satisfactory, with Minor Flaws	• Shows understanding of the concepts of *inequality, compound inequality, absolute value, solving inequalities, compound events,* and *box-and-whisker plot.* • Uses appropriate strategies to solve problems. • Computations are mostly correct. • Written explanations are effective. • Word problem concerning inequality with more than one operation is appropriate and makes sense. • Satisfies all requirements of problems.
1 Nearly Satisfactory, with Serious Flaws	• Shows understanding of most of the concepts of *inequality, compound inequality, absolute value, solving inequalities, compound events,* and *box-and-whisker plot.* • May not use appropriate strategies to solve problems. • Computations are mostly correct. • Written explanations are satisfactory. • Word problem concerning inequality with more than one operation is mostly appropriate and sensible. • Satisfies most requirements of problems.
0 Unsatisfactory	• Shows little or no understanding of the concepts of *inequality, compound inequality, absolute value, solving inequalities, compound events,* and *box-and-whisker plot.* • May not use appropriate strategies to solve problems. • Computations are incorrect. • Written explanations are not satisfactory. • Word problem concerning inequality with more than one operation is not appropriate or sensible. • Does not satisfy requirements of problems.

Chapter 7 Answer Key
Performance Assessment

Page 182

1. a. $91 - l \geq 20$ or $l \leq 71$

   b. $2800 \leq 71w \leq 3200$ or $40 \leq w \leq \dfrac{320}{7}$

   c. $|\,\$175{,}000 - x\,| \leq \$20{,}000$; $\$155{,}000 \leq x < \$195{,}000$; The cost of the house may vary from $\$155{,}000$ to $\$195{,}000$.

2. a. Sample answer: The cost of six roses and an $8 vase must be no more than $26; how much can one pay per rose?

   b. $6r + \$8 \leq \$26$; one can pay no more than $3 per rose.

3.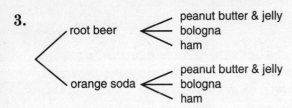

   $$P = \left(\frac{1}{2}\right)\left(\frac{2}{3}\right) = \frac{1}{3}$$

4. Students' answers should include the median (80), lower and upper quartiles (65 and 89, respectively), and the least and greatest values (44 and 99, respectively). They may mention that 25% of the data is between 44 and 65, 50% is between 65 and 89, and 25% is between 89 and 99. Students may say that they cannot tell how many members of the data set there are.

Chapter 7 Answer Key

Mid-Chapter Test
Page 183

1. $\{n \mid n \geq 27\}$
2. $\{x \mid x > 5 \text{ or } x < -3\}$
3. $\{t \mid t < 15.2\}$
4. $\{d \mid d < 1\frac{1}{5}\}$
5. $\{w \mid w \geq -8\}$
6. $\{y \mid 3 < y < 5\}$
7. $\{w \mid w > -15\}$
8. $\{v \mid v < \frac{4}{9}\}$
9. $\{a \mid a > 70\}$
10. $\{x \mid x < 2\}$
11. $\{n \mid n \geq 28\}$
12. $\{d \mid -2 < d < 5\}$
13. $\{w \mid w \geq 2\}$
14. $\{x \mid 2 < x < 4\}$
15. $l = \text{length}; l + 63 \leq \leq 85; 22 \text{ in. or less}$
16. $a = \text{no. of apples};$ $6a \geq 50; \text{at least } 8\frac{1}{3}$ apples
17. $s = \text{score};$ $\frac{75 + 64 + 83 + 91 + 95 + s}{6} \geq$ $80; \text{at least } 72$
18. $b = \text{no. of biscuits};$ $b + 2b \leq 27; 9 \text{ or}$ less
19. $b = \text{no. of books};$ $1.5b + 30 \leq 60; \text{no}$ more than 20
20. $n = \text{number};$ $3 < \frac{1}{2}n + 6 < 8;$ $-6 < n < 4$

Bonus   10 points

Quiz A
Page 184

1. $\{w \mid w \leq -14\}$
2. $\{m \mid m \geq \frac{1}{2}\}$
3. $\{x \mid x > -10\}$
4. $\{r \mid r < 15\}$
5. $\{n \mid n \geq -28\}$
6. $\{m \mid m > -78\}$
7. $\{r \mid r < 1\frac{1}{15}\}$
8. $\{w \mid w \leq -2.3\}$
9. $2n \geq 16; n \geq 8$
10. $s = \text{amt. on skirt};$ $2(38.95) + s \leq 115;$ $\$37.10 \text{ or less}$

Quiz B
Page 184

1. $\{r \mid r < -1\frac{19}{21}\}$
2. $\{d \mid d \leq -100\}$
3. $\{y \mid y > 3\}$
4. $\{x \mid x \geq 0\}$
5. $\{y \mid y > -5\}$
6. $\{x \mid x < -2\}$
7.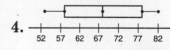
8. $y \leq 5 \text{ or } y \geq 6$
   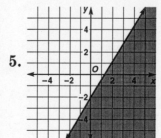
9. $-7 < x \leq 4$
10. $16 < 8x < 40; 3, 4$

Quiz C
Page 185

1. $2 < m < 8$
   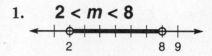
2. $x \leq -3\frac{2}{3} \text{ or } x \geq 1$
   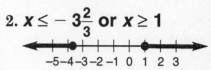
3. $x = 3$
   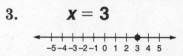
4. The absolute value of x is greater than or equal to 1.
5.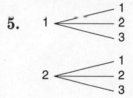

Quiz D
Page 185

1. 68.4
2. UQ = 78.6; LQ = 58.15
3. 20.45
4. [box-and-whisker plot: 52 57 62 67 72 77 82]
5. [graph]

Chapter 7 Answer Key

Standardized Test Practice
Page 186

1. C
2. D
3. D
4. B
5. D
6. A
7. D
8. D
9. A
10. B

Cumulative Review
Page 187

1. $44\frac{4}{9}$
2. multiplicative identity
3. $7r + 9t$
4. $23a + 6b$
5. 21
6. $-1\frac{1}{3}$
7. $\begin{bmatrix} 0 & 0 \\ -12 & 6 \end{bmatrix}$
8. 102
9. Elisa is 7 and Elisabeth is 13.
10. mean = 54.5; median = 53; mode = 65
11. 27°; 117°
12. 48°, 48°
13. 6 pounds
14. 8
15. 2.436
16. 70

Page 188

17. $\frac{25}{102}$
18. 3:23
19. 10
20. $a = 12$; $e = 12$
21. $y = -\frac{1}{2}x + \frac{1}{2}$
22. 33
23. 42
24. 37
25. 55
26. 18
27. $-\frac{3}{2}$
28.
29. $\left(3, 8\frac{1}{2}\right)$
30. $\{y \mid y \le 5\}$
31. $\{a \mid a < -5\frac{3}{13}\}$
32.
33. 5

Chapter 8 Test, Form 1A

Write the letter for the correct answer in the blank at the right of each problem.

Use the graph to answer questions 1–4.

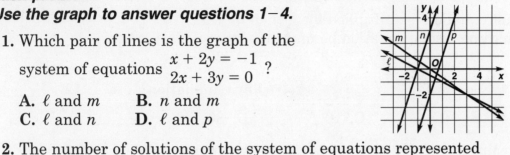

1. Which pair of lines is the graph of the system of equations $\begin{array}{l} x + 2y = -1 \\ 2x + 3y = 0 \end{array}$?

   A. ℓ and m **B.** n and m
   C. ℓ and n **D.** ℓ and p

   1. _____

2. The number of solutions of the system of equations represented by lines n and p is
   A. exactly one. **B.** none.   **C.** exactly two. **D.** infinitely many.

   2. _____

3. The equation for line p and the equation $y = 3x - 2$ form a system of equations. The number of solutions is
   A. exactly one. **B.** none.   **C.** exactly two. **D.** infinitely many.

   3. _____

4. Which ordered pair is the solution of the system of equations represented by lines ℓ and n?
   A. $(3, -2)$ **B.** $(0, 3)$ **C.** $(0, -1)$ **D.** $(-1, 0)$

   4. _____

5. If the system $\begin{array}{l} x + 2y = 15 \\ 5x + y = 21 \end{array}$ is to be solved by substitution, which expression can be replaced for x in the second equation?
   A. $15 - 2y$ **B.** $21 - 5x$ **C.** $\dfrac{15 - x}{2}$ **D.** $\dfrac{21 - y}{5}$

   5. _____

6. Solve the system $\begin{array}{l} x = 2y + 3 \\ 4x - 5y = 9 \end{array}$ by substitution.
   A. $\{(2, 7)\}$ **B.** $\{(1, -1)\}$ **C.** $\{(5, 1)\}$ **D.** none of these

   6. _____

Use the graph for questions 7 and 8.

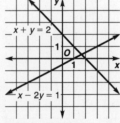

7. Identify the best estimate of the solution of this system.
   A. $\{(0, 2)\}$ **B.** $\{(2, 0)\}$
   C. $\{(0, 0)\}$ **D.** $\{(3, 0)\}$

   7. _____

8. Use elimination to solve the system.
   A. $\left\{\left(2, \frac{1}{3}\right)\right\}$ **B.** $\left\{\left(\frac{1}{3}, \frac{1}{3}\right)\right\}$ **C.** $\left\{\left(\frac{5}{3}, \frac{1}{3}\right)\right\}$ **D.** $\left\{\left(\frac{1}{3}, \frac{5}{3}\right)\right\}$

   8. _____

9. If the system $\begin{array}{l} x + 7y = 16 \\ 3x - 7y = 4 \end{array}$ is solved by elimination, what is the value of x?
   A. 3   **B.** 4   **C.** 5   **D.** -6

   9. _____

10. Half the perimeter of a garden is 18 feet. The garden is 8 feet longer than it is wide. If w = the width in feet and ℓ = the length in feet, which system must be true?

    A. $\frac{1}{2}(\ell + w) = 18$ **B.** $\frac{1}{2}(\ell + w) = 18$ **C.** $\ell + w = 8$ **D.** $\ell - w = 8$
    $\quad\ \ \ell = w + 8$ $\qquad\ \ w = \ell + 8$ $\qquad \ell - w = 18$ $\quad\ \ell + w = 18$

    10. _____

11. If the system $\begin{array}{l} 2x - 5y = 1 \\ -3x + 7y = -3 \end{array}$ is to be solved by elimination of   11. _____

    x, and the first equation is multiplied by 3, then by which
    number should the second equation be multiplied?
    A. 3   **B.** 5   **C.** −3   **D.** 2

12. What is the value of x if $\begin{array}{l} x - 5y = 20 \\ x + 3y = -4 \end{array}$ is solved by elimination?   12. _____

    A. 5   **B.** −13   **C.** 10   **D.** 80

13. What is the value of y if $\begin{array}{l} 8x - 7y = 5 \\ 3x - 5y = 9 \end{array}$ is solved by elimination?   13. _____

    A. −2   **B.** 8   **C.** −3   **D.** none of these

14. Solve the system $\begin{array}{l} 4x + 6y = 8 \\ 2x - 5y = 1 \end{array}$.   14. _____

    A. $\left\{\left(\dfrac{17}{16}, \dfrac{5}{8}\right)\right\}$ **B.** $\left\{\left(\dfrac{23}{16}, \dfrac{3}{8}\right)\right\}$ **C.** $\left\{\left(\dfrac{23}{4}, -\dfrac{5}{2}\right)\right\}$ **D.** $\left\{\left(\dfrac{17}{4}, -\dfrac{3}{2}\right)\right\}$

15. State which region in the
    graph is the solution of the
    system. $y \geq -x + 1$
    $y \leq \dfrac{2}{3}x + 2$ 15. _____

16. Which system of inequalities
    is graphed?   16. _____

    A. $x < y + 1$
    $y < x + 2$
    B. $y > x - 1$
    $x < y - 2$
    C. $y > x + 2$
    $y < x - 1$
    D. $x > y + 1$
    $x > y - 2$

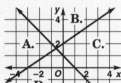

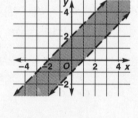

17. A 2-digit number is 12 times its tens digit. The sum of the   17. _____
    digits is 12. What is the tens digit?
    A. 8   **B.** 1   **C.** 2   **D.** 4

18. The difference of the digits of a 2-digit number is 5. If the   18. _____
    digits are reversed, the new number is 7 greater than twice the
    original number. What is the units digit of the original number?
    A. 5   **B.** 8   **C.** 7   **D.** 6

19. A company is going to mix two kinds of coffee. The first kind   19. _____
    costs $7 per pound. The second kind costs $4 per pound. It wants
    90 pounds worth $6 per pound. How much of the first kind should it use?
    A. 30 pounds   **B.** 40 pounds   **C.** 50 pounds   **D.** 60 pounds

20. A boat took 1 hour 50 minutes to go 55 miles downstream   20. _____
    and 3 hours 40 minutes to return. Find the rate of the current.
    A. 22.5 mi/h   **B.** 7.5 mi/h   **C.** 30 mi/h   **D.** 15 mi/h

Bonus   Where on the graph of $2x - 6y = 7$ is the x-coordinate   **Bonus** _____
    twice the y-coordinate?

Write the letter for the correct answer in the blank at the right of each problem. Use the graph to answer questions 1–4.

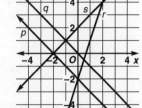

1. Which ordered pair is the solution of the system of equations represented by lines q and s?
   A. $(0, -2)$ **B.** $(2, 4)$ **C.** $(1, -1)$ **D.** $(-1, 1)$

   1. _____

2. Which pair of lines is the graph of the system of equations $\begin{array}{l} x - y = -2 \\ 3x - y = 2 \end{array}$?
   A. p and q **B.** q and s
   C. r and p **D.** r and s

   2. _____

3. How many solutions are there of the system of equations represented by the line q and the equation $y = -x$?
   A. exactly one **B.** exactly two **C.** no solutions **D.** infinitely many

   3. _____

4. How many solutions are there of the system of equations represented by lines p and q?
   A. exactly one **B.** exactly two **C.** no solutions **D.** infinitely many

   4. _____

5. If the system of equations $\begin{array}{l} 3x + y = 14 \\ x + 4y = 3 \end{array}$ is to be solved by substitution, which expression can be substituted for y in the second equation?
   A. $3 - 4y$ **B.** $14 - 3x$ **C.** $\dfrac{14 - y}{3}$ **D.** $\dfrac{3 - x}{4}$

   5. _____

6. Solve the system of equations $\begin{array}{l} x = 5y \\ 2x + 5y = 15 \end{array}$ by substitution.
   A. $\{(1, 5)\}$ **B.** $\{(0, 3)\}$ **C.** $\{(5, 1)\}$ **D.** none of these

   6. _____

7. Use substitution to solve the system of equations $\begin{array}{l} x + 6y = 12 \\ 2x + 12y = 1 \end{array}$.
   A. $\{(0, 2)\}$ **B.** $\{(12, 0)\}$
   C. There are infinitely   **D.** There are no solutions.
       many solutions.

   7. _____

8. Identify the best estimate of the solution of this system.
   A. $\{(0, 0)\}$ **B.** $\{(0, -3)\}$
   C. $\{(-1, 1)\}$ **D.** $\{(1, -1)\}$

   $y = -\frac{1}{3}x - 3$
   $y = 2x - 3$

   8. _____

9. The sum of the digits of a 2-digit number is 6. The number is 6 times the units digit. If t = the tens digit, and u = the units digit, which system must be true?
   A. $t = 6 - u$ **B.** $t + u = 6$ **C.** $t + u = 6u$ **D.** $t + u = 6$
      $10t + 6u = 6$ $10t + u = 6u$ $10t + u = 6u$ $10t = 6u$

   9. _____

10. If the system of equations $\begin{array}{l} 3x + 5y = 16 \\ 8x - 5y = 28 \end{array}$ is solved by elimination, what is the value of x?
    A. 4   **B.** 5   **C.** -6 **D.** 7

    10. _____

11. What is the value of y if the system of equations $\begin{array}{l} x + y = 5 \\ x + 2y = 3 \end{array}$ is solved by elimination?

    A. -2 **B.** 3 **C.** $\dfrac{8}{3}$ **D.** $-\dfrac{8}{3}$

11. _____

12. The system of equations $\begin{array}{l} 4x + 7y = 8 \\ -3x - 2y = 5 \end{array}$ is to be solved by elimination of x. If the first equation is multiplied by 3, then by which number should the second equation be multiplied?

    A. 3 **B.** -3 **C.** 7 **D.** 4

12. _____

13. What is the value of x if the system of equations $\begin{array}{l} 4x + 7y = -4 \\ 8x + 5y = 28 \end{array}$ is solved by elimination?

    A. 2 **B.** 6 **C.** 4 **D.** -4

13. _____

14. Solve the system of equations $\begin{array}{l} 5x + 4y = -10 \\ 3x + 6y = -6 \end{array}$ by elimination.

    A. $\{(0, -2)\}$ **B.** $\{(2, -5)\}$ **C.** $\{(-2, 0)\}$ **D.** none of these

14. _____

15. Which system of inequalities is graphed?

    A. $y > 2$
         $y > x - 2$

    B. $y < 2$
         $y < x - 2$

    C. $y < 2$
         $x < y + 2$

    D. $y > 2$
         $x > y - 2$

16. State which region in the graph is the solution of the system $|x + 1| \le y$.

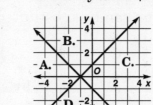

15. _____

16. _____

17. A lab technician has a 15% alcohol solution and a 35% alcohol solution. She wants to make 100 gallons of a 29% alcohol solution. How much of the 15% solution should she use?

    A. 70 gal   **B.** 30 gal   **C.** 40 gal   **D.** 55 gal

17. _____

18. How many pounds of cashew nuts that sell for $2 a pound should be mixed with peanuts, which sell for 80¢ a pound, to make a 10-pound mixture that sells for $1.28 a pound?

    A. 4 pounds   **B.** 6 pounds   **C.** 8 pounds   **D.** 10 pounds

18. _____

19. An airplane travels 1560 miles in 3 hours flying with the wind. The return trip takes 4 hours. Find the rate of the plane in still air.

    A. 65 mi/h   **B.** 195 mi/h   **C.** 455 mi/h   **D.** 260 mi/h

19. _____

20. Roger reversed the digits in the amount of a check and overpaid a customer by $9. The sum of the digits in the two-digit amount was 7. Find the amount of the check.

    A. $43   **B.** $34   **C.** $63   **D.** $54

20. _____

Bonus   Find the value of a and b so that the graph of $y = ax^2 + b$ will pass through the points $(3, 1)$ and $(-2, -1)$.

Bonus _____

NAME_____ DATE _____

Chapter 8 Test, Form 1C

Write the letter for the correct answer in the blank at the right of each problem.
Use the graph for questions 1–4.

1. The ordered pair (3, 2) is the solution of the
   system of equations represented by lines
   A. a and b.   **B.** a and c.
   C. a and d.   **D.** b and d.

   1. _____

2. Lines c and d represent a system of equations.
   How many solutions does this system have?
   A. exactly one **B.** exactly two **C.** none   **D.** infinitely many

   2. _____

3. Suppose that line c and the equation $4x - 2y = 0$ represent
   a system of equations. How many solutions does this system have?
   A. exactly one **B.** exactly two **C.** none   **D.** infinitely many

   3. _____

4. Which pair of lines is the graph of the system of equations
   $3x + y = 2$
   $-2x + y = 0$?
   A. a and b **B.** b and c **C.** c and d **D.** c and a

   4. _____

5. Jewel is using substitution to solve the following system of
   equations: $\begin{array}{c} r + s = 4 \\ 3r + 2s = 15 \end{array}$. Which of these expressions should
   she substitute for r in the second equation?
   A. $4 - s$ **B.** $4 - r$ **C.** $s - 4$ **D.** $\dfrac{4}{s}$

   5. _____

6. Use substitution to solve the system
   of equations. $x = 2$
                        $3x + y = 5$
   A. $\{(-1, 2)\}$ **B.** $\{(2, -1)\}$ **C.** $\{(2, 11)\}$ **D.** none of these

   6. _____

7. Use substitution to solve the system $3m - n = 11$
   of equations. $2m + 3n = 0$
   A. $\{(-2, 3)\}$ **B.** $\{(-3, 2)\}$ **C.** $\{(3, -2)\}$ **D.** none of these

   7. _____

8. An art museum's general admission fee is $5, but certain age
   groups pay a reduced rate of $3. Yesterday, the museum collected a total
   of $902 from 216 people. In each of the following systems of equations,
   $s =$ the number of people who paid the reduced rate and $t =$ the number
   of people who paid the full rate. Which system would you use to find the
   number of $3 and $5 admission fees collected by the museum yesterday?
   A. $s + t = 216$ **B.** $s + t = 902$ **C.** $s + t = 216$ **D.** $t = s - 216$
   $\quad$ $3s + 5t = 902$ $\quad$ $3s + 5t = 216$ $\quad$ $5s + 3t = 902$ $\quad$ $3s + 5t = 902$

   8. _____

9. Use elimination to find the value of x $x - y = 5$
   in the system of equations. $x + y = 3$
   A. 8   **B.** 4   **C.** 2   **D.** $\dfrac{1}{4}$

   9. _____

10. Use elimination to find the value of y $x + 6y = 10$
    in the system of equations. $x + 5y = 1$
    A. 1   **B.** 9   **C.** 11   **D.** 10

    10. _____

11. Estimate the solution of the system of linear equations.
    A. {(−1, −2)}   **B.** {(−2, −1)}
    C. {(0, 2)}   **D.** {(−3, 0)}

11. _____

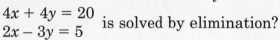

12. What is the value of x if the system of equations
    $4x + 4y = 20$
    $2x − 3y = 5$ is solved by elimination?
    A. 1   **B.** 10   **C.** 4   **D.** −2

12. _____

13. To eliminate the variable y in the system of
    equations $\begin{matrix} 5x + 4y = 22 \\ 2x − y = 1 \end{matrix}$, multiply the second equation by
    A. −4.   **B.** 9.   **C.** $−\frac{1}{3}$.   **D.** 4.

13. _____

14. Use elimination to solve the system $2x + 5y = 7$
    of equations. $3x + 6y = 3$
    A. {(−9, 5)}   **B.** {(5, −9)}   **C.** {(−1, 1)}   **D.** none of these

14. _____

15. Which point is a solution to the system of inequalities in the graph?
    A. (2, 1)   **B.** (−3, −1)
    C. (1, 3)   **D.** (−2, 3)

15. _____

16. Which system of inequalities is graphed?
    A. $y > −3x + 3$ **B.** $y \ge −3x + 3$
       $y < −3x − 1$ $y \le −3x − 1$
    C. $y < −3x + 3$ **D.** $y \le −3x + 3$
       $y > −3x − 1$ $y \ge −3x − 1$

16. _____

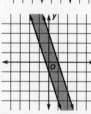

17. The sum of two numbers is 17. The lesser number is 10 less than twice the greater number. What are the two numbers?
    A. 6 and 11   **B.** 7 and 10   **C.** 8 and 9   **D.** 5 and 12

17. _____

18. A promoter priced tickets to a concert as follows: $17 when purchased in advance and $20 when purchased at the door. The total number of tickets purchased was 514, and ticket sales totaled $9,158. How many tickets were sold at the door?
    A. 420   **B.** 140   **C.** 374   **D.** 514

18. _____

19. The sum of the digits of a 2-digit number is 12. If you reverse the digits, you get a number that is 15 more than twice the original number. What is the original number?
    A. 39   **B.** 48   **C.** 57   **D.** 93

19. _____

20. A boat can travel upstream 60 miles in 6 hours. The boat can travel downstream the same distance in 5 hours. What is the rate of the current?
    A. 12 mi/h   **B.** 10 mi/h   **C.** 2 mi/h   **D.** 1 mi/h

20. _____

Bonus   Manuel is 8 years older than his sister. Three years ago he was 3 times older than his sister. How old is each now?

Bonus _____

Chapter 8 Test, Form 2A

8

Graph each system of equations using the coordinate plane provided. Then determine whether the system has one solution, no solution, or infinitely many solutions. If the system has one solution, name it.

1. $y = 3x$
   $y + x - 4 = 0$

1. _____

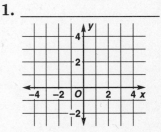

2. $x + 3y = 3$
   $y = -\dfrac{1}{3}x + 3$

2. _____

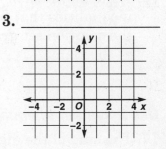

3. $x = 3y - 3$
   $2x - 6y = -6$

3. _____

Solve each system of equations.

4. $y = 2x - 7$
   $3x - 4y = 8$

5. $4y - 3x = 5$
   $\dfrac{3}{4}x = y - 4$

4. _____

5. _____

6. $\dfrac{1}{2}x - 5y = 19$
   $x - 2y = -10$

7. $3x - y = 4$
   $2x - 3y = -9$

6. _____

7. _____

8. $6x - 7y = 21$
   $3x + 7y = 6$

9. $5x + y = 12$
   $2x = 3y - 19$

8. _____

9. _____

10. $2x + \dfrac{2}{3}y = -8$
    $\dfrac{1}{2}x - \dfrac{1}{3}y = 1$

11. $0.5x + 0.4y = -1$
    $0.3x + 0.6y = -0.6$

10. _____

11. _____

Solve a system of equations to find the two numbers described.

12. The sum of two numbers is 16. Three times the greater number equals the sum of four times the lesser number and 6.

12. _____

13. The difference of two numbers is 5. Five times the lesser number is 9 greater than the greater number.

13. _____

Solve each system of inequalities by graphing. Use the coordinate planes provided.

14. $y \geq 2x$
    $y < x + 1$

15. $x - y < 2$
    $x \leq 1$

14.

15.

16. Write a system of inequalities that has the solution set graphed at the right.

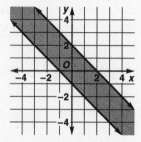

16. _____

Use a system of equations to solve each problem.

17. The sum of the digits of a 2-digit number is 7. The tens digit is one less than 3 times the units digit. Find the number.

17. _____

18. The sum of the digits of a 2-digit number is 13. If the digits are reversed, the new number is 9 more than the original number. Find the original number.

18. _____

19. Candy worth $2.45 per pound is mixed with candy worth $2.30 per pound. How much of each kind must be used to have 30 pounds of a mixture worth $2.35 a pound?

19. _____

20. A boat travels 60 miles downstream in the same time it takes to go 36 miles upstream. The speed of the boat in still water is 15 mi/h greater than the speed of the current. Find the speed of the current.

20. _____

Bonus Graph the solution set of $-3 \leq y - 2x < 1$.

Bonus

8

Chapter 8 Test, Form 2B

Graph each system of equations using the coordinate plane provided. Then determine whether the system has one solution, no solution, or infinitely many solutions. If the system has one solution, name it.

1. $x + y = 4$
   $x - y = 4$

1. _____

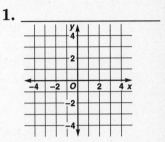

2. $2x - y = -3$
   $6x - 3y = -9$

2. _____

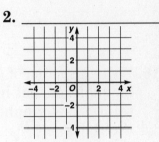

3. $x + y = -2$
   $x + y = 3$

3. _____

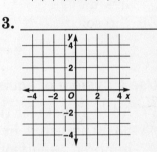

Solve each system of equations.

4. $y = 3x$
   $x + y = 4$

5. $5x - y = 10$
   $7x - 2y = 11$

6. $x - 6y = 4$
   $3x - 18y = 4$

7. $x - 5y = 10$
   $2x - 10y = 20$

8. $x + 4y = -8$
   $x - 4y = -8$

9. $2x + 5y = 3$
   $-x + 3y = -7$

10. $2x - 5y = -16$
    $3y = 2x + 12$

11. $2x - 3y = 1$
    $5x + 4y = 14$

4. _____

5. _____

6. _____

7. _____

8. _____

9. _____

10. _____

11. _____

Solve a system of equations to find the two numbers described.

12. The sum of two numbers is 17 and their difference is 29.

12. _____

13. The sum of a number and twice a greater number is 8. The sum of the greater number and twice the lesser number is −6.

13. _____

Solve each system of inequalities by graphing.

14. $y < x - 1$
    $y \leq 2x + 1$

15. $y \geq -x + 2$
    $y > 2x - 1$

14. _____

15. _____

16. Write a system of inequalities that has the solution set graphed at the right.

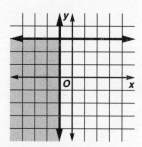

16. _____

Use a system of equations to solve each problem.

17. Adult tickets for the school musical sold for $3.50 and student tickets sold for $2.50. Three hundred twenty-one tickets were sold altogether for $937.50. How many of each kind of ticket were sold?

17. _____

18. Trinidad has $2.35 in nickels and dimes. If she has 33 coins in all, find the number of nickels and dimes.

18. _____

19. Amal reversed the digits in the amount of a check and underpaid a customer by $36. The sum of the digits in the 2-digit amount was 8. Find the amount of the check.

19. _____

20. A boat travels 12 miles downstream in $1\frac{1}{2}$ hours. On the return trip the boat travels the same distance upstream in 2 hours. Find the rate of the boat in still water and the rate of the current.

20. _____

Bonus   Graph the solution set of $-3 \leq 4x + y < 1$.

Bonus

8

Chapter 8 Test, Form 2C

Graph each system of equations using the coordinate plane provided. Then determine whether the system has one solution, no solution, or infinitely many solutions. If the system has one solution, name it.

1. $x + y = 3$
   $x - y = 3$

1. _____

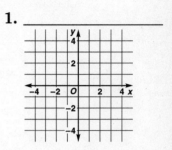

2. $2x - y = 6$
   $4x - 2y = 12$

2. _____

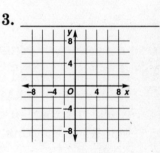

3. $x + y = 0$
   $x + y = 2$

3. _____

Solve each system of equations.

4. $c = 2d$
   $c + 2d = 8$

5. $2m - n = 3$
   $4m + 3n = 11$

4. _____

5. _____

6. $x - 5y = 2$
   $9x - 29y = 50$

7. $r + s = 8$
   $r - s = 2$

6. _____

7. _____

8. $7a + 3b = 1$
   $9a + 3b = -3$

9. $6x + 4y = 20$
   $4x - 2y = 4$

8. _____

9. _____

10. $2u - 3v = -11$
    $3u - 5v = 12$

11. $5m = 2n + 7$
    $2m + 5n = -3$

10. _____

11. _____

Solve a system of equations to find the two numbers described.

12. The sum of two numbers is 16. Their difference is 20.

12. _____

13. The sum of two numbers is 10. Three times the lesser number is 5 less than twice the greater number.

13. _____

Solve each system of inequalities by graphing.

14. $y > -2$
$y \leq x + 1$

14.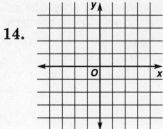

15. $y \geq 2x + 3$
$y \leq 2x - 1$

15.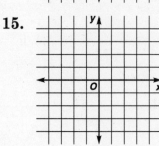

16. Write a system of inequalities that has the solution set graphed at the right.

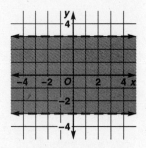

16. _____

Use a system of equations to solve each problem.

17. Kyle just started a new job that pays $7 per hour. He had been making $5 per hour at his old job. Kyle worked a total of 54 hours last month and made $338 before deductions. How many hours did he work at his new job?

17. _____

18. So far this basketball season, all of Nikki's points have come from two-point and three-point field goals. She has scored a total of 43 points. She has made 1 more than twice as many three-pointers as two-pointers. How many of each kind of field goal has Nikki made?

18. _____

19. The sum of the digits of a 2-digit number is 9. If the digits are reversed, the number is decreased by 27. What is the original number?

19. _____

20. A certain plane can travel 1500 miles in 5 hours when flying into the wind. The same plane can travel 2000 miles in 5 hours when flying with the wind. Find the rate of the wind.

20. _____

Bonus Write the system of equations whose solution is shown in the graph.

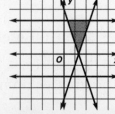

Bonus _____

8
Chapter 8 Calculator-Based Test

Use a graphing calculator to graph each system of equations. In which quadrant or on which axis does the solution lie?

1. $3x + y = 0$
   $x + y = 2$

2. $y = x + 4$
   $5x - 3y = -6$

3. $4x + 3y = 12$
   $7x + y = 4$

1. _____

2. _____

3. _____

Use a graphing calculator to graph each system of equations. Determine whether each system has no solution, one solution, or infinitely many solutions. If the system has one solution, name it.

4. $4x + 2y = -6$
   $6x + 3y = -11$

5. $4.2x + y = 3.6$
   $2.1x + 0.5y = 1.8$

6. $5.2x + 2.6y = 13$
   $3.8x + 1.9y = 22.8$

4. _____

5. _____

6. _____

7. $3(y + 4) = 2x$
   $x = 6y - 3$

8. $y + 3 = 4(x - 1)$
   $3y + 8 = 3(4x - 5)$

9. $0.35x + 0.5y = 2$
   $1.5x + y = 20$

7. _____

8. _____

9. _____

Use a graphing calculator to graph each system of inequalities. Determine in which quadrant(s) the solutions lie.

10. $y < \frac{1}{4}x - 1$
    $y > 5x + 10$

11. $y \geq x + 4$
    $2x + y \leq -3$

12. $2x + 5y \leq 10$
    $x - y \leq 5$

10. _____

11. _____

12. _____

Write a system of equations. Then solve.

13. A movie theater sold 450 tickets, receiving a total of $1800. If each adult paid $5 and each child paid $2, find the number of adult tickets that were sold.

13. _____

14. A company sells one unit of its product for $5.75. Making the product costs $400 in set-up fees, plus $2.50 per unit. Use d for dollars and n for the number of units sold. About how many units does the company need to sell in order to break even?

14. _____

15. A teacher accidentally reversed the digits in a student's test score. The sum of the digits was still 12, but the score was 18 points lower than the actual score. Find the student's correct score.

15. _____

16. Jenny babysits for two families on a regular basis. The Greenes pay $5 per hour, since they have more children, and the Browns pay $2.50 per hour. Jenny's parents allow her to babysit up to 10 hours each weekend. Find the greatest whole number of hours Jenny can babysit for the Browns and still earn at least $36.

16. _____

Chapter 8 Performance Assessment

Instructions: *Demonstrate your knowledge by giving a clear, concise solution to each problem. Be sure to include all relevant drawings and justify your answers. You may show your solution in more than one way or investigate beyond the requirements of the problem.*

1. **a.** Tell how you know that a system of two linear equations has no solutions.

   b. Write a system of two linear equations that has no solution.

   c. Tell how you know that a system of two linear equations has more than one solution. How many solutions will such a system have? Justify your answer.

   d. Write a system of two linear equations that has more than one solution.

   e. Write a system of two linear equations that has only one solution.

   f. Solve the system of equations in part e in at least two ways.

   g. Write a word problem that can be solved using a system of two linear equations. Solve the problem and give the meaning of the answer.

2. **a.** Write a system of inequalities whose solution is represented by the shaded region shown on the graph at the right.

   b. Name a point that is a solution of the system of inequalities.

   c. Name a point that is not a solution of the system of inequalities.

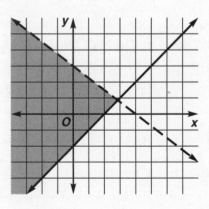

8

Chapter 8 Mid-Chapter Test (Lessons 8-1 through 8-3)

Use the graph below to determine whether each system has one solution, no solution, or infinitely many solutions. If the system has one solution, name it.

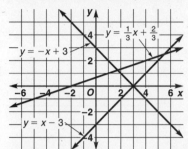

1. $x + y = 3$

 $x - y = 3$

1. _____

2. $x - 3y = -2$

 $\frac{1}{3}x - y = -\frac{2}{3}$

2. _____

Graph each system of equations. Then determine whether the system has one solution, no solution, or infinitely many solutions. If the system has one solution, name it.

3. $y = 4$

 $y = -2$

4. $x - 3y = -9$

 $x + 3y = 3$

3. _____

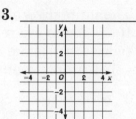

4. _____

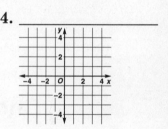

Use substitution to solve each system of equations.

5. $\frac{1}{2}x + 2y = 12$

 $x - 2y = 6$

6. $4x + y = 0$

 $2y + x = -7$

5. _____

6. _____

Use elimination to solve each system of equations.

7. $r - 5s = -6$

 $r + 2s = 8$

8. $\frac{1}{2}w + v = 7$

 $-\frac{1}{2}w + 3v = -11$

7. _____

8. _____

Use a system of equations to solve each problem.

9. The sum of two numbers is 30. The sum of the greater number and 3 times the lesser number is 54. Find the numbers.

9. _____

10. You invest $10,000, part at 7% annual interest and the rest at 10% annual interest. If you receive $910 in interest after one year, how much did you invest at each rate?

10. _____

Bonus Find the point on the graph of $3x - 4y = 9$ where the y-coordinate is 3 times the x-coordinate.

Bonus _____

8

Chapter 8, Quiz A (Lessons 8-1 and 8-2)

Use the graph at the right to determine whether each system has one solution, no solution, or infinitely many solutions. If the system has one solution, name it.

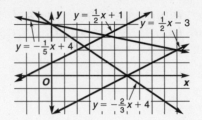

1. $2x + 3y = 12$ **2.** $x - 2y = -2$
    $x + 5y = 20$ $x - 2y = 6$

1. _____

2. _____

Use substitution to solve each system of equations.

3. $3x - 2y = -7$ **4.** $2x - 6y = 5$
    $y = x + 4$ $y = x + 3$

3. _____

4. _____

5. The units digit of a number is 4 more than the tens digit. If the digits are reversed, the new number is 1 less than twice the original number. Use a system of equations and substitution to find the number.

5. _____

8

Chapter 8, Quiz B (Lesson 8-3)

Use elimination to solve each system of equations.

1. $x + y = 4$ **2.** $-2x + y = 5$
   $x - y = 7$ $2x + 3y = 3$

1. _____

2. _____

3. $5r - 3s = 17$ **4.** $3x = 2 - 7y$
   $2r - 3s = 9$ $-4x = 30 - 7y$

3. _____

4. _____

5. Find two numbers whose sum is 26 and whose difference is 42.

5. _____

NAME_____ DATE _____

Chapter 8, Quiz C (Lesson 8-4)

Use elimination to solve each system of equations.

1. $x - 4y = 11$
   $5x - 7y = -10$

2. $2r + 3s = 9$
   $3r + 2s = 12$

3. $4c + 6d = -10$
   $8c - 3d = -5$

4. $0.7x + 0.5y = 2.9$
   $2.1x - 2.5y = -3.3$

5. Twice one number equals 3 more than 3 times a second number. The sum of 4 times the first number and 5 times the second number is 50. Find both numbers.

1. _____

2. _____

3. _____

4. _____

5. _____

NAME_____ DATE _____

Chapter 8, Quiz D (Lesson 8-5)

Solve each system of inequalities by graphing.

1. $y \geq 2$
   $x + y \leq 3$

2. $y < 2x - 1$
   $y \leq -x + 4$

1.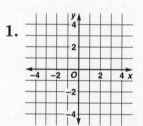

2.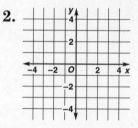

Write a system of inequalities for each graph.

3.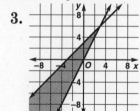

4.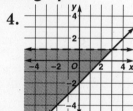

3. _____

4. _____

5. Adult tickets to the school musical are $5 and student tickets are $2. There are 300 seats in the auditorium where the musical is being performed. The goal for ticket sales for one performance is $900. Use the coordinate plane provided to graph a system of inequalities. Then find how many of each type of ticket will be sold if the goal is to be reached. Give three solutions.

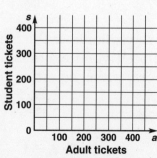

5. _____

_____

_____

Choose the best answer. Write A, B, C, or D.

1. If $x + 3 = y$, then $(x - y)^5 =$
   A. -243.   B. -15.   C. 15.   D. 243.

   1. _____

2. What is the average of $3c - 2$, $2c + 6$, and $c + 2$?
   A. $\dfrac{2c + 1}{3}$ B. $2c + 2$ C. $\dfrac{2c + 2}{3}$ D. $2c + 6$

   2. _____

3. If $a + t = 7$ and $a^2 - t^2 = 35$, find $a - t$.
   A. $\dfrac{1}{5}$ B. 5 C. 28 D. 42

   3. _____

4. If $mn = 30$ and $m^2 + n^2 = 109$, find $(m + n)^2$.
   A. 49 B. 79 C. 139 D. 169

   4. _____

5. Joshua spent one-third of his money on a shirt and then spent two-thirds of what was left on a pair of slacks. What part of his money did he have left?
   A. none   B. $\dfrac{2}{9}$ C. $\dfrac{4}{9}$ D. $\dfrac{2}{3}$

   5. _____

6. If $\dfrac{x}{4}$, $\dfrac{x}{5}$, and $\dfrac{x}{8}$ are integers, x could be
   A. 20.   B. 30.   C. 32.   D. 40.

   6. _____

7. If d is a negative integer and $d^2 - 12d = a$, a could be
   A. -28.   B. -10.   C. 0.   D. 28.

   7. _____

8. If $(24)(y)(9) = 27$, then $y =$
   A. $\dfrac{1}{3}$.   B. $\dfrac{1}{6}$.   C. $\dfrac{1}{8}$.   D. $\dfrac{1}{9}$.

   8. _____

9. If Carlota can type a word every 1.5 seconds, how many words can she type in $1\dfrac{1}{2}$ hours?
   A. 36 B. 40 C. 360 D. 3600

   9. _____

10. The difference of the squares of the least and greatest of three consecutive positive integers is 88. If x is the least of the three integers, which equation must be true?
    A. $4x + 4 = 88$ B. $8x + 16 = 88$
    C. $(x + 2)^2 - x^2 = 88$ D. $x^2 - (x + 4)^2 = 88$

    10. _____

Chapter 8 Cumulative Review

1. State the property shown in $3a + 7c = 7c + 3a$. (Lesson 1-6)

1._____

2. Simplify $6(-4) + (-12)(-3)$. (Lesson 2-6)

2._____

Solve each equation. (Lessons 3-2, 3-3, and 3-5)

3. $-\frac{3}{4}x = 30$

3._____

4. $2p - 3(p + 2) = 5(2p + 1)$

4._____

5. $\frac{7}{10} = \frac{3}{x + 1}$

5._____

Solve each inequality. (Lessons 7-1 and 7-3)

6. $-6 + d > -14$

6._____

7. $10y - 3(y + 4) \le 0$

7._____

8. Solve the compound inequality $t - 1 > -4$ and $2t - 4 \le 6$. Then graph the solution set. (Lesson 7-4)

8._____

9. A clothing store makes a profit of $5.50 on each tie sold. How many ties must the store sell to make a profit of at least $352.00? (Lesson 7-2)

9._____

10. A price decreased from $85 to $72.25. Find the percent of decrease. (Lesson 4-5)

10._____

11. Sara leaves home at 7 A.M. traveling at a rate of 45 mi/h. Her son discovers that she has forgotten her briefcase and starts out to catch up with her. Her son leaves at 7:30 A.M. traveling at a rate of 55 mi/h. At what time will he overtake his mother? (Lesson 4-7)

11._____

12. Tracey Tierney invested $6,000 for one year, part at 10% annual interest and the balance at 13% annual interest. Her total interest for the year was $712.50. How much money did she invest at each rate? (Lesson 4-7)

12._____

Tell in which quadrant or on which axis the given point lies. (Lesson 5-1)

13. $(-2, 0)$

13._____

14. $(5, -3)$

14._____

For exercises 15 and 16, refer to the triangle shown below. (Lesson 4-3)

15. Find b to the nearest tenth.

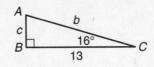

16. Find c to the nearest tenth.

15. _____

16. _____

17. Determine the slope of the line passing through $(-2, 1)$ and $(-6, 5)$. (Lesson 6-1)

17. _____

18. Find the x- and y-intercepts for the graph of $x - 4y = 4$. (Lesson 6-4)

18. _____

19. Write an equation in slope-intercept form for the line that is perpendicular to the graph of $y - 3x = -4$ and passes through $(1, 2)$. (Lesson 6-6)

19. _____

20. Find the coordinates of the midpoint of the line segment whose endpoints have the coordinates $(-1, 4)$ and $(2, 7)$. (Lesson 6-7)

20. _____

21. Use the coordinate plane provided to graph the equations $x + y = 4$ and $y = x$. Then state the solution set. (Lesson 8-1)

21. _____

22. Use substitution to solve the system of equations $-x - 5y = 7$ and $x + y = 1$. (Lesson 8-2)

22. _____

Use elimination to solve each system of equations. (Lessons 8-3 and 8-4)

23. $2x + 4y = 1$
    $x - 4y = 5$

23. _____

24. $2x - 2y = 6$
    $x + y = 3$

24. _____

25. With the wind, an airplane travels 2200 miles in 4 hours. Against the wind, it takes 5 hours to travel 2350 miles. Find the rate of the wind and the rate of the plane in still air. (Lesson 8-4)

25. _____

Chapter 8 Answer Key

1. __A__

2. __B__

3. __D__

4. __D__

5. __A__

6. __B__

7. __B__

8. __C__

9. __C__

10. __D__

11. __D__

12. __A__

13. __C__

14. __B__

15. __C__

16. __A__

17. __D__

18. __B__

19. __D__

20. __D__

Bonus $\left(-7, -\dfrac{7}{2}\right)$

1. __D__

2. __D__

3. __D__

4. __C__

5. __B__

6. __C__

7. __D__

8. __D__

9. __B__

10. __A__

11. __A__

12. __D__

13. __B__

14. __C__

15. __C__

16. __B__

17. __B__

18. __A__

19. __C__

20. __B__

Bonus $a = \dfrac{2}{5}$;

$b = -\dfrac{13}{5}$

Chapter 8 Answer Key

Form 1C		Form 2A	
Page 201	**Page 202**	**Page 203**	**Page 204**

Form 1C

Page 201

1. __C__

2. __C__

3. __D__

4. __B__

5. __A__

6. __B__

7. __C__

8. __A__

9. __B__

10. __B__

Page 202

11. __B__

12. __C__

13. __D__

14. __A__

15. __D__

16. __D__

17. __C__

18. __B__

19. __A__

20. __D__

Bonus **Manuel: 15; sister: 7**

Form 2A

Page 203

1. **(1, 3)**

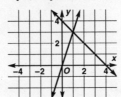

2. **no solution**

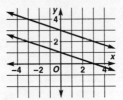

3. **infinitely many**

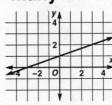

4. __(4, 1)__

5. __no solution__

6. __(−22, −6)__

7. __(3, 5)__

8. $\left(3, -\dfrac{3}{7}\right)$

9. __(1, 7)__

10. __(−2, −6)__

11. __(−2, 0)__

12. __10, 6__

13. $3\dfrac{1}{2}, 8\dfrac{1}{2}$

Page 204

14.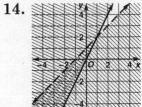

15.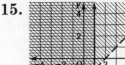

16. $y \geq -x - 1$
    $y \leq -x + 2$

17. __52__

18. __67__

19. **10 lb at $2.45; 20 lb at $2.30**

20. __5 mi/h__

Bonus

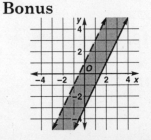

Algebra 1

Chapter 8 Answer Key

Form 2B

Page 205

1. **(4, 0)**

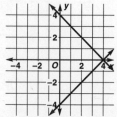

2. **infinitely many**

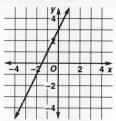

3. **no solution**

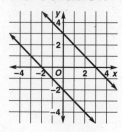

4. _____ **(1, 3)** _____

5. _____ **(3, 5)** _____

6. _____ **no solution** _____

7. **infinitely many**

8. _____ **(−8, 0)** _____

9. _____ **(4, −1)** _____

10. _____ **(−3, 2)** _____

11. _____ **(2, 1)** _____

12. _____ **23, −6** _____

13. _____ **$-6\frac{2}{3}, 7\frac{1}{3}$** _____

Page 206

14.

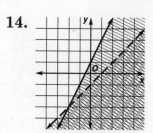

15.

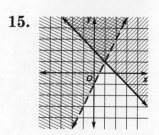

16. _____ **$y \leq 3, x \leq -1$** _____

17. **135 adult; 186 student**

18. **14 dimes; 19 nickels**

19. _____ **$62** _____

20. _____ **7 mi/h; 1 mi/h** _____

Bonus

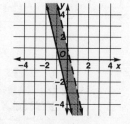

Algebra 1

Chapter 8 Answer Key

Form 2C

Page 207

1. **one solution; (3, 0)**

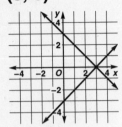

2. **infinitely many**

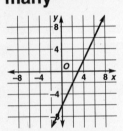

3. **no solution**

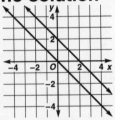

4. _____ **(4, 2)** _____

5. _____ **(2, 1)** _____

6. _____ **(12, 2)** _____

7. _____ **(5, 3)** _____

8. _____ **(−2, 5)** _____

9. _____ **(2, 2)** _____

10. _____ **(−91, −57)** _____

11. _____ **(1, −1)** _____

12. _____ **18, −2** _____

13. _____ **3, 7** _____

Page 208

14.

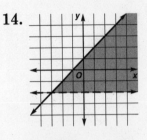

15.

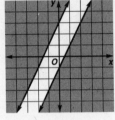

16. _____ $y < 3$ $y > -3$ _____

17. _____ **34 hours** _____

18. **5 two-pointers; 11 three-pointers**

19. _____ **63** _____

20. _____ **50 mi/h** _____

Bonus

$y \le 3$
$y \ge -2$
$y \ge 3x - 4$
$y \ge -3x + 4$

Calculator Based

Page 209

1. _____ **II** _____

2. _____ **I** _____

3. _____ **y-axis** _____

4. _____ **no solution** _____

5. _____ **infinitely many** _____

6. _____ **no solution** _____

7. _____ **one solution; (9, 2)** _____

8. _____ **no solution** _____

9. _____ **one solution; (20, −10)** _____

10. _____ **III** _____

11. _____ **II and III** _____

12. _____ **I, II, III, and IV** _____

13. **sample: $x + y = 450$; $5x + 2y = 1800$; 300 adult tickets**

14. _____ **about 123 units** _____

15. _____ **75** _____

16. _____ **5 hours** _____

Scoring Guide
Chapter 8
Performance Assessment

Level	Specific Criteria
3 Superior	• Shows thorough understanding of the concepts of *systems of linear equations and inequalities* and *solving such systems graphically and algebraically.* • Uses appropriate strategies to solve problems. • Computations are correct. • Written explanations are exemplary. • Word problem concerning a system of two linear equations is appropriate and makes sense. • Graphs are accurate and appropriate. • Goes beyond requirements of some or all problems.
2 Satisfactory, with Minor Flaws	• Shows understanding of the concepts of *systems of linear equations and inequalities* and *solving such systems graphically and algebraically.* • Uses appropriate strategies to solve problems. • Computations are mostly correct. • Written explanations are effective. • Word problem concerning a system of two linear equations is appropriate and makes sense. • Graphs are mostly accurate and appropriate. • Satisfies all requirements of problems.
1 Nearly Satisfactory, with Serious Flaws	• Shows understanding of most of the concepts of *systems of linear equations and inequalities* and *solving such systems graphically and algebraically.* • May not use appropriate strategies to solve problems. • Computations are mostly correct. • Written explanations are satisfactory. • Word problem concerning a system of two linear equations is mostly appropriate and sensible. • Graphs are mostly accurate and appropriate. • Satisfies most requirements of problems.
0 Unsatisfactory	• Shows little or no understanding of the concepts of *systems of linear equations and inequalities* and *solving such systems graphically and algebraically.* • May not use appropriate strategies to solve problems. • Computations are incorrect. • Written explanations are not satisfactory. • Word problem concerning a system of two linear equations is not appropriate or sensible. • Graphs are not accurate or appropriate. • Does not satisfy requirements of problems.

Chapter 8 Answer Key
Performance Assessment

Page 210

1. **a.** When the graphs of a system of two linear equations are parallel, the system has no solutions.

   b. $y = 3x - 4$, $y = 3x - 5$

   c. When the graphs of a system of two linear equations are the same line, the system has more than one solution. There are an infinite number of solutions.

   d. $y = 3x - 4$, $2y = 6x - 8$

   e. $y = x + 1$, $x + y = 3$

   f. Method 1: Substitute $x + 1$ for y in the second equation.
   $$x + (x + 1) = 3$$
   $$2x = 2$$
   $$x = 1$$
   $$y = x + 1$$
   $$= 1 + 1 \text{ or } 2$$

   Method 2:
   $$-x + y = 1$$
   $$\underline{x + y = 3}$$
   $$2y = 4$$
   $$y = 2$$
   $$x + y = 3$$
   $$x + 2 = 3$$
   $$x = 1$$

   The solution is (1, 2).

   g. If the sum of two numbers is 5 and their difference is 1, what are the numbers?

$x + y = 5$	$3 + y = 5$
$\underline{x - y = 1}$	$y = 2$
$2x = 6$	
$x = 3$	

   The numbers are 3 and 2.

2. **a.** $3x + 4y < 12$, $x - y \leq 2$
   b. (0, 0)
   c. (4, 0)

Chapter 8 Answer Key

1. **one solution; (3, 0)**

2. **infinitely many**

3. **no solution**

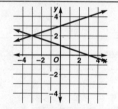

4. **one solution; (−3, 2)**

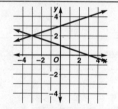

5. **(12, 3)**

6. **(1, −4)**

7. **(4, 2)**

8. **(−1, 16)**

9. **18 and 12**

10. **$3000 at 7%;
$7000 at 10%**

Bonus   **(−1, −3)**

---

1. **one solution; (0, 4)**

2. **no solution**

3. **(1, 5)**

4. $\left(-\dfrac{23}{4}, -\dfrac{11}{4}\right)$

5. **37**

---

1. $\left(\dfrac{11}{2}, -\dfrac{3}{2}\right)$

2. $\left(-\dfrac{3}{2}, 2\right)$

3. $\left(\dfrac{8}{3}, -\dfrac{11}{9}\right)$

4. **(−4, 2)**

5. **34 and −8**

---

1. **(−9, −5)**

2. $\left(\dfrac{18}{5}, \dfrac{3}{5}\right)$

3. **(−1, −1)**

4. **(2, 3)**

5. **first number: 7.5;
second number: 4**

1.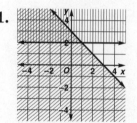

2.

3. $y \leq x + 3$
   $y \geq 2x$

4. $y \geq x - 2$
   $y < 1$

5. **Possible answers—
   a: 100, s: 200;
   a: 200, s: 50;
   a: 250, s: 20**

Chapter 8 Answer Key

Standardized Test Practice — Page 214

1. __A__

2. __B__

3. __B__

4. __D__

5. __B__

6. __D__

7. __D__

8. __C__

9. __D__

10. __C__

Cumulative Review — Page 215

1. __commutative of addition__

2. __12__

3. __−40__

4. __−1__

5. $3\frac{2}{7}$

6. $d > -8$

7. $y \le \frac{12}{7}$

8. $\{t \mid -3 < t \le 5\}$
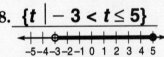

9. __at least 64__

10. __15%__

11. __9:45 A.M.__

12. __$2250 at 10%; $3750 at 13%__

13. __x-axis__

14. __Quadrant IV__

Page 216

15. __13.5__

16. __3.7__

17. __−1__

18. __4; −1__

19. $y = -\frac{1}{3}x + \frac{7}{3}$

20. $\left(\frac{1}{2}, 5\frac{1}{2}\right)$

21. __(2, 2)__
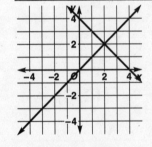

22. __(3, −2)__

23. $\left(2, -\frac{3}{4}\right)$

24. __(3, 0)__

25. __40 mi/h; 510 mi/h__

9

Chapter 9 Test, Form 1A

Write the letter for the correct answer in the blank at the right of each problem.

1. What is the simplest form of $(9c^3d^4)(-6c^4d^5)$?
   A. $3c^7d^9$ B. $3cd$ C. $-54c^7d^9$ D. $-54c^{12}d^{20}$

   1. _____

2. What is the simplest form of $(x^3)^8$?
   A. x^{24} B. x^{11} C. $8x^{24}$ D. $8x^{11}$

   2. _____

3. What is the simplest form of $(-2hk)^4(4h^3k^5)^2$?
   A. $2h^{24}k^{40}$ B. $-64h^9k^{11}$ C. $-256h^{10}k^{14}$ D. $256h^{10}k^{14}$

   3. _____

4. What is the simplest form of $\frac{a^9}{a^3}$? Assume the denominator is not equal to zero.
   A. a^3 B. a^{12} C. a^6 D. a^{27}

   4. _____

5. What is the simplest form of $\frac{36b^4c^2}{9b^{-1}c^5}$? Assume the denominator is not equal to zero.
   A. $\frac{27b^4}{c^3}$ B. $\frac{4b^4}{c^3}$ C. $\frac{27b^3}{c^3}$ D. $\frac{4b^5}{c^3}$

   5. _____

6. What is the simplest form of $\frac{(3y^4n^6)^2}{(y^2n^{-3})^4}$? Assume the denominator is not equal to zero.
   A. $\frac{9}{y^{16}}$ B. $\frac{9}{n^{24}}$ C. $9y^{16}$ D. $9n^{24}$

   6. _____

7. What is 4173 expressed in scientific notation?
   A. 4.173×10^3 B. 41.73×10^2 C. 417.3×10 D. 4.173×10^{-3}

   7. _____

8. What is the value of $(4 \times 10^{-2})(2 \times 10^8)$?
   A. 8×10^{-16} B. 8×10^6 C. 6×10^6 D. 6×10^{-16}

   8. _____

9. What is the degree of $3xy - 8x^2y^5 + x^7y$?
   A. 2   B. 7   C. 8   D. 10

   9. _____

10. Which of the following shows the terms of $4x^3 - 6x + 2x^5 + 3$ arranged so that the powers of x are in descending order?
    A. $3 - 6x + 4x^3 + 2x^5$ B. $4x^3 + 3 + 2x^5 - 6x$
    C. $2x^5 + 4x^3 - 6x + 3$ D. $-6x + 4x^3 + 2 + 2x^5$

    10. _____

11. What is the simplest form of $(9t^2 + 4t - 6) + (t^2 - 2t + 4)$?
    A. $10t^2 + 2t - 2$ B. $9t^2 + 2t - 2$
    C. $10t^2 + 2t + 2$ D. $9t^2 + 2t + 2$

    11. _____

12. Find the difference.

$$7a^2 \qquad - 8$$
$$(-)\ 10a^2 + 6a + 2$$

A. $-3a^2 - 6a - 6$ **B.** $-3a^2 + 6a - 6$
C. $-3a^2 + 6a - 10$ **D.** $-3a^2 - 6a - 10$

12._____

13. What is the simplest form of
$2a^2(5a - 6) - 5a(a^2 - 3a + 4) - 7(a - 5)$?
A. $5a^3 + 3a^2 - 27a + 35$ **B.** $5a^3 - 27a^2 + 13a - 35$
C. $5a^3 - 10a - 7$ **D.** none of these

13._____

14. What is the simplest form of $(c - 5)(c - 7)$?
A. $c^2 + 12c + 35$ **B.** $c^2 - 12c - 35$
C. $c^2 - 12c + 35$ **D.** $c^2 + 35$

14._____

15. What is the simplest form of $(3y - 4)(2y^2 + y - 1)$?
A. $6y^3 - 5y^2 - 7y - 4$ **B.** $6y^3 - 5y^2 - 7y + 4$
C. $6y^3 - 7y^2 - 7y + 4$ **D.** $6y^2 - 5y^2 + 7y + 4$

15._____

16. What is the simplest form of $(3a - 2b)(3a + 2b)$?
A. $9a^2 - 4b^2$ **B.** $9a^2 + 4b^2$
C. $9a^2 - 12ab + 4b^2$ **D.** $9a^2 + 12ab + 4b^2$

16._____

17. What is the simplest form of $(4a^2 + \frac{1}{2}b)^2$?

A. $16a^4 + \frac{1}{4}b^2$ **B.** $16a^4 + b^2$

C. $16a^4 + 4a^2b + \frac{1}{4}b^2$ **D.** $16a^4 + 9a^2b + b^2$

17._____

18. Find the solution of $6(n - 11) = 12 + 4(2n - 3)$.
A. -11 **B.** 11 **C.** -33 **D.** 33

18._____

19. Find the solution of $5x^2 - 3x = (7x^2 + 5x) - (2x^2 + 16)$.
A. 2 **B.** -2 **C.** 8 **D.** -8

19._____

20. The length of a rectangle is 4 units less than twice the width. If the
length is decreased by 3 units and the width is increased by 1 unit,
the area is decreased by 16 square units. If w is the original width,
which equation must be true?
A. $(2w - 3)(w - 3) = w(2w - 4) - 16$
B. $2(2w - 3) + 2(w - 3) = 2w + 2(2w - 4) - 16$
C. $(2w - 7)(w + 1) = w(2w - 4) - 16$
D. $2(2w - 7) + 2(w + 1) = 2w + (2w - 4) - 16$

20._____

Bonus   Solve $\dfrac{7^{x-3}}{7^{3x-1}} = 1$ for x.   **Bonus** _____

9

Chapter 9 Test, Form 1B

Write the letter for the correct answer in the blank at the right of each problem.

1. What is the simplest form of $m^4 \cdot m^2$?
   A. m^2 **B.** m^8 **C.** m^6 **D.** $2m^8$

   1. _____

2. What is the simplest form of $(3w^2v)(-2w^5v^2)(4w^6v^5)$?
   A. $-24w^{13}v^8$ **B.** $5w^{60}v^{10}$ **C.** $-24w^{60}v^{10}$ **D.** $5w^{13}v^8$

   2. _____

3. What is the simplest form of $(y^2n^3)^4 + (3y^4n^6)^2$?
   A. $10y^8n^{12}$ **B.** $9y^{16}n^{27}$ **C.** $10y^8 + 2n^{12}$ **D.** $y^6n^7 + 9y^6n^8$

   3. _____

4. What is the simplest form of $\dfrac{m^6n^3}{m^2n^6}$? Assume the denominator is not equal to zero.

   A. $\dfrac{m^4}{n^3}$ **B.** $-\dfrac{m^4}{n^3}$ **C.** $-\dfrac{m^8}{n^3}$ **D.** $\dfrac{m^8}{n^3}$

   4. _____

5. What is the simplest form of $\dfrac{6n^{-3}yw^{-5}}{2n^{-1}y^{-3}w^2}$? Assume the denominator is not equal to zero.

   A. $\dfrac{4y^3}{n^2w^3}$ **B.** $\dfrac{3y^4}{n^2w^7}$ **C.** $\dfrac{3}{n^4w^3y^2}$ **D.** $\dfrac{3n^2}{y^4w^7}$

   5. _____

6. What is the simplest form of $\dfrac{(a^{-2}b^4)^{-6}}{(a^4b^{-8})^3}$? Assume the denominator is not equal to zero.

   A. ab^3 **B.** 1 **C.** $\dfrac{a^{24}}{b^{48}}$ **D.** $\dfrac{b^{48}}{a^{24}}$

   6. _____

7. What is 0.000543 expressed in scientific notation?
   A. 5.43×10^4 **B.** 5.43×10^{-3}
   C. 543×10^6 **D.** 5.43×10^{-4}

   7. _____

8. What is the value of $\dfrac{2.88 \times 10^3}{2.4 \times 10^{-7}}$?

   A. 0.48×10^{-4} **B.** 1.2×10^{-4} **C.** 1.2×10^{10} **D.** 0.48×10^{10}

   8. _____

9. What is the degree of $2x^3y - 4xy^2 + 9x^3y^2$?
   A. 4   **B.** 3   **C.** 12   **D.** 5

   9. _____

10. Which of the following shows the terms of $x^2y^3 + 4xy^2 - 3x^3y + 6$ arranged so that the powers of x are in ascending order?
    A. $6 + 4xy^2 + x^2y^3 - 3x^3y$ **B.** $x^2y^3 - 3x^3y + 4xy^2 + 6$
    C. $6 + 4xy^2 - 3x^3y + x^2y^3$ **D.** $6 - 3x^3y + 4xy^2 + x^2y^3$

    10. _____

11. What is the simplest form of $(3c^2 - 8c + 5) + (c^2 - 8c - 6)$?
    A. $3c^2 - 1$ **B.** $4c^2 + 11$
    C. $4c^2 - 16c - 1$ **D.** $2c^2 - 16c - 1$

    11. _____

12. What is the simplest form of $(6w^2 - 5wz - 3z^2) - (4w^2 + 6wz - 8z^2)$?   12. _____
    A. $10w^2 + wz - 11z^2$ B. $2w^2 - 11wz + 5z^2$
    C. $2w^2 + wz - 11z^2$ D. $2w^2 - 11wz - 5z^2$

13. What is the simplest form of $8a^2b(3a + 2ab^3)$?   13. _____
    A. $24a^2b + 16a^2b^3$ B. $24a^3b + 2ab^3$
    C. $24a^3b + 16a^3b^4$ D. $11a^2b + 10a^2b^3$

14. What is the simplest form of $(x + 2)(x + 4)$?   14. _____
    A. $x^2 + 8$ B. $2x + 6$ C. $2x + 8$ D. $x^2 + 6x + 8$

15. What is the simplest form of $(2n - 6)(4n + 2)$?   15. _____
    A. $6n^2 + 28n - 12$ B. $8n^2 - 12$
    C. $8n^2 - 20n - 12$ D. $8n^2 + 20n - 12$

16. What is the simplest form of $(x + 6)^2$?   16. _____
    A. $x^2 + 36$ B. $x^2 + 12x + 36$
    C. $x^2 + 12$ D. $2x + 12$

17. What is the simplest form of $(3y + 4z)(3y - 4z)$?   17. _____
    A. $9y^2 - 16z^2$ B. $9y^2 - 24yz - 16z^2$
    C. $9y^2 + 16z^2$ D. $9y^2 - 24yz + 16z^2$

18. Find the solution of $-4(5 - 2n) = 8(-6 - 5n)$.   18. _____
    A. $-\dfrac{1}{9}$ B. $-\dfrac{28}{3}$ C. $-\dfrac{7}{8}$ D. $-\dfrac{7}{12}$

19. Find the solution of $x(x + 3) - 2 = 2 + x(x + 1)$.   19. _____
    A. 2   B. -2 C. 1   D. 0

20. A picture is 4 inches longer than it is wide. It is surrounded by a   20. _____
    mat 2 inches wide. The total area of the mat is 112 square inches.
    If w is the width of the picture, which equation is true?
    A. $(w + 4)(w + 8) + w(w + 4) = 112$
    B. $(w + 2)(w + 6) - w(w + 4) = 112$
    C. $(w + 4)(w + 8) - w(w + 4) = 112$
    D. $(w + 2)(w + 6) + w(w + 4) = 112$

Bonus   Solve $3^{2n-1} \cdot 3^{5n} = (3^4)^{n+2}$ for n.   Bonus _____

9

Chapter 9 Test, Form 1C

Write the letter for the correct answer in the blank at the right of each problem.

1. What is the simplest form of $y^5 \cdot y^3$?

   A. y^2 **B.** y^8 **C.** y^{15} **D.** $2y^8$

   1. _____

2. What is the simplest form of $(5c^2d^3)(-2c^5d^2)$?

   A. $10c^7d^5$ **B.** $-10c^7d^5$ **C.** $10c^{10}d^6$ **D.** $-10c^{10}d^6$

   2. _____

3. What is the simplest form of $(x^2)^6 + (2x^4)^3$?

   A. $7x^{12}$ **B.** $9x^{12}$ **C.** $x^8 + 6x^7$ **D.** $3x^{12}$

   3. _____

4. What is the simplest form of $\frac{a^7}{a^4}$? Assume the denominator is not equal to zero.

   A. a^{11} **B.** a^{28} **C.** a^3 **D.** 1

   4. _____

5. What is the simplest form of $\frac{6m^5n^2}{2m^2n^3}$? Assume the denominator is not equal to zero.

   A. $3m^7n^5$ **B.** $\frac{3m^3}{n}$ **C.** $3m^3n$ **D.** $\frac{4m^3}{n}$

   5. _____

6. What is the simplest form of $\frac{(z^2w^{-1})^3}{(z^3w^2)^2}$? Assume the denominator is not equal to zero.

   A. $\frac{1}{w^7}$ **B.** $\frac{z^{12}}{w^7}$ **C.** w **D.** $\frac{1}{w}$

   6. _____

7. What is 3851 expressed in scientific notation?

   A. 3.851×10^3 **B.** 38.51×10^2 **C.** 385.1×10 **D.** 3.851×10^{-3}

   7. _____

8. What is the value of $(3 \times 10^4)(3 \times 10^5)$?

   A. 6×10^9 **B.** 9×10^9 **C.** 6×10^{20} **D.** 9×10^{20}

   8. _____

9. What is the degree of $4x^2y^3 + 2xy^2 - 5x^3y$?

   A. 4 **B.** 3 **C.** 6 **D.** 5

   9. _____

10. Which of the following shows the terms of $x^2 + 5x^3 - 4 - 2x$ arranged so that the powers of x are in descending order?

    A. $5x^3 - 2x + x^2 - 4$ **B.** $-4 - 2x + x^2 + 5x^3$
    C. $5x^3 - 4 - 2x + x^2$ **D.** $5x^3 + x^2 - 2x - 4$

    10. _____

11. What is the simplest form of $(5n^2 + 3n - 2) + (2n^2 - 7n - 1)$?

    A. $7n^2 + 4n + 3$ **B.** $7n^2 - 4n - 3$
    C. $3n^2 + 10n - 1$ **D.** $3n^2 - 4n - 1$

    11. _____

12. What is the simplest form of $(2a - 5) - (3a + 1)$?   12._____
    A. $5a + 6$ B. $a - 4$ C. $-a - 6$ D. $-a - 4$

13. What is the simplest form of $2ab^2(4a + 3a^3b)$?   13._____
    A. $6a^2b^2 + 5a^4b^3$ B. $8a^2b^2 + 6a^4b^3$
    C. $8ab^2 + 6a^3b^2$ D. $14a^5b^3$

14. What is the simplest form of $(x + 3)(x + 5)$?   14._____
    A. $x^2 + 8x + 15$ B. $x^2 + 15$ C. $2x + 8$ D. $2x + 15$

15. What is the simplest form of $(2n - 3)(n + 4)$?   15._____
    A. $3n + 1$ B. $2n^2 - 12$
    C. $2n^2 + 5n - 12$ D. $2n^2 + 11n + 1$

16. What is the simplest form of $(2x - 5)(2x + 5)$?   16._____
    A. $4x$ B. $4x^2 - 25$ C. $4x^2 - 20x - 25$ D. $4x^2 + 25$

17. What is the simplest form of $(y + 5)^2$?   17._____
    A. $y^2 + 25$ B. $2y + 10$ C. $y^2 + 10y + 10$ D. $y^2 + 10y + 25$

18. Find the solution of $3(2n - 6) = -4(n - 3)$.   18._____
    A. 3   B. 20   C. 6   D. -3

19. Find the solution of $x(x + 2) = x^2 + x + 2$.   19._____
    A. 2   B. 1   C. 0   D. -1

20. The length of a rectangle is 4 cm longer than its width. The area of   20._____
    the rectangle is 50 cm^2. If w is the width of the rectangle, which
    equation is true?
    A. $4w = 50$ B. $w + w + 4 = 50$
    C. $2w + 2(w + 4) = 50$ D. $w(w + 4) = 50$

Bonus   Solve $3^{n-1} \cdot 3^{n+4} = 3^5$ for n.   Bonus _____

9

Chapter 9 Test, Form 2A

1. Simplify $(ab^8)(3a^6b^2)$.

1._____

2. Simplify $\left(\dfrac{2}{3}h^3\right)^4$.

2._____

3. Simplify $(4a^2n)^3 + 4a^2n^3 + 4(a^2n)^3$.

3._____

4. Simplify $\dfrac{-54c^2d^5}{9c^6d^2}$. Assume the denominator is not equal to zero.

4._____

5. Simplify $\dfrac{36v^{-7}}{9v^{-5}}$. Assume the denominator is not equal to zero.

5._____

6. Simplify $\dfrac{(4xy^{-2})^2}{(2x^3y)^3}$. Assume the denominator is not equal to zero.

6._____

7. Express 196,783 in scientific notation.

7._____

8. Express 2.71×10^{-5} in decimal notation.

8._____

9. Evaluate $(5 \times 10^{10})(3 \times 10^{-12})$. Express the result in scientific notation.

9._____

10. Evaluate $\dfrac{7.2 \times 10^{-5}}{4 \times 10^{-3}}$. Express the result in scientific notation.

10._____

11. Arrange the terms of $2x - 6 + 4x^5 + 7x^6$ so that the powers of x are in ascending order.

11._____

12. Find the degree of $n^3 + m^2 + n^2m^2$.

12._____

13. Simplify $(8w^2 + 4w - 2) + (2w^2 - w + 6)$.

13._____

14. Find the difference.

$$5x^2 + x + 7$$
$$(-)\ x^2 - 10x + 4$$

14. _____

15. Simplify $5n^2(n - 6) - 2n(3n^2 + n - 6) + 7(n^2 - 3)$.

15. _____

16. Simplify $(x + 4)(x + 1)$.

16. _____

17. Simplify $(2y - 7)(4y + 4)$.

17. _____

18. Simplify $\left(\dfrac{2}{3}m - 1\right)\left(\dfrac{1}{2}m - 2\right)$.

18. _____

19. Simplify $(z + 2)^2$.

19. _____

20. Simplify $(2m - 3n)(2m + 3n)$.

20. _____

21. Simplify $(3x - 1)^2$.

21. _____

22. Simplify $(x + 3)(x^2 - 2x + 4)$.

22. _____

23. Solve $y(y - 6) = (5y^2 - 36) - (4y^2 - 3y)$.

23. _____

24. The length of a picture is 1 inch less than twice its width. The frame around the picture has a uniform width of 2 inches and an area of 96 square inches. What are the dimensions of the picture?

24. _____

25. The length of a rectangle is 4 centimeters more than the width. If the length is increased by 8 centimeters and the width is decreased by 4 centimeters, the area will remain unchanged. Find the original dimensions of the rectangle.

25. _____

Bonus Graph the solution set of
$(x + 3)(x + 5) - (x + 1)^2 < 2(x + 1)$.

Bonus

Chapter 9 Test, Form 2B

9

1. Simplify $y^5 \cdot y^3$.

1. _____

2. Simplify $(9m^3n^5)(-2mn^2)(6m^2n^8)$.

2. _____

3. Simplify $(w^5y^4)^3$.

3. _____

4. Simplify $4a^3n^6 + 4(a^3n)^6 + 4(an^2)^3$.

4. _____

5. Simplify $\dfrac{p^6q^2}{p^3q}$. Assume the denominator is not equal to zero.

5. _____

6. Simplify $\dfrac{16r^3s^{-5}}{4r^{-1}s^2}$. Assume the denominator is not equal to zero.

6. _____

7. Simplify $\dfrac{(-8x^2y^2)^2}{(4x^3y)^3}$. Assume the denominator is not equal to zero.

7. _____

8. Express 0.000498 in scientific notation.

8. _____

9. Express 1.27×10^5 in decimal notation.

9. _____

10. Evaluate $(2.5 \times 10^{-2})(4 \times 10^6)$. Express the result in scientific notation.

10. _____

11. Evaluate $\dfrac{5.4 \times 10^{-8}}{1.5 \times 10^2}$. Express the result in scientific notation.

11. _____

12. Find the degree of $2x^3y^3 + 4xy - 10x^3y$.

12. _____

13. Arrange the terms $4 + 3x^3y^3 - x^5y + xy$ so that the powers of x are in descending order.

13. _____

14. Find the difference.

$$5n^2 - 2ny + 3y^2$$
$$(-)\ 9n^2 - 8ny - 10y^2$$

14. _____

15. Simplify $(11m^2 - 2mn + 8n^2) + (8m^2 + 4mn - 2n^2)$.

15. _____

16. Simplify $5hk^2(2h^2k - hk^3 + 4h^2k^2)$.

16. _____

17. Simplify $(x + 5) - (x + 6)$.

17. _____

18. Simplify $(4x^2 + 2y^2)(2x^2 - y^2)$.

18. _____

19. Simplify $(3s + 5)(2s^2 - 8s + 6)$.

19. _____

20. Simplify $(5c - 4)^2$.

20. _____

21. Simplify $(7a - 3b)(7a + 3b)$.

21. _____

22. Simplify $(4n + 1)^2$.

22. _____

23. Solve $-6(3n - 2) = 4(-3 - 2n)$.

23. _____

24. Solve $8n + 11 = 4 + 5(2n - 1)$.

24. _____

25. The length of a rectangular garden is 8 feet longer than the width. The garden is surrounded by a 4-foot sidewalk. The sidewalk has an area of 320 square feet. Find the dimensions of the garden.

25. _____

Bonus If $(x + 1)^{20}$ is multiplied out, how many terms will there be? (*Hint:* Look at the smaller powers of $(x + 1)$. Find a pattern.)

Bonus _____

Chapter 9 Test, Form 2C

1. Simplify $x^4 \cdot x^3$.

1. _____

2. Simplify $(3a^2b^5)(4a^2b)$.

2. _____

3. Simplify $(w^3z^7)^3$.

3. _____

4. Simplify $5a^4b^6 + (2a^2b^3)^2$.

4. _____

5. Simplify $\dfrac{-8n^7}{4n^4}$. Assume the denominator is not equal to zero.

5. _____

6. Simplify $\dfrac{15t^2v^5}{3t^5v^4}$. Assume the denominator is not equal to zero.

6. _____

7. Simplify $\dfrac{(4x^{-2}y)^2}{(2x^2y^{-1})^3}$. Assume the denominator is not equal to zero.

7. _____

8. Express 12,556 in scientific notation.

8. _____

9. Express 7.43×10^{-3} in decimal notation.

9. _____

10. Evaluate $(6 \times 10^{-2})(4 \times 10^6)$. Express the result in scientific notation.

10. _____

11. Evaluate $\dfrac{5.4 \times 10^4}{2.7 \times 10^{-3}}$. Express the result in scientific notation.

11. _____

12. Find the degree of $2x^2y - 4x^5 + 6xy^3$.

12. _____

13. Arrange the terms of $3x^2 - x - 3 + x^3$ so that the powers of x are in descending order.

13. _____

14. Find the difference.

$$7m^2 + 3m - 4$$
$$\underline{(-)\ 3m^2 + 9m - 5}$$

14. _____

15. Simplify $(4y^2 + 3y - 7) + (4y^2 - 7y - 2)$.

15. _____

16. Simplify $3x^2(2x^2 - 5x + 8)$.

16. _____

17. Simplify $(3x - 4) - (2x - 1)$.

17. _____

18. Simplify $(m + 5)(m + 7)$.

18. _____

19. Simplify $(2n + 3)(4n - 1)$.

19. _____

20. Simplify $(y + 6)^2$.

20. _____

21. Simplify $(2k + 5)(2k - 5)$.

21. _____

22. Simplify $(2c - 1)^2$.

22. _____

23. Solve $5x + 8 = 3 + 2(3x - 4)$.

23. _____

24. Solve $-5(2n - 3) = 7(3 - n)$.

24. _____

25. The length of a rectangular garden is 5 feet longer than the width. The garden is surrounded by a 2-foot-wide sidewalk. The sidewalk has an area of 76 square feet. Find the dimensions of the garden.

25. _____

Bonus If $(x + 1)^{10}$ is multiplied out, how many terms will there be? (*Hint*: Look at the smaller powers of $(x + 1)$. Find a pattern.)

Bonus _____

NAME _____ DATE _____

Chapter 9 Calculator-Based Test

Simplify.

1. $[(2.4)^2]^3$

2. $(4^3)^2 - (2^3)^4$

3. Use the formula $T = p(1 + r)^t$ to determine how much money you will have in $9\frac{1}{2}$ years (t) if you invest $8000 ($p$) at 8% ($r$).

4. The formula $P = A\left[\dfrac{i}{1 - (1 + i)^{-n}}\right]$ can be used to determine the monthly payment on a home. P represents the monthly payment, A represents the price of the home less the down payment, i represents the *monthly* interest rate, and n is the total number of monthly payments. Find the monthly payment on a $150,000 home with 20% down and an *annual* interest rate of $8\frac{5}{8}$% over 30 years.

Evaluate. Express each answer in scientific notation.

5. $(8.12 \times 10^8)(4.6 \times 10^3)$

6. $(3.78 \times 10^{-5})(9.1 \times 10^{-4})$

7. $(1.8 \times 10^9) \div (7.2 \times 10^{-4})$

8. $\dfrac{6.75 \times 10^5}{(36,000)(1.25 \times 10^8)}$

9. The area of a circle can be found using $A = \pi r^2$. Find the area of the shaded region.

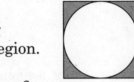

10. The sum of the angle measures of a triangle is 180.
   a. Write a polynomial to represent the measure of $\angle C$.
   b. If $x = 12.5$, find the measure of $\angle A$, $\angle B$, and $\angle C$.

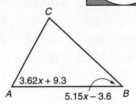

Find each product.

11. $(4.5y - 3.1)(2.6y + 7.3)$

12. $(5.2x - 3.8)^2$

13. $(9.3c + 1.8)(9.3c - 1.8)$

14. $(2.3x - 3)(1.9x^2 + 0.8x - 4)$

15. The diameter of the center of the target shown at the right is 4 inches. The radii of the successive circles increase by 3 inches each time. Find the total area of the shaded regions.

16. A picture is 1 foot wider than it is tall. The picture is mounted in a $\frac{3}{4}$-inch-wide frame. The frame has an area of $45\frac{9}{16}$ square inches. Find the dimensions of the picture.

1. _____

2. _____

3. _____

4. _____

5. _____

6. _____

7. _____

8. _____

9. _____

10. _____

_____

_____

11. _____

12. _____

13. _____

14. _____

15. _____

16. _____

NAME_____ DATE _____

Chapter 9 Performance Assessment

Instructions: *Demonstrate your knowledge by giving a clear, concise solution to each problem. Be sure to include all relevant drawings and justify your answers. You may show your solution in more than one way or investigate beyond the requirements of the problem.*

1. Rectangular areas can be used to represent products of binomials.
   a. Find the product $(2x + 3)(x + 1)$. Tell how the product and the area at the right are related.

   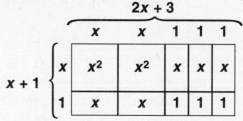

   b. Draw an area model demonstrating the product $(3x + 1)(x + 2)$. Find the product algebraically to verify your model.

   c. Write the two binomials whose product is demonstrated by the area model at the right. Find the product and show how it relates to the model.

   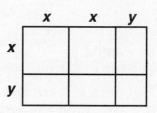

   d. If the shaded regions represent a negative area and can be used to subtract or remove area from positive areas, tell how $x(2x - 1) = 2x^2 - x$ relates to the model.

   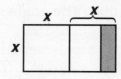

   e. Draw an area model demonstrating the product $x(3x - 2)$. Find the product and tell how it relates to the model.

   f. The product of two binomials is $x^2 + 3x + 2$. Use the area models at the right to form a rectangle and find the two binomials. Check your answer.

2. Simplify $\dfrac{(-3a^3b^2)(4ab)}{2a^7b}$ in at least two ways. Explain each step.

3. Write a product of two numbers in scientific notation. Find the product and explain each step.

Chapter 9 Mid-Chapter Test (Lessons 9-1 through 9-4)

Simplify. Assume no denominator is equal to zero.

1. $n^5 \cdot n^2 \cdot m^3 \cdot m^4$ 2. $6(a^3)^4 + (3a^6)^2$

3. $(-2m^5n^6)^2$ 4. $(-3a^3n^4)(-3a^3n)^4$

5. $\frac{1}{3}(2a^3b)(6b^3)$ 6. $\frac{n^{-2}}{n^7}$

7. $\frac{x^0}{x^{-17}}$ 8. $\frac{10x^3y^5}{15x^7y^3}$

9. $\frac{-10m^{-1}y^0r}{-14m^{-7}y^{-3}r^{-4}}$ 10. $\frac{2x^3y^5}{5(x^4y^2)^3}$

Express each number in scientific notation.

11. $31{,}000{,}000$ 12. 0.76×10^{-3}

Evaluate. Express each result in scientific notation.

13. $\frac{5.1 \times 10^6}{1.5 \times 10^2}$ 14. $\frac{1.17 \times 10^2}{5 \times 10^{-1}}$

15. $(8.3 \times 10^2)(9.1 \times 10^{-7})$ 16. $(3.1 \times 10^{-7})(2 \times 10^{-5})$

Find the degree of each polynomial.

17. $5c^2 - 3c^4 + 2c^3 - 1$ 18. $8x^3y - 6x^2y^3 + 3xy$

Arrange the terms of each polynomial so that the powers of x are in descending order.

19. $6 + 2x^2 - 3x + 4x^3$ 20. $2a^2x^3 + 8x^4 - 3a^4x^2 + 8x$

Bonus Simplify $\frac{-83t^5}{stw}\left(sw^6 \cdot w^{-5} + \frac{sww^0}{-3-(-2)} \right)$.

1. _____

2. _____

3. _____

4. _____

5. _____

6. _____

7. _____

8. _____

9. _____

10. _____

11. _____

12. _____

13. _____

14. _____

15. _____

16. _____

17. _____

18. _____

19. _____

20. _____

Bonus _____

Chapter 9, Quiz A (Lessons 9-1 and 9-2)

Simplify.

1. $(x^3y^4)(x^2y^3)$

2. $(r^3n^5)(-5r^3n^5)$

3. $(-4x^2y^3z)(3xyz^2)$

4. $(x^5)^4$

5. $(-5x^4y^2)^3$

6. $(5y^2w^4)^2 + 2(yw^2)^4$

Simplify. Assume no denominator is equal to zero.

7. $\dfrac{y^9}{y^6}$

8. $\dfrac{r^6n^{-7}}{r^4n^2}$

9. $\dfrac{6x^5y^7w^3}{8x^2y^{10}w^3}$

10. $\dfrac{(4x^2y^3)^0}{8x^3}$

1. _____

2. _____

3. _____

4. _____

5. _____

6. _____

7. _____

8. _____

9. _____

10. _____

Chapter 9, Quiz B (Lessons 9-3 and 9-4)

Express each number in scientific notation.

1. 57,600

2. 0.0000061

3. Write 6.4871×10^{-3} in decimal notation.

Evaluate. Express each result in scientific notation.

4. $\dfrac{7.2 \times 10^{-5}}{4.5 \times 10^2}$

5. $(3.5 \times 10^6)(8.2 \times 10^3)$

Find the degree of each polynomial.

6. $5a - 2b^2 + 1$

7. $24xy - xy^3 + x^2$

Arrange the terms of each polynomial so that the powers of x are in descending order.

8. $4x^2 - 3x^3 + 2x + 12$

9. $5x^3y + 3xy^4 - x^2y^3 + y^4$

10. Arrange the terms of the polynomial $-3 + x^2 + 4x$ so that the powers of x are in ascending order.

1. _____

2. _____

3. _____

4. _____

5. _____

6. _____

7. _____

8. _____

9. _____

10. _____

NAME_____ DATE _____

Chapter 9, Quiz C (Lessons 9-5 and 9-6)

Find each sum or difference.

1. $(-2x^2 + x + 6) + (5x^2 - 4x - 2)$　　　　1. _____

2. $(5a + 9b) - (2a + 4b)$　　　　2. _____

3. 　　　　$3a^2 - 7a + 4$　　　　3. _____
　　$(-)\ a^2 + 14a - 4$

Simplify.

4. $3xy(2x^2 + 5xy - 7y^2)$　　　　4. _____

5. $5c^2(c + 10) - 4c(2c^2 - 6c + 1)$　　　　5. _____

NAME_____ DATE _____

Chapter 9, Quiz D (Lessons 9-7 and 9-8)

Find each product.

1. $(4m - n)(5m + 8n)$　　　2. $(2c - 3)(c^2 - 4c + 5)$　　　1. _____

　　　　　　　　　　　　　　　　　　　　　　2. _____

3. $(4h + 3)^2$　　　4. $(a - 9)^2$　　　3. _____

　　　　　　　　　　　　　　　　　　　　　4. _____

5. $(2x + 6y)(2x - 6y)$　　　6. $(m^2 + 2n)^2$　　　5. _____

　　　　　　　　　　　　　　　　　　　　　　6. _____

7. $(9x - 7)^2$　　　7. _____

Use the diagram at the right for exercises 8–10.

8. Write a polynomial expression that represents the surface　　8. _____
area of the top side of the prism.

9. Write a polynomial expression that
represents the volume of the prism.

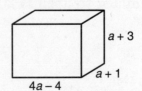

$a + 3$

$a + 1$

9. _____

10. Find the volume if $a = 3$ cm.　　$4a - 4$　　10. _____

Choose the best answer. Write A, B, C, or D.

1. If $(2m - 1)(6m + 2) = 12m^2 - 2m - 2$, then $(2m + 1)(6m - 2) =$
   A. $12m^2 - 2m + 2$.
   B. $12m^2 + 2m - 2$.
   C. $12m^2 + 2m + 2$.
   D. $12m^2 + 10m + 2$.

   1. _____

2. If $4f - g = 10$ and $4f + g = 12$, then $16f^2 - g^2 =$
   A. -2.
   B. 2.
   C. 22.
   D. 120.

   2. _____

3. 16% of 980 is 9.8% of
   A. 1.6.
   B. 16.
   C. 160.
   D. 1600.

   3. _____

4. Which number is closest to $\frac{2}{5}$?

   A. $\frac{1}{2}$
   B. $\frac{2}{3}$
   C. $\frac{3}{7}$
   D. $\frac{5}{9}$

   4. _____

5. If $3y + 3 \neq 6y$, then
   A. $y = 1$.
   B. $y > 1$.
   C. $y < 1$.
   D. $y \neq 1$.

   5. _____

6. For what value(s) of r is $3r - 6$ equal to $7 + 3r$?
   A. all positive integers
   B. all numbers
   C. all negative integers
   D. no values of r

   6. _____

7. If $-|a| = a$, then
   A. $a = 0$.
   B. $a \leq 0$.
   C. $a \geq 0$.
   D. $a < 0$.

   7. _____

8. $\dfrac{195 + 195 + 195 + 195}{4} =$

   A. 23.75
   B. 195
   C. 390
   D. 780

   8. _____

9. If $xyz = 10$ and $y = z$, then $x =$
   A. z^2.
   B. $\dfrac{1}{y^2}$.
   C. $\dfrac{10}{y^2}$.
   D. $\dfrac{1}{10y^2}$.

   9. _____

10. Two-thirds of a number added to itself is 20. What is the number?
    A. 12
    B. $13\frac{1}{3}$
    C. 30
    D. $33\frac{1}{3}$

    10. _____

11. If $a:b = c:d$, then
    A. $ad = bc$.
    B. $ac = bd$.
    C. $ab = cd$.
    D. $ad > bc$.

    11. _____

Chapter 9 Cumulative Review

9

1. Evaluate $a^2 + b^2(c^2)$ if $a = -2$, $b = 3$, and $c = \frac{1}{2}$.
   (Lesson 1-3)

   1. _____

2. Simplify $\frac{-48a}{6}$. (Lesson 2-7)

   2. _____

3. Replace __?__ with <, >, or = to make $-\frac{3}{5}$ __?__ $-\frac{5}{7}$
   a true sentence. (Lesson 2-4)

   3. _____

4. Find the missing terms in the following sequence.
   (Lesson 1-2) 14, 9, ___, ___, ___, -11, ___

   4. _____

5. Solve $3 + 2.1m = -13.8$. (Lesson 3-3)

   5. _____

6. Solve $5(c + 3) = 15 + 2(2c - 1)$. (Lesson 3-5)

   6. _____

7. Carla is 5 years older than Meredith. In 3 years,
   the sum of their ages will be 45. How old is
   Meredith now? (Lesson 2-9)

   7. _____

8. Three is 0.24% of what number? (Lesson 4-4)

   8. _____

9. If y varies directly as x and $x = 12$ when $y = 10$,
   find y when $x = 40$. (Lesson 4-8)

   9. _____

10. Given $f(x) = x^2 - 2x - 4$, find $f(-4)$. (Lesson 5-5)

    10. _____

11. Graph $x = -2$. (Lesson 5-4)

    11.

12. Write an equation in standard form for the line
    through $(-1, 2)$ and $(7, -6)$. (Lesson 6-2)

    12. _____

13. Write an equation in slope-intercept form for the
    line with a slope of -2 and passing through $(3, 6)$.
    (Lesson 6-4)

    13. _____

14. Write an equation of the line that is perpendicular
    to the graph of $y = 3x - 5$ and passes through $(6, -2)$.
    (Lesson 6-6)

    14. _____

15. Solve the open sentence $|2n - 6| \geq 8$. (Lesson 7-6)

15._____

16. Graph $3x - y \geq -1$. (Lesson 7-8)

16.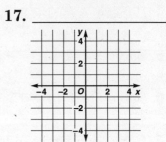

17. Graph the equations $2y - x = 1$ and $2y - x = -2$. Then state the number of solutions of the system of equations. (Lesson 8-1)

17._____

18. Use substitution to solve the system of equations $\frac{1}{2}x + y = 4$ and $x = 2y$. (Lesson 8-2)

18._____

19. Use elimination to solve the system of equations $4x + 3y = -1$ and $-3x - 2y = 3$. (Lesson 8-4)

19._____

20. The product of the digits of a two-digit number is 8. The units digit is 7 more than the tens digit. Find the number. (Lesson 8-4)

20._____

21. Simplify $(2d^2h^3y)(-4dhy^4)$. (Lesson 9-1)

21._____

22. Simplify $\frac{51x^{-1}y^3}{17x^2y}$. (Lesson 9-2)

22._____.

23. Evaluate $(6 \times 10^5)(2.3 \times 10^3)$. Express the result in scientific notation. (Lesson 9-3)

23._____

24. Find $\left(\frac{2}{3}a^2 - \frac{1}{4}a - \frac{1}{5}\right) - \left(\frac{1}{3}a^2 + \frac{3}{4}a + \frac{2}{5}\right)$. (Lesson 9-5)

24._____

25. Find $(2x - 3)^2$. (Lesson 9-8)

25._____

Chapter 9 Answer Key

Page 225	Page 226	Page 227	Page 228
1. **C**	12. **D**	1. **C**	12. **B**
2. **A**		2. **A**	
	13. **A**		13. **C**
3. **D**		3. **A**	
4. **C**	14. **C**	4. **A**	14. **D**
5. **D**	15. **B**	5. **B**	15. **C**
6. **D**	16. **A**	6. **B**	16. **B**
7. **A**	17. **C**	7. **D**	17. **A**
8. **B**	18. **C**	8. **C**	18. **D**
9. **C**	19. **A**	9. **D**	19. **A**
10. **C**	20. **C**	10. **A**	20. **B**
11. **A**		11. **C**	
	Bonus **−1**		Bonus **3**

Chapter 9 Answer Key

Form 1C

Page 229

1. __B__
2. __B__
3. __B__
4. __C__
5. __B__
6. __A__
7. __A__
8. __B__
9. __D__
10. __D__
11. __B__

Page 230

12. __C__
13. __B__
14. __A__
15. __C__
16. __B__
17. __D__
18. __A__
19. __A__
20. __D__

Bonus __1__

Form 2A

Page 231

1. $3a^7b^{10}$
2. $\frac{16}{81}h^{12}$
3. $68a^6n^3 + 4a^2n^3$
4. $\frac{-6d^3}{c^4}$
5. $\frac{4}{v^2}$
6. $\frac{2}{x^7y^7}$
7. 1.96783×10^5
8. 0.0000271
9. 1.5×10^{-1}
10. 1.8×10^{-2}
11. $-6 + 2x + 4x^5 + 7x^6$
12. 4
13. $10w^2 + 3w + 4$

Page 232

14. $4x^2 + 11x + 3$
15. $-n^3 - 25n^2 + 12n - 21$
16. $x^2 + 5x + 4$
17. $8y^2 - 20y - 28$
18. $\frac{1}{3}m^2 - \frac{11}{6}m + 2$
19. $z^2 + 4z + 4$
20. $4m^2 - 9n^2$
21. $9x^2 - 6x + 1$
22. $x^3 + x^2 - 2x + 12$
23. 4
24. $7 \text{ in.} \times 13 \text{ in.}$
25. $12 \text{ cm} \times 16 \text{ cm}$

Bonus

Chapter 9 Answer Key

Form 2B

Page 233

1. y^8

2. $-108m^6n^{15}$

3. $w^{15}y^{12}$

4. $8a^3n^6 + 4a^{18}n^6$

5. p^3q

6. $\dfrac{4r^4}{s^7}$

7. $-\dfrac{y}{x^5}$

8. 4.98×10^{-4}

9. $127{,}000$

10. 1×10^5

11. 3.6×10^{-10}

12. 6

13. $-x^5y + 3x^3y^3 + xy + 4$

Page 234

14. $-4n^2 + 6ny + 13y^2$

15. $19m^2 + 2mn + 6n^2$

16. $10h^3k^3 - 5h^2k^5 + 20h^3k^4$

17. -1

18. $8x^4 - 2y^4$

19. $6s^3 - 14s^2 - 22s + 30$

20. $25c^2 - 40c + 16$

21. $49a^2 - 9b^2$

22. $16n^2 + 8n + 1$

23. 2.4

24. 6

25. $12 \text{ ft} \times 20 \text{ ft}$

Bonus 21

Chapter 9 Answer Key

Form 2C — Page 235

1. x^7

2. $12a^4b^6$

3. w^9z^{21}

4. $9a^4b^6$

5. $-2n^3$

6. $\dfrac{5v}{t^3}$

7. $\dfrac{2y^5}{x^{10}}$

8. 1.2556×10^4

9. 0.00743

10. 2.4×10^5

11. 2×10^7

12. 5

13. $x^3 + 3x^2 - x - 3$

Page 236

14. $4m^2 - 6m + 1$

15. $8y^2 - 4y - 9$

16. $6x^4 - 15x^3 + 24x^2$

17. $x - 3$

18. $m^2 + 12m + 35$

19. $8n^2 + 10n - 3$

20. $y^2 + 12y + 36$

21. $4k^2 - 25$

22. $4c^2 - 4c + 1$

23. 13

24. -2

25. $5\text{ ft} \times 10\text{ ft}$

Bonus ___ 11

Calculator-Based — Page 237

1. $(2.4)^6$, or 191.102976

2. 0

3. $\$16,619.41$

4. $\$933.35$

5. 3.7352×10^{12}

6. 3.4398×10^{-8}

7. 2.5×10^{12}

8. 1.5×10^{-7}

9. about 21.46 square units

10. a. $174.3 - 8.77x$
    b. $m \angle A = 54.55$
    $m \angle B = 60.775$
    $m \angle C = 64.675$

11. $11.7y^2 + 24.79y - 22.63$

12. $27.04x^2 - 39.52x + 14.44$

13. $86.49c^2 - 3.24$

14. $4.37x^3 - 3.86x^2 - 11.6x + 12$

15. about 370.71 sq in.

16. $8\dfrac{7}{16}$ in. $\times\ 20\dfrac{7}{16}$ in.

Algebra 1

Scoring Guide
Chapter 9
Performance Assessment

Level	Specific Criteria
3 Superior	• Shows thorough understanding of the concepts of *multiplication of binomials, multiplication and division of monomials,* and *scientific notation.* • Computations are correct. • Written explanations are exemplary. • Diagrams are accurate and appropriate. • Goes beyond requirements of some or all problems.
2 Satisfactory, with Minor Flaws	• Shows understanding of the concepts of *multiplication of binomials, multiplication and division of monomials,* and *scientific notation.* • Computations are mostly correct. • Written explanations are effective. • Diagrams are mostly accurate and appropriate. • Satisfies all requirements of problems.
1 Nearly Satisfactory, with Serious Flaws	• Shows understanding of most of the concepts of *multiplication of binomials, multiplication and division of monomials,* and *scientific notation.* • Computations are mostly correct. • Written explanations are satisfactory. • Diagrams are mostly accurate and appropriate. • Satisfies most requirements of problems.
0 Unsatisfactory	• Shows little or no understanding of the concepts of *multiplication of binomials, multiplication and division of monomials,* and *scientific notation.* • Computations are incorrect. • Written explanations are not satisfactory. • Diagrams are not accurate or appropriate. • Does not satisfy requirements of problems.

Chapter 9 Answer Key
Performance Assessment

Page 238

1. a. $(2x + 3)(x + 1) = 2x^2 + 5x + 3$
Each rectangle is defined by the product of the measures of its sides. That is, $x^2 = x \cdot x$, $x = 1 \cdot x$, and $1 = 1 \cdot 1$. The rectangular area is made up of 2 x^2-areas, 5 x-areas, and 3 1-areas.

b.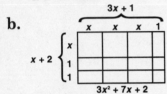

c. The length of the rectangular region is $2x + y$. The width of the region is $x + y$. The area of the rectangular region is $(2x + y)(x + y)$ or $2x^2 + 3xy + y^2$. The regions in the model include 2 x^2-areas, 3 xy-areas, and 1 y^2-area, which when combined describe the algebraic product of the binomials.

d. Without considering the shaded region, the model shows $2x \cdot x$ or $2x^2$. The shaded region represents $-(1)(x)$ or $-x$. Together, the model parts represent $2x^2 - x$. The length of the model represents $2x$ and -1 or $2x - 1$. The width of the model shows x. Thus $x(2x - 1) = 2x^2 - x$.

e.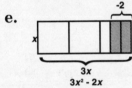

f. $(x + 2)(x + 1) = x^2 + x + 2x + 2$
$= x^2 + 3x + 2$

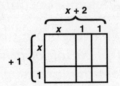

2. method 1:

$$\frac{(-3a^3b^2)(4ab)}{2a^7b} = \frac{-3 \cdot 4 \cdot a \cdot a \cdot a \cdot a \cdot b \cdot b \cdot b}{2 \cdot a \cdot a \cdot a \cdot a \cdot a \cdot a \cdot a \cdot b}$$

$$= \frac{-6b^2}{a^3}$$

method 2:

$$\frac{(-3a^3b^2)(4ab)}{2a^7b} = \frac{-12a^4b^3}{2a^7b}$$

$$= -6a^{-3}b^2$$

$$= \frac{-6b^2}{a^3}$$

3. $(3 \times 10^{12})(4 \times 10^{-5}) = 12 \times 10^7 = 1.2 \times 10^8$

Chapter 9 Answer Key

Mid-Chapter Test
Page 239

1. $n^7 m^7$
2. $15a^{12}$
3. $4m^{10}n^{12}$
4. $-243a^{15}n^8$
5. $4a^3b^4$
6. $\dfrac{1}{n^9}$
7. $\dfrac{x^{17}}{2y^2}$
8. $\dfrac{3x^4}{5m^6y^3r^5}$
9. $\dfrac{7}{2}$
10. $\dfrac{2}{5x^9y}$

11. 3.1×10^7
12. 7.6×10^{-4}

13. 3.4×10^4
14. 2.34×10^2
15. 7.553×10^{-4}
16. 6.2×10^{-12}

17. 4
18. 5

19. $4x^3 + 2x^2 - 3x + 6$

20. $8x^4 + 2a^2x^3 - 3a^4x^2 + 8x$

Bonus 0

Quiz A
Page 240

1. x^5y^7
2. $-5r^6m^{10}$
3. $-12x^3y^4z^3$
4. x^{20}
5. $-125x^{12}y^6$
6. $27y^4w^8$
7. y^3
8. $\dfrac{r^2}{n^9}$
9. $\dfrac{3x^3}{4y^3}$
10. $\dfrac{1}{8x^3}$

Quiz B
Page 240

1. 5.76×10^4
2. 6.1×10^{-6}
3. 0.0064871

4. 1.6×10^{-7}
5. 2.87×10^{10}

6. 2
7. 4

8. $-3x^3 + 4x^2 + 2x + 12$

9. $5x^3y - x^2y^3 + 3xy^4 + y^4$

10. $-3 + 4x + x^2$

Quiz C
Page 241

1. $3x^2 - 3x + 4$
2. $3a + 5b$
3. $2a^2 - 21a + 8$
4. $6x^3y + 15x^2y^2 - 21xy^3$
5. $-3c^3 + 74c^2 - 4c$

Quiz D
Page 241

1. $20m^2 + 27mn - 8n^2$
2. $2c^3 - 11c^2 + 22c - 15$
3. $16h^2 + 24h + 9$
4. $a^2 - 18a + 81$
5. $4x^2 - 36y^2$
6. $m^4 + 4m^2n + 4n^2$
7. $81x^2 - 126x + 49$
8. $4a^2 - 4$
9. $4a^3 + 12a^2 - 4a - 12$
10. 192 cm^3

Chapter 9 Answer Key

Standardized Test Practice
Page 242

1. <u>**B**</u>

2. <u>**D**</u>

3. <u>**D**</u>

4. <u>**C**</u>

5. <u>**D**</u>

6. <u>**D**</u>

7. <u>**B**</u>

8. <u>**B**</u>

9. <u>**C**</u>

10. <u>**A**</u>

11. <u>**A**</u>

Cumulative Review
Page 243

1. $6\frac{1}{4}$

2. $-8a$

3. $>$

4. $4; -1; -6; -16$

5. -8

6. -2

7. **17 years**

8. **1250**

9. $33\frac{1}{3}$

10. **20**

11.

12. $x + y = 1$

13. $y = -2x + 12$

14. $y = -\frac{1}{3}x$

Page 244

15. $n \le -1 \text{ or } n \ge 7$

16.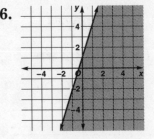

17. **no solutions**

18. $(4, 2)$

19. $(-7, 9)$

20. **18**

21. $-8d^3h^4y^5$

22. $\dfrac{3y^2}{x^3}$

23. 1.38×10^9

24. $\frac{1}{3}a^2 - a - \frac{3}{5}$

25. $4x^2 - 12x + 9$

10

Chapter 10 Test, Form 1A

Write the letter for the correct answer in the blank at the right of each problem.

1. What is the prime factorization of 684?
   A. $2 \cdot 2 \cdot 3 \cdot 57$ **B.** $1 \cdot 2 \cdot 2 \cdot 3 \cdot 57$
   C. $2 \cdot 2 \cdot 3 \cdot 3 \cdot 19$ **D.** none of these

   1. _____

2. Find the GCF of $18n^3y^4w$ and $24n^5y$.
   A. $6n^5y^4w$ **B.** $6n^3y$ **C.** $243n^56y^4w$ **D.** $243n^3y$

   2. _____

3. Find the GCF of $4a^2b$, $5b^3c$, and $6ac$.
   A. 0   **B.** 1   **C.** $2ac$ **D.** $120a^3b^4c^2$

   3. _____

4. Factor $14xy^2 - 2xy$.
   A. $2xy(7y - 1)$ **B.** $2x(7y^2 - y)$ **C.** $-2xy(-7y)$ **D.** prime

   4. _____

5. If the polynomial $3a^2 - 3an^2 - 2an + 2n^3$ is to be factored by grouping pairs of terms, which grouping is *not* helpful?
   A. $3a^2$ paired with $-3an^2$ and $-2an$ paired with $2n^3$
   B. $3a^2$ paired with $-2an$ and $-3an^2$ paired with $2n^3$
   C. $3a^2$ paired with $2n^3$ and $-3an^2$ paired with $-2an$
   D. All the above pairings are helpful.

   5. _____

6. Which polynomials have $w + 5$ as a factor?
   A. $3w^2n + 6w^2 - 75n - 150$ **B.** $2w^2 + 50$
   C. Both do.   **D.** Neither do.

   6. _____

7. If $2a^3 + 16a^2 + 30a$ is factored completely, one of the factors is
   A. $a + 5$.   **B.** $2a + 6$.   **C.** $a + 6$.   **D.** $2a + 25$.

   7. _____

8. Factor $6x^2 + 20x - 16$.
   A. $(x + 4)(6x - 4)$ **B.** $(2x + 4)(3x + 4)$
   C. $2(3x - 2)(x + 4)$ **D.** $2(3x + 4)(x + 2)$

   8. _____

9. Which polynomial is prime?
   A. $2x^2 - 5x + 3$ **B.** $10x^2 - 11xw + 6w^2$
   C. $9y^2 + 29yn + 6n^2$ **D.** none of the above

   9. _____

10. How many values of k can be found so that $m^2 + km + 9$ can be factored using integers?
    A. 2   **B.** 4   **C.** 3   **D.** 6

    10. _____

11. Factor $16 - n^4$.
    A. $(4 - n^2)(4 + n^2)$ **B.** $(n + 2)(n - 2)(4 + n^2)$
    C. $(2 - n)(2 + n)(n^2 + 4)$ **D.** $(2 - n)(2 + n)(2 - n)(2 + n)$

    11. _____

12. If $8x^2 - 72y^2$ is factored completely, one of the factors is
    A. $2x^2 - 18y^2$. **B.** $x + 3$. **C.** $x - 9y^2$. **D.** $x - 3y$.

12. _____

13. 47×53 is 9 less than
    A. 50. **B.** 100. **C.** 1600. **D.** 2500.

13. _____

14. Each of the following is a perfect square except
    A. $x^2 + 8x + 16$. **B.** $4x^2 - 20x + 25$.
    C. $9x^2 + 12x - 4$. **D.** All are perfect squares.

14. _____

15. If $80y^2 - 120y + 45$ is factored completely, one of the factors is
    A. $4y - 3$. **B.** $8y - 9$. **C.** $10y - 9$. **D.** $8y - 15$.

15. _____

16. Find the value of c that makes $cn^2 + 72ny + 81y^2$ a perfect square trinomial.
    A. 1 **B.** 4 **C.** 16 **D.** none of these

16. _____

17. What is the solution set of the equation $4(3m - 2)(m + 9) = 0$?
    A. $\left\{\frac{2}{3}, -9\right\}$ **B.** $\left\{0, \frac{2}{3}, -9\right\}$ **C.** $\left\{-\frac{2}{3}, 9\right\}$ **D.** $\left\{0, -\frac{2}{3}, 9\right\}$

17. _____

18. What is the solution set of the equation $75x^2 - 50x = -8$?
    A. $\left\{-\frac{4}{15}, -\frac{2}{5}\right\}$ **B.** $\left\{\frac{4}{15}, \frac{2}{5}\right\}$ **C.** $\left\{\frac{2}{15}, -\frac{4}{5}\right\}$ **D.** $\left\{-\frac{2}{15}, \frac{4}{5}\right\}$

18. _____

19. What is the solution set of the equation $n^3 + 2n^2 - 35n = 0$?
    A. $\{-7, 0, 5\}$ **B.** $\{-5, 0, 7\}$ **C.** $\{-5, 7\}$ **D.** $\{-7, 5\}$

19. _____

20. The length of a rectangle is twice the width. The area is 72 square centimeters. What is the length?
    A. 48 cm **B.** 24 cm **C.** 12 cm **D.** 6 cm

20. _____

Bonus Find the least integer greater than 1 that is a perfect square, a perfect cube, and a perfect fourth power.

Bonus _____

10

Chapter 10 Test, Form 1B

Write the letter for the correct answer in the blank at the right of each problem.

1. What is the prime factorization of 342?
   A. $2 \cdot 3 \cdot 57$ B. $1 \cdot 2 \cdot 3 \cdot 57$ C. $2 \cdot 3 \cdot 3 \cdot 19$ D. none of these

   1. _____

2. Find the GCF of $18abc^3$ and $54ab^2$.
   A. $18ab^2c^3$ B. $9ab$ C. $18ab$ D. $432a^2b^3c^3$

   2. _____

3. Find the GCF of $3ab$, $4bc$, and $5ac$.
   A. 0   B. 1   C. $2c$ D. $60a^2b^2c^2$

   3. _____

4. Factor $3x^2 + 75$.
   A. $3(x + 5)(x + 5)$ B. $3(x^2 + 25)$
   C. $3(x - 5)(x - 5)$ D. none of these

   4. _____

5. Factor $6y(y^2 - 6) + 5(6 - y^2)$.
   A. $(6y - 5)(y^2 - 6)$ B. $(6y + 5)(6 - y^2)$
   C. $(6y + 5)(y^2 - 6)$ D. none of these

   5. _____

6. If $x^3 - 7x^2 + 4x - 28$ is factored completely, one of the factors is
   A. $x + 2$.   B. $x + 7$.   C. $x^2 + 7$.   D. $x^2 + 4$.

   6. _____

7. Factor $5x^2 - 13x + 6$.
   A. $(x + 3)(5x - 2)$ B. $(x - 3)(5x + 2)$
   C. $(x + 2)(5x + 3)$ D. $(x - 2)(5x - 3)$

   7. _____

8. If $14a^2 - 15a + 4$ is factored completely, one of the factors is
   A. $7a + 2$.   B. $7a - 4$.   C. $7a - 1$.   D. $14a - 1$.

   8. _____

9. If $6x^2 + 11x - 2$ is factored completely, one of the factors is
   A. $3x - 1$.   B. $6x - 1$.   C. $2x + 1$.   D. $3x - 2$.

   9. _____

10. Which polynomial is prime?
    A. $x^2 + 13x - 114$ B. $n^2 - 2ny - 195y^2$
    C. $x^2 + 2x - 18$ D. More than one of these is prime.

    10. _____

11. Factor $100v^2 - 64y^2$.
    A. $(10v - 8y)(10v + 8y)$ B. $(10v - 8y)(10v - 8y)$
    C. $(10v + 8y)(10v + 8y)$ D. none of these

    11. _____

12. Factor $n^4 - 5n^2 - 36$.

    A. $(n + 2)(n - 2)(n + 3)(n - 3)$ **B.** $(n^2 + 9)(n + 2)(n - 2)$

    C. $(n^2 - 4)(n^2 + 9)$ **D.** none of these

12. _____

13. How much less than 1600 is the product of 38 and 42?

    A. 1   **B.** 2   **C.** 4   **D.** 16

13. _____

14. Each of the following is a perfect square except

    A. $4x^2 + 4x + 1$.   **B.** $x^2 - 6x + 9$.

    C. $x^2 + 10x - 25$.   **D.** All are perfect squares.

14. _____

15. If $6x^2 + 48x + 96$ is factored completely, one of the factors is

    A. $x + 4$.   **B.** $3x + 8$.   **C.** $3x + 12$.   **D.** $6x + 16$.

15. _____

16. Find the value of c that makes $25y^2 - 40y + c$ a perfect square trinomial.

    A. 64   **B.** 25   **C.** 20   **D.** 16

16. _____

17. What is the solution set of the equation $(3w + 4)(2w - 7) = 0$?

    A. $\left\{-\frac{3}{4}, \frac{2}{7}\right\}$ **B.** $\left\{\frac{3}{4}, -\frac{2}{7}\right\}$ **C.** $\left\{-\frac{4}{3}, \frac{7}{2}\right\}$ **D.** $\left\{\frac{4}{3}, -\frac{7}{2}\right\}$

17. _____

18. What is the solution set of the equation $4x^2 = 20x - 25$?

    A. $\left\{0, \frac{5}{4}\right\}$ **B.** $\left\{0, -\frac{2}{5}\right\}$ **C.** $\left\{-\frac{4}{5}\right\}$ **D.** $\left\{\frac{5}{2}\right\}$

18. _____

19. What is the solution set of the equation $x^2 - 16x = 0$?

    A. $\{4, -4\}$ **B.** $\{0, 4, -4\}$ **C.** $\{0, 16\}$ **D.** $\{16\}$

19. _____

20. The width of a rectangle is 6 centimeters less than the length. The area of the rectangle is 112 square centimeters. What is the length?

    A. 16 cm   **B.** 31 cm   **C.** 7 cm   **D.** 14 cm

20. _____

Bonus   Insert parentheses so that a true equation results.

     $7 + 3 \cdot 5 - 6 - 2 \cdot 4 = 6$

Bonus _____

10

Chapter 10 Test, Form 1C

Write the letter for the correct answer in the blank at the right of each problem.

1. What is the prime factorization of 198?
   A. $2 \cdot 3 \cdot 33$ **B.** $2 \cdot 9 \cdot 11$ **C.** $2 \cdot 3 \cdot 3 \cdot 11$ **D.** none of these

1. _____

2. Find the GCF of $12x^3y^4z$ and $6x^2y$.
   A. $6x^3y^4z$ **B.** $6x^2y$ **C.** $72x^2y$ **D.** $72x^3y^4z$

2. _____

3. Find the GCF of $3x$, $4y$, and $5xy$.
   A. 0   **B.** 1   **C.** $2xy$ **D.** $60x^2y^2$

3. _____

4. Factor $15x^2 - 5x$.
   A. $5x(3x - 1)$ **B.** $5(3x^2 - x)$ **C.** $-5x(-3x)$ **D.** none of these

4. _____

5. Factor $3n(n + 4) - 2(n + 4)$.
   A. $(n + 4)(3n - 2)$ **B.** $(3n - 2)(n + 4)^2$
   C. $(3n + 2)(n - 4)$ **D.** none of these

5. _____

6. If $x^3 - 5x^2 + 6x - 30$ is factored completely, one of the factors is
   A. $x^2 + 5$.   **B.** $x + 5$.   **C.** $x^2 - 6$.   **D.** $x^2 + 6$.

6. _____

7. Factor $3m^2 + 14m - 5$.
   A. $(3m + 1)(m - 5)$ **B.** $(3m - 1)(m + 5)$
   C. $(3m + 5)(m - 1)$ **D.** $(3m - 5)(m + 1)$

7. _____

8. If $4x^2 - 13x + 3$ is factored completely, one of the factors is
   A. $2x - 3$.   **B.** $2x - 1$.   **C.** $4x - 3$.   **D.** $4x - 1$.

8. _____

9. If $15n^2 - n - 2$ is factored completely, one of the factors is
   A. $5n - 2$.   **B.** $3n - 2$.   **C.** $5n - 1$.   **D.** $3n - 1$.

9. _____

10. Which polynomial is prime?
    A. $x^2 - 6x + 8$ **B.** $x^2 + 5x + 4$
    C. $x^2 - 3x + 10$ **D.** none of these

10. _____

11. Factor $25x^2 - 16y^2$.
    A. $(5x + 4y)(5x + 4y)$ **B.** $(5x + 4y)(5x - 4y)$
    C. $(5x - 4y)(5x - 4y)$ **D.** none of these

11. _____

12. If $2n^2 - 32n$ is factored completely, one of the factors is   12. _____
    A. $2n - 8$.   B. $n + 16$.   C. $n - 16$.   D. $n + 4$.

13. How much less than 900 is 29×31?   13. _____
    A. 9   B. 5   C. 4   D. 1

14. Which of the following is a perfect square trinomial?   14. _____
    A. $3x^2 - 6x + 9$ B. $x^2 + 10x + 25$
    C. $x^2 + 8x - 16$ D. $x^2 + 12x - 36$

15. If $3k^2 - 36k + 108$ is factored completely, one of the factors is   15. _____
    A. $3k - 18$.   B. $3k + 12$.   C. $k - 6$.   D. $k - 12$.

16. Find the value of c that makes $9x^2 + 24x + c$ a perfect square   16. _____
    trinomial.
    A. 8   B. 16   C. 216   D. 12

17. What is the solution set of the equation $(5x - 3)(x + 4) = 0$?   17. _____
    A. $\left\{\frac{3}{5}, 4\right\}$ B. $\left\{-\frac{3}{5}, -4\right\}$ C. $\left\{\frac{3}{5}, -4\right\}$ D. $\left\{-\frac{3}{5}, 4\right\}$

18. What is the solution set of the equation $2x^2 - 5x = 3$?   18. _____
    A. $\left\{-\frac{1}{2}, 3\right\}$ B. $\left\{-\frac{1}{2}, -3\right\}$ C. $\left\{\frac{1}{2}, 3\right\}$ D. $\left\{\frac{1}{2}, -3\right\}$

19. What is the solution set of the equation $x^3 - 4x = 0$?   19. _____
    A. $\{-4, 0, 4\}$ B. $\{-2, 0, 2\}$ C. $\{-4, 4\}$ D. $\{-2, 2\}$

20. The length of a rectangle is 5 centimeters more than the width.   20. _____
    The area of the rectangle is 36 square centimeters. What is the
    length?
    A. 4 cm   B. 9 cm   C. 14 cm   D. 26 cm

Bonus   Find the least integer greater than 1 that is a perfect   Bonus _____
          square and a perfect cube.

NAME_____ DATE _____

Chapter 10 Test, Form 2A

State whether each number is prime or composite. If the number is composite, find its prime factorization.

1. 630

1. _____

   _____

2. 1160

2. _____

   _____

Find the GCF of the given monomials.

3. $-24, 36$

3. _____

4. $148, -555$

4. _____

5. $30n^6y^2t, 12n^3t^4$

5. _____

6. $4x^3y^2, 7x^2z^3, 15yz^2$

6. _____

Factor each polynomial.

7. $13x - 78xy^2$

7. _____

8. $15ay + 40a + 6ny + 16n$

8. _____

9. $3a^2x - 15xa + 3x$

9. _____

10. $2n(n^2 - 7) + 5(7 - n^2)$

10. _____

Factor each polynomial, if possible. If the polynomial cannot be factored using integers, write prime.

11. $3x^2 - 24xy + 48y^2$

11. _____

12. $10x^2 + 29x - 21$

12. _____

13. $(a + n)^2 - 4$

13. _____

14. $3p^2 - 13pw + 12w^2$

14. _____

15. $n^3 - 16n$

15. _____

16. $x^2 + 23x + 7$

16. _____

17. $25x^2 + 20xy + 4y^2$

17. _____

18. Find the value of c that will make $9x^2 + 12xy + c$ a perfect square trinomial.

18. _____

19. Find all values of k so that $t^2 + kt - 8$ can be factored using integers.

19. _____

20. The area of a square is $(169 - 234x + 81x^2)$ square feet. If x is a positive integer, what is the least possible perimeter measure for the square?

20. _____

21. Show how to use a difference of squares to multiply 68×72. Then find the product.

21. _____

Solve each equation.

22. $(3x - 5)(2x + 9) = 0$

22. _____

23. $r^3 + 54r = 15r^2$

23. _____

For each problem, define a variable. Then use an equation to solve each problem.

24. Find two consecutive even integers whose product is 224.

24. _____

25. The sum of the squares of the least and greatest of three consecutive negative even integers is 80. Find the three integers.

25. _____

Bonus   Factor $x^4 + x^2y^2 + y^4$.

Bonus _____

10

Chapter 10 Test, Form 2B

State whether each number is prime or composite. If the number is composite, find its prime factorization.

1. 89

1. _____

   _____

2. 132

2. _____

   _____

Find the GCF of the given monomials.

3. 305, 55

3. _____

4. -80, 45

4. _____

5. $12x^3y^2$, $44xy^3$

5. _____

6. $2a^2b^2$, $5b^2c^2$, $9a^2c^2$

6. _____

Factor each polynomial.

7. $7x - 19xy^2$

7. _____

8. $5s^3 + 45s$

8. _____

9. $3x^2 + 21x + 27$

9. _____

10. $v^2n + 2v^2 - 4n - 8$

10. _____

Factor each polynomial, if possible. If the polynomial cannot be factored using integers, write prime.

11. $36m^2 - 64$

11. _____

12. $u^4 - 15u^2 - 16$

12. _____

13. $n^2 + nw - 42w^2$

13. _____

14. $54 + 3y - y^2$

14. _____

15. $b^2 - 6b + 10$

15. _____

16. $25w^2 - 60w + 36$

16. _____

17. $8n^2y - 36ny + 40y$

17. _____

18. $y^4 - v^4$

18. _____

19. $36x^3 - 84x^2 + 49x$

19. _____

20. The area of a square is $(49 - 56x + 16x^2)$ square feet. If x is a positive integer, what is the least possible perimeter measure for the square?

20. _____

21. Find the value of c that will make $9x^2 + 30x + c$ a perfect square trinomial.

21. _____

Solve each equation.

22. $8y(2y - 1) = 0$

22. _____

23. $9n^2 = 12n - 4$

23. _____

For each problem, define a variable. Then use an equation to solve each problem.

24. The sum of two positive integers is 25. The difference of their squares is 275. Find the two integers.

24. _____

25. The area of a rectangular room is 238 square feet. The width is 3 feet less than the length. What are the dimensions?

25. _____

Bonus   Factor $v^2x^2 + 9n^2 - 9x^2 - v^2n^2$.

Bonus _____

Chapter 10 Test, Form 2C

State whether each number is prime or composite. If the number is composite, find its prime factorization.

1. 39

1. _____

_____

2. 73

2. _____

_____

Find the GCF of the given monomials.

3. 16, 60

3. _____

4. 252, 126

4. _____

5. $9x^2y^3$, $6xy^3$

5. _____

6. $5ab$, $6ac$, $7bc$

6. _____

Factor each polynomial.

7. $5x - 11xy^2$

7. _____

8. $8rs^2 + 16rs$

8. _____

9. $3x^3 + 27x$

9. _____

10. $a^3 - 4a^2 + 7a - 28$

10. _____

Factor each polynomial, if possible. If the polynomial cannot be factored using integers, write prime.

11. $x^2 - 25$

11. _____

12. $n^2 - 7n - 18$

12. _____

13. $5t^2 + 17t - 12$

13. _____

14. $2x^2 - 16x + 32$

14. _____

15. $y^4 - 16$

15. _____

16. $x^2 + 12x + 5$

16. _____

17. $5n^3 - 5n^2 + 15n$

17. _____

18. $4c^2 + 4cd + d^2$

18. _____

19. $4p^2 - 28p + 48$

19. _____

20. $c^2d^2 - 9$

20. _____

21. Find the value of c that will make $4x^2 + 28x + c$ a perfect square trinomial.

21. _____

Solve each equation.

22. $(x - 5)(2x - 1) = 0$

22. _____

23. $y^2 + 4y = 45$

23. _____

24. $n^3 - 3n^2 - 10n = 0$

24. _____

25. Define a variable for the following problem. Then use an equation to solve the problem.

25. _____

The area of a rectangular room is 90 square feet. The length of the room is 1 foot longer than the width. Find the dimensions of the room.

Bonus Factor $x^2y^2 - 4x^2 - 9y^2 + 36$.

Bonus _____

NAME_____ DATE _____

Chapter 10 Calculator-Based Test

Find the prime factorization of each number.

1. 3940

1. _____

2. 12,870

2. _____

Find the GCF of the given monomials.

3. 325, 2695

3. _____

4. 1188, 1760

4. _____

5. 648, 972, 4725

5. _____

6. 5508; 31,104

6. _____

7. $825x^6y^4$, $693x^3y^5$

7. _____

8. $18x^2y^2$, $85y^2z^2$, $143x^2z^2$

8. _____

Determine whether each equation is a true statement by graphing the polynomial and the factored expression. If the statement is not correct, state the correct factorization of the trinomial.

9. $x^2 - 3x - 4 = (x + 1)(x - 4)$

9. _____

10. $5x^2 + 7x - 6 = (5x - 3)(x + 2)$

10. _____

11. $15x^2 - 4x - 4 = (3x - 2)(5x + 2)$

11. _____

12. $12x^2 + 5x - 3 = (6x + 1)(2x - 3)$

12. _____

13. Find a Pythagorean triple that includes 114 as one of its numbers.

13. _____

14. Two positive real numbers differ by 2. Their product is 31. Find the numbers.

14. _____

15. Find two consecutive odd integers whose product is 9603.

15. _____

16. The area of a rectangle is 59 square feet. The length of the rectangle is 3 feet shorter than twice the width. What is the length of the rectangle?

16. _____

Instructions: *Demonstrate your knowledge by giving a clear, concise solution to each problem. Be sure to include all relevant drawings and justify your answers. You may show your solution in more than one way or investigate beyond the requirements of the problem.*

1. One way to factor a trinomial such as $x^2 - 2x - 3$ is to assign a value such as 10 to x and evaluate the expression.

$$
\begin{aligned}
x^2 - 2x - 3 &= 10^2 - 2(10) - 3 \\
&= 100 - 20 - 3 \\
&= 77
\end{aligned}
$$

A factorization of 77 is 7×11. Since $x = 10$, $7 = (x - 3)$ and $11 = (x + 1)$. Multiply to see if $(x - 3)(x + 1) = x^2 - 2x - 3$.

a. Try the above method to factor $x^2 - 8x + 15$. Show your work and explain each step. Did the method give you the correct factors?

b. Try the above method to factor $2x^2 - 13x - 24$. *Hint: The factors will be of the form* $(2x + a)(x + b)$. Show your work and explain each step.

c. Try the above method to factor $x^2 - 2x - 8$. Why is it difficult to find the correct factors for this trinomial using the above method?

d. Evaluate the expression in part c for $x = 7$. Then use the above method to find the factors. Explain each step. Remember in finding your factors that $x = 7$.

2. a. Tell how to factor a polynomial with four terms by grouping.

b. Use grouping to factor $10ax - 5ay + 2bx - by$. Explain each step.

c. Factor $6x^3 + 3x^2y - 2xy - y^2$ in two different ways. Show your work.

NAME_____ DATE _____

Chapter 10 Mid-Chapter Test (Lessons 10-1 through 10-3)

Find the GCF of the given monomials.

1. $42, 60$

2. $36, 64$

3. $32xyz, 48xy^4$

4. $18m^2n^2, 66m^3$

1. _____

2. _____

3. _____

4. _____

Factor each polynomial.

5. $2y + 6xy$

6. $8ax - 56a$

7. $36xy^2 - 48x^2y$

8. $75b^2c^3 + 60bc^6$

9. $4x^3 - 12x^2 + 24x$

10. $64a^2b - 16a^3b^2 + 8a^2b^2$

5. _____

6. _____

7. _____

8. _____

9. _____

10. _____

Factor each polynomial, if possible. If the polynomial cannot be factored using integers, write prime.

11. $6ab + 4a + 3b + 2$

11. _____

12. $6mn - 9m - 4n + 6$

12. _____

13. $2x^2y + 6xy - x - 3$

13. _____

14. $6xy^2 - 3xy + 8y - 4$

14. _____

15. $y^2 - 7y - 10$

15. _____

16. $48 - 16e + e^2$

16. _____

17. $w^2 - 16w - 36$

17. _____

18. $2b^2 + 14b - 16$

18. _____

19. $6a^2 + 12ab - 18b^2$

19. _____

20. The measure of the area of a rectangle is $6a^2 + 7a + 2$. The width is a binomial of the form $ap + q$. What is the measure of the perimeter of the rectangle?

20. _____

Bonus   Factor $12a^3 - 4a^2 - 408a$.

Bonus _____

NAME_____ DATE _____

Chapter 10, Quiz A (Lessons 10-1 and 10-2)

State whether each number is prime or composite. If the number is composite, find its prime factorization.

1. 57   2. 175

Find the GCF of the given monomials.

3. 12, 90   4. 45, 72, 117

5. $20xy$, $48xy^2$ 6. $12a^2b^2$, $36ab^3$

Factor each polynomial.

7. $48a^2b^2 - 12ab$ 8. $6x^2y - 21y^2w + 24xw$

9. $xy - 2xz + 5y - 10z$ 10. $a^2 + 6a + ab + 6b$

1. _____

2. _____

_____

3. _____

4. _____

5. _____

6. _____

7. _____

8. _____

9. _____

10. _____

NAME_____ DATE _____

Chapter 10, Quiz B (Lesson 10-3)

Factor each trinomial, if possible. If the trinomial cannot be factored using integers, write prime.

1. $a^2 - 10a + 21$ 2. $x^2 + 9x + 20$

3. $x^2 + 9x + 27$ 4. $y^2 + 23y - 24$

5. $m^2 + 5mp - 6p^2$

1. _____

2. _____

3. _____

4. _____

5. _____

NAME_____ DATE_____

Chapter 10, Quiz C (Lessons 10-4 and 10-5)

Factor each polynomial, if possible. If the polynomial cannot be factored using integers, write prime.

1. $a^2 - 25$

2. $49x^2 - 64y^2$

3. $9x^2 - 1$

4. $0.04m^2 - 0.49n^4$

5. $2y^2 + 32$

6. $a^2 + 14a + 49$

7. $n^2 + 18n + 81$

8. $16x^2 - 40x + 25$

9. $6z^2 - 12z + 30$

10. $\frac{1}{4}b^2 + 4bc + 16c^2$

1. _____
2. _____
3. _____
4. _____
5. _____
6. _____
7. _____
8. _____
9. _____
10. _____

10

NAME_____ DATE_____

Chapter 10, Quiz D (Lesson 10-6)

Solve. Check each solution.

1. $(y + 4)(6y + 10) = 0$

2. $y^2 = -11y$

3. $3n^2 + 6 = 11n$

4. $(x - 3)(2x + 1) = 22$

5. The product of two consecutive odd integers is 195. Find the integers.

1. _____
2. _____
3. _____
4. _____
5. _____

Chapter 10 Standardized Test Practice

Choose the best answer. Write A, B, C, or D.

1. If $a^2 > c^2$, then
   A. $a > c$.   B. $a < c$.   C. $|a| > |c|$.   D. $a = c$.

   1. _____

2. If r and s are integers and rs is a negative integer, which of the following can be true?
   A. $r < 0$ and $s < 0$ B. $r < 0$ and $s \geq 0$
   C. $r > 0$ and $s > 0$ D. $r < 0$ and $s > 0$

   2. _____

3. If $m^2 + 2m - 8 = 0$, then $m - 2 =$
   A. -2 or 0.   B. -4 or 0.
   C. -6 or 0.   D. none of the above

   3. _____

4. Which fraction is greater than $\frac{1}{8}$ but less than $\frac{1}{5}$?
   A. $\frac{1}{4}$ B. $\frac{2}{11}$ C. $\frac{5}{13}$ D. $\frac{1}{3}$

   4. _____

5. Which group of numbers is arranged from least to greatest?
   A. $-8, -10, \frac{1}{3}, 0.6, 1$ B. $1, 0.6, \frac{1}{3}, -8, -10$
   C. $-10, -8, 0.6, \frac{1}{3}, 1$ D. $-10, -8, \frac{1}{3}, 0.6, 1$

   5. _____

6. If $2x - 2y = 10$, then
   A. $x > y$.   B. $y > x$.
   C. $x > y$ and $y \geq 0$.   D. $y > x$ and $y \geq 0$.

   6. _____

7. What is the total length of fencing needed to enclose a square region that measures 12 feet on a side?
   A. 4 yards   B. 8 yards   C. 12 yards   D. 16 yards

   7. _____

8. The discount price for a \$65 item is \$58.50. What is the discount price for a \$110 item if the rate of discount is $2\frac{1}{2}$ times the rate of discount for the \$65 item?
   A. \$16.25   B. \$25   C. \$27.50   D. \$82.50

   8. _____

9. If $\frac{x + y}{z} = xy + z$, then $x =$

   A. $\frac{z^2 + y}{1 - yz}$.   B. $\frac{z^2 - y}{1 - yz}$.   C. $\frac{z^2 + y}{1 + yz}$.   D. $\frac{z^2 - y}{1 + yz}$.

   9. _____

10. If $m + 8$ is an even integer, which of the following is not an even integer?
    A. $2m + 8$ B. $2m - 10$ C. $m + 10$ D. $m + 9$

    10. _____

1. Find $-\dfrac{3}{8} + \dfrac{5}{16}$. (Lesson 2-5)

    1. _____

2. Simplify $\dfrac{2}{3}(6a - 9b) - \dfrac{1}{2}(2a - 12b)$. (Lesson 2-6)

    2. _____

3. Solve $\dfrac{3y - 2}{5} = \dfrac{1}{10}y$. (Lesson 3-5)

    3. _____

4. Find two consecutive even integers whose sum is 74. (Lesson 3-3)

    4. _____

5. Two airplanes leave Atlanta at the same time and fly in opposite directions. One plane travels 60 mi/h faster than the other. After $2\dfrac{1}{2}$ hours they are 1700 miles apart. What is the rate of each plane? (Lesson 4-7)

    5. _____

Find the probability of each outcome if two marbles are selected from a bag containing 3 red marbles, 4 blue marbles, and 2 green marbles. The first marble is not replaced before the second marble is selected. (Lesson 4-6)

6. selecting a blue marble first

    6. _____

7. selecting a yellow marble first

    7. _____

8. selecting a red marble followed by a blue marble

    8. _____

9. selecting a green marble after selecting two marbles that are not green

    9. _____

10. Write an equation for the relationship between the variables in the chart at the right. (Lesson 5-6)

x	0	2	4	6
y	4	8	12	16

    10. _____

11. If $f(x) = 2x^2 - 5x + 4$, find $f(-3)$. (Lesson 5-5)

    11. _____

12. Graph $4x + 2y = 1$ using the slope and y-intercept. (Lesson 6-5)

    12.
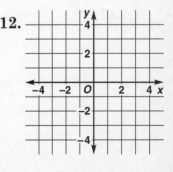

13. Write an equation in slope-intercept form of the line that is parallel to the graph of $2y - 6x = 3$ and passes through $(-3, 2)$. (Lesson 6-6)

13. _____

14. Solve $\frac{2}{3}x > -10$. (Lesson 7-2)

14. _____

15. Graph the inequality $x + 2y < 4$. (Lesson 7-8)

15.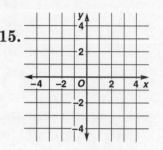

16. Solve the system of equations $3y - 2x = 4$ and $2y + 4x = 8$. (Lesson 8-4)

16. _____

17. Simplify $(-2x^2y^3)^4$. (Lesson 9-1)

17. _____

18. Evaluate $\frac{3.6 \times 10^{-4}}{1.2 \times 10^{-8}}$. Express the result in scientific notation. (Lesson 9-3)

18. _____

19. Simplify $5(2y^2 + 3y - 2) - 8(3y^2 + 4y - 2)$. (Lesson 9-5)

19. _____

20. Find $(a + 6)(a - 5)$. (Lesson 9-8)

20. _____

Factor each polynomial, if possible. (Lessons 10-2 and 10-3)

21. $m^2 + 12m + 36$

21. _____

22. $2ar + 2rt - a - t$

22. _____

23. $36c^3 + 6c^2 - 6c$

23. _____

24. Solve $x(x + 12) = 0$. (Lesson 10-6)

24. _____

25. Find two consecutive odd integers whose product is 255. (Lesson 10-6)

25. _____

Chapter 10 Answer Key

1. __C__

2. __B__

3. __B__

4. __A__

5. __C__

6. __A__

7. __A__

8. __C__

9. __B__

10. __B__

11. __C__

12. __D__

13. __D__

14. __C__

15. __A__

16. __C__

17. __A__

18. __B__

19. __A__

20. __C__

Bonus __4096__

1. __C__

2. __C__

3. __B__

4. __B__

5. __A__

6. __D__

7. __D__

8. __B__

9. __B__

10. __C__

11. __A__

12. __D__

13. __C__

14. __C__

15. __A__

16. __D__

17. __C__

18. __D__

19. __C__

20. __D__

Bonus $7 + 3 \cdot 5 - (6 - 2) \cdot 4 = 6$

Chapter 10 Answer Key

Form 2A

1. __C__	12. __C__	1. **composite;** $2 \cdot 3 \cdot 3 \cdot 5 \cdot 7$	14. $(3p - 4w)(p - 3w)$
2. __B__	13. __D__	2. **composite;** $2 \cdot 2 \cdot 2 \cdot 5 \cdot 29$	15. $n(n - 4)(n + 4)$
3. __B__	14. __B__		16. **prime**
4. __A__		3. __12__	17. $(5x + 2y)^2$
5. __A__	15. __C__	4. __37__	18. $4y^2$
6. __D__	16. __B__	5. $6n^3t$	19. $2, -2, 7, -7$
7. __B__	17. __C__	6. __1__	20. __16 ft__
8. __D__	18. __A__	7. $13x(1 - 6y^2)$	21. $(70 - 2)(70 + 2); 4896$
9. __A__	19. __B__	8. $(5a + 2n)(3y + 8)$	
10. __C__	20. __B__	9. $3x(a^2 - 5a + 1)$	22. $\frac{5}{3}, -\frac{9}{2}$
11. __B__		10. $(2n - 5)(n^2 - 7)$	23. __0, 6, 9__
	Bonus __64__	11. $3(x - 4y)^2$	24. **14 and 16 or −16 and −14**
		12. $(5x - 3)(2x + 7)$	25. $-4, -6, -8$
		13. $(a + n - 2)(a + n + 2)$	Bonus $(x^2 + y^2 - xy)(x^2 + y^2 + xy)$

Chapter 10 Answer Key

Form 2B

1. _____ prime _____

2. _____ composite; _____
   _____ $2 \cdot 2 \cdot 3 \cdot 11$ _____

3. _____ 5 _____

4. _____ 5 _____

5. _____ $4xy^2$ _____

6. _____ 1 _____

7. _____ $x(7 - 19y^2)$ _____

8. _____ $5s(s^2 + 9)$ _____

9. _____ $3(x^2 + 7x + 9)$ _____

10. _____ $(n + 2)(v - 2)(v + 2)$ _____

11. _____ $4(3m + 4)(3m - 4)$ _____

12. _____ $(u^2 + 1)(u + 4)(u - 4)$ _____

13. _____ $(n + 7w)(n - 6w)$ _____

14. _____ $(9 - y)(6 + y)$ _____

15. _____ prime _____

16. _____ $(5w - 6)^2$ _____

17. _____ $4y(2n - 5)(n - 2)$ _____

18. _____ $(y^2 + v^2)(y - v)(y + v)$ _____

19. _____ $x(6x - 7)^2$ _____

20. _____ 12 ft _____

21. _____ 25 _____

22. _____ $0, \dfrac{1}{2}$ _____

23. _____ $\dfrac{2}{3}$ _____

24. _____ 7 and 18 _____

25. _____ 17 ft by 14 ft _____

Bonus _____ $(x + n)(x - n)$ _____
   _____ $(v + 3)(v - 3)$ _____

Chapter 10 Answer Key

Page 263   **Page 264**   **Page 265**

1. composite; $3 \cdot 13$

2. prime

3. 4

4. 126

5. $3xy^3$

6. 1

7. $x(5 - 11y^2)$

8. $8rs(s + 2)$

9. $3x(x^2 + 9)$

10. $(a^2 + 7)(a - 4)$

11. $(x + 5)(x - 5)$

12. $(n - 9)(n + 2)$

13. $(5t - 3)(t + 4)$

14. $2(x - 4)^2$

15. $(y^2 + 4)(y + 2)(y - 2)$

16. prime

17. $5n(n^2 - n + 3)$

18. $(2c + d)^2$

19. $4(p - 3)(p - 4)$

20. $(cd + 3)(cd - 3)$

21. 49

22. $5, \dfrac{1}{2}$

23. $-9, 5$

24. $0, -2, 5$

25. 9 ft by 10 ft

Bonus $\dfrac{(x - 3)}{(x + 3)(y - 2)}(y + 2)$

1. $2^2 \cdot 5 \cdot 197$

2. $2 \cdot 3^2 \cdot 5 \cdot 11 \cdot 13$

3. 5

4. 44

5. 27

6. 324

7. $33x^3y^4$

8. 1

9. yes

10. yes

11. yes

12. no; $(3x - 1)(4x + 3)$

13. 114, 3248, 3250

14. 4.66 and 6.66

15. 97 and 99 or -97 and -99

16. about 9.46 ft

Scoring Guide
Chapter 10
Performance Assessment

Level	Specific Criteria
3 Superior	• Shows thorough understanding of the concepts of *prime factorization of integers, factorization of polynomials, evaluating polynomials,* and *the guess-and-check strategy for problem solving.* • Computations are correct. • Written explanations are exemplary. • Goes beyond requirements of some or all problems.
2 Satisfactory, with Minor Flaws	• Shows understanding of the concepts of *prime factorization of integers, factorization of polynomials, evaluating polynomials,* and *the guess-and-check strategy for problem solving.* • Computations are mostly correct. • Written explanations are effective. • Satisfies all requirements of problems.
1 Nearly Satisfactory, with Serious Flaws	• Shows understanding of most of the concepts of *prime factorization of integers, factorization of polynomials, evaluating polynomials,* and *the guess-and-check strategy for problem solving.* • Computations are mostly correct. • Written explanations are satisfactory. • Satisfies most requirements of problems.
0 Unsatisfactory	• Shows little or no understanding of the concepts of *prime factorization of integers, factorization of polynomials, evaluating polynomials,* and *the guess-and-check strategy for problem solving.* • Computations are incorrect. • Written explanations are not satisfactory. • Does not satisfy requirements of problems.

Chapter 10 Answer Key
Performance Assessment

1. a. $x^2 - 8x + 15 = 10^2 - 8(10) + 15$
$$= 100 - 80 + 15$$
$$= 35$$

$35 = 7 \cdot 5$
If $x = 10$, then $7 = (x - 3)$ and $5 = (x - 5)$.
So, $(x - 3)(x - 5) = x^2 - 8x + 15$.

b. $2x^2 - 13x - 24 = 2(10^2) - 13(10) - 24$
$$= 200 - 130 - 24$$
$$= 46$$

$46 = 2 \cdot 23$
If $x = 10$, then $2 = x - 8$ and $23 = 2x + 3$.
Thus, $(x - 8)(2x + 3) = 2x^2 - 13x - 24$.

c. $x^2 - 2x - 8 = 10^2 - 2(10) - 8$
$$= 100 - 20 - 8$$
$$= 72$$

$72 = 36(2)$ or $4(18)$ or $8(9)$ or $24(3)$ or $1(72)$ or $6(12)$

Since the coefficient of x is 1, you can eliminate any factors greater than $1x \pm n$. That leaves $4(18)$, $8(9)$, and $6(12)$. Now try each pair of factors to find the ones that will result in the desired last term.

$4(18) \rightarrow (x - 6)(x + 8)$; last term is -48.
$8(9) \rightarrow (x - 2)(x - 1)$; last term is 2.
$6(12) \rightarrow (x - 4)(x + 2)$; last term is -8.
Thus, $(x - 4)(x + 2) = x^2 - 2x - 8$.

d. $x^2 - 2x - 8 = 7^2 - 2(7) - 8$
$$= 49 - 14 - 8$$
$$= 27$$

$27 = 3 \cdot 9$
For $x = 7$, $3 = x - 4$ and $9 = x + 2$.
Thus, $(x - 4)(x + 2) = x^2 - 2x - 8$.

2. a. Group the terms by twos and factor out the greatest common factor of each group. Factor out the common binomial factor.

b. $(10ax - 5ay) + (2bx - by) = 5a(2x - y) + b(2x - y)$
$$= (2x - y)(5a + b)$$

c. method 1:
$(6x^3 + 3x^2y) + (-2xy - y^2) = 3x^2(2x + y) - y(2x + y)$
$$= (2x + y)(3x^2 - y)$$

method 2:
$(6x^3 - 2xy) + (3x^2y - y^2) = 2x(3x^2 - y) + y(3x^2 - y)$
$$= (3x^2 - y)(2x + y)$$

Chapter 10 Answer Key

Mid-Chapter Test
Page 267

1. 6
2. 4

3. $16xy$
4. $6m^2$

5. $2y(1 + 3x)$
6. $8a(x - 7)$

7. $12xy(3y - 4x)$
8. $15bc^3(5b + 4c^3)$

9. $4x(x^2 - 3x + 6)$
10. $8a^2b(8 - 2ab + b)$

11. $(2a + 1)(3b + 2)$

12. $(3m - 2)(2n - 3)$

13. $(2xy - 1)(x + 3)$

14. $(3xy + 4)(2y - 1)$

15. prime

16. $(12 - e)(4 - e)$

17. $(w - 18)(w + 2)$

18. $2(b + 8)(b - 1)$

19. $6(a + 3b)(a - b)$

20. $10a + 6$

Bonus $4a(3a + 17)$ $(a - 6)$

Quiz A
Page 268

1. composite; $3 \cdot 19$
2. composite; $5 \cdot 5 \cdot 7$

3. 6

4. 9

5. $4xy$

6. $12ab^2$

7. $12ab(4ab - 1)$

8. $3(2x^2y - 7y^2w + 8xw)$

9. $(x + 5)(y - 2z)$

10. $(a + b)(a + 6)$

Quiz B
Page 268

1. $(a - 7)(a - 3)$

2. $(x + 5)(x + 4)$

3. prime

4. $(y + 24)(y - 1)$

5. $(m + 6p)(m - p)$

Quiz C
Page 269

1. $(a - 5)(a + 5)$
2. $(7x - 8y)(7x + 8y)$
3. $(3x - 1)(3x + 1)$
4. prime
5. $2(y^2 + 16)$
6. $(a + 7)^2$
7. $(n + 9)^2$
8. $(4x - 5)^2$
9. $6(z^2 - 2z + 5)$
10. prime

Quiz D
Page 269

1. $-4, -\dfrac{5}{3}$

2. $0, -11$

3. $\dfrac{2}{3}, 3$

4. $5, -\dfrac{5}{2}$

5. -15 and -13 or 13 and 15

Algebra 1

Chapter 10 Answer Key

Standardized Test Practice
Page 270

1. __C__

2. __D__

3. __C__

4. __B__

5. __D__

6. __A__

7. __D__

8. __D__

9. __B__

10. __D__

Cumulative Review
Page 271

1. $-\dfrac{1}{16}$

2. $3a$

3. $\dfrac{4}{5}$

4. $3\ 6\text{ and }38$

5. 310 mi/h; 370 mi/h

6. $\dfrac{4}{9}$

7. 0

8. $\dfrac{1}{6}$

9. $\dfrac{1}{6}$

10. $y = 2x + 4$

11. 37

12.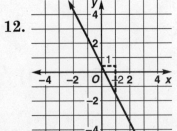

Page 272

13. $y = 3x + 11$

14. $x > -15$

15.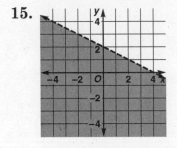

16. $(1, 2)$

17. $16x^8y^{12}$

18. 3×10^4

19. $-14y^2 - 17y + 6$

20. $a^2 + a - 30$

21. $(m + 6)^2$

22. $(2r - 1)(a + z)$

23. $6c(3c - 1)(2c + 1)$

24. $0, -12$

25. 15 and 17 or -17 and -15

Write the letter for the correct answer in the blank at the right of each problem.

1. What are the equation of the axis of symmetry and the coordinates   1. _____
   of the vertex of the graph of $y = 2x^2 - 12x + 6$?
   A. $x = -3; (-3, 60)$ **B.** $x = 3; (3, -12)$
   C. $x = -3; (-3, 78)$ **D.** $x = 3; (3, 6)$

2. Find the equation of the axis of symmetry for the graph of   2. _____
   $y = -4x^2 + 5x + 1$, and state whether this axis contains the
   maximum point or the minimum point of the graph.
   A. $x = -\frac{5}{8}$; maximum   **B.** $x = -\frac{5}{8}$; minimum
   C. $x = \frac{5}{8}$; maximum   **D.** $x = \frac{5}{8}$; minimum

3. What are the coordinates of the vertex of the graph of   3. _____
   $y = -2x^2 - 8$?
   A. $(-2, -16)$ **B.** $(-2, 8)$ **C.** $(2, -16)$ **D.** $(0, -8)$

4. Which of the following equations   4. _____
   describes the graph at the right?
   A. $y - 2 = \frac{1}{2}(x + 1)^2$ **B.** $y + 2 = \frac{1}{2}(x + 1)^2$
   C. $y = x^2 + 4x + 9$ **D.** $y = x^2 - 9x + 4$

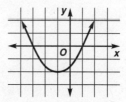

5. If a quadratic equation has exactly one real root, then its graph   5. _____
   intersects the x-axis at how many points?
   A. two   **B.** one   **C.** none   **D.** It varies.

6. If the roots of $x^2 + 4x + 1 = 0$ are located by graphing the related   6. _____
   function, between which pair of integers does a root of the equation lie?
   A. -4 and -3 **B.** -2 and -1 **C.** 0 and 1   **D.** 2 and 3

7. What must be the value of c in the function $y = x^2 - 5x + c$ 7. _____
   if its graph has a minimum point of $\left(\frac{5}{2}, 0\right)$?

   A. $-\frac{5}{2}$ **B.** $\frac{25}{4}$ **C.** $\frac{25}{2}$ **D.** -5

8. How many real roots does $x^2 - x + 2 = 0$ have?   8. _____
   A. 0   **B.** 1   **C.** 2   **D.** cannot be
                                                             determined

9. Solve $3x^2 + 4x - 1 = 0$.   9. _____
   A. $\frac{-2 \pm 2\sqrt{7}}{3}$ **B.** $\frac{-4 \pm \sqrt{7}}{6}$ **C.** $-1, \frac{1}{3}$ **D.** $\frac{-2 \pm \sqrt{7}}{3}$

10. Solve $2y^2 - 5 = 1$.   10. _____
    A. $\pm \sqrt{3}$ **B.** $\frac{5 \pm \sqrt{17}}{4}$ **C.** $\frac{5 \pm \sqrt{33}}{4}$ **D.** 9

11. Solve $x^2 + 5x - 6 = 0$.   11. _____
    A. $6, -1$ **B.** $-6, 1$ **C.** $-3, -2$ **D.** 3, 2

12. The perimeter of a rectangle is 49 cm. Its area is 117 cm². If
    x represents the width of the rectangle in centimeters, which
    equation must be true?

    A. $x(49 - x) = 117$ **B.** $x(x - 49) = 117$

    C. $x\left(\dfrac{49}{2} - x\right) = 117$ **D.** $x\left(x - \dfrac{49}{2}\right) = 117$

    12. _____

13. Which of the following is the graph of $y = \dfrac{1}{4} \cdot 4^x$?

    A.   **B.**   **C.**   **D.** none of them

    13. _____

14. Which table of values displays exponential behavior?

    A.
x	0	1	2	3
y	1	$\frac{3}{2}$	$\frac{9}{4}$	$\frac{27}{8}$

    B.
x	0	1	2	3
y	0	1	4	9

    C.
x	0	1	2	3
y	0	1	$\frac{1}{2}$	$\frac{1}{3}$

    D. none of them

    14. _____

15. Solve $16^x = 4^{x^2 - 15}$.

    A. $\{6, -2.5\}$ **B.** $\{-6, 2.5)$ **C.** $\{-5, -3\}$ **D.** $\{-3, 5\}$

    15. _____

16. A certain fast-growing bacteria can reproduce in 12 minutes.
    If you begin with 100 bacteria, how many will there be
    36 minutes later?

    A. 36,000   **B.** approximately 800

    C. approximately 300   **D.** 3,200,000

    16. _____

17. First City Bank's "Perfect Ten" account pays 10% annual interest
    compounded monthly for a 10-month period. How much
    will a $50,000 investment be worth at the end of the 10 months?

    A. $55,000   **B.** $129,687.12

    C. $54,326.44   **D.** $156,921.42

    17. _____

18. An $18,000 car depreciates in value at the rate of 12% per year.
    After how many years will the car be worth less than $10,000?

    A. 5   **B.** 8   **C.** 4   **D.** 3

    18. _____

19. If $10,000 is invested for 3 years at 7.5% per year, how much
    more will it be worth if interest is compounded daily rather
    than quarterly?

    A. $99.97   **B.** $11,394.83   **C.** $25.78   **D.** $1718.40

    19. _____

20. In 1980, a city's population was about 954,000. Since then,
    the population has been declining at the rate of 0.1% per year.
    What will the population of the city be in 2030 if it continues to
    decrease at the same rate?

    A. about 577,000   **B.** about 1,003,200

    C. about 1,569,000   **D.** about 907,000

    20. _____

Bonus Solve the equation $x + 5 + \dfrac{4}{x} = 0$.

Bonus _____

NAME_____ DATE _____

Chapter 11 Test, Form 1B

11

Write the letter for the correct answer in the blank at the right of each problem.

1. What are the equation of the axis of symmetry and the coordinates of the vertex of the graph of $y = -x^2 - 10x + 17$?
   A. $x = -5; (-5, -8)$ B. $x = -5; (-5, 42)$
   C. $x = 5; (5, 92)$ D. $x = 5; (5, 32)$

   1. _____

2. Find the equation of the axis of symmetry for the graph of $y = -2x^2 + x + 17$, and state whether the axis of symmetry contains the minimum or maximum point of the graph.
   A. $x = \frac{1}{4}$; maximum B. $x = -\frac{1}{4}$; maximum
   C. $x = \frac{1}{4}$; minimum D. $x = -\frac{1}{4}$; minimum

   2. _____

3. The equation of the axis of symmetry of a parabola is $x = -1$. If the point $(0, 1)$ is on the parabola, which of the following points is also on the parabola?
   A. $(-1, 0)$ B. $(0, -2)$ C. $(-2, 1)$ D. $(-1, -2)$

   3. _____

4. Which of the following equations describes the graph at the right?
   A. $y = x^2 - 1$ B. $y = x^2 + 1$
   C. $y = -x^2 - 1$ D. $y = x^2$

   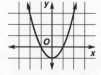

   4. _____

5. If a quadratic equation has no real roots, then its graph intersects the x-axis at how many points?
   A. two B. one C. none D. It varies.

   5. _____

6. If the roots of $x^2 - 3x - 3 = 0$ are located by graphing the related function, between which pair of integers does a root of the equation lie?
   A. -1 and 0 B. 1 and 2 C. 2 and 3 D. -2 and -1

   6. _____

7. What must be the value of c in the function $y = x^2 + 3x + c$ if its graph has a minimum point at $\left(-\frac{3}{2}, 0\right)$?
   A. $-\frac{3}{2}$ B. $-\frac{9}{4}$ C. $\frac{9}{4}$ D. $\frac{3}{2}$

   7. _____

8. How many real roots does $x^2 - 2x - 3 = 0$ have?
   A. 0 B. 1 C. 2 D. cannot be determined

   8. _____

9. Solve $9x^2 + 16 = 24x$.
   A. 24 B. 0 C. $\frac{4}{3}$ D. $\frac{-8 \pm 2\sqrt{70}}{9}$

   9. _____

10. Solve $3x^2 + 5x - 16 = 0$.
    A. $\frac{-3 \pm 6\sqrt{3}}{5}$ B. $\frac{-5 \pm 6\sqrt{3}}{5}$ C. $\frac{-5 \pm \sqrt{167}}{6}$ D. $\frac{-5 \pm \sqrt{217}}{6}$

    10. _____

11. Solve $d^2 - 6d + 4 = 0$.
    A. $3 \pm \sqrt{5}$ B. $6 \pm 2\sqrt{5}$ C. $\frac{-6 \pm \sqrt{5}}{2}$ D. $\frac{3 \pm 2\sqrt{5}}{2}$

    11. _____

12. If $3x^2 - \frac{2}{3}x = \frac{1}{2}$ is to be solved using the quadratic formula, which of these would be best to do first?   12._____

   A. Add $\frac{1}{9}$ to each side.   **B.** Divide each side by 3.

   C. Multiply each side by 3.   **D.** Multiply each side by 6.

13. Use a calculator to determine the value of $0.5(2.5^{-2.5})$ to the nearest hundredth.   13._____

   A. 0.10   **B.** -3.13 **C.** 0.05   **D.** 0.57

14. Which of the following is the graph of $y = 3^x + 1$?   14._____

   A.   **B.**   **C.** 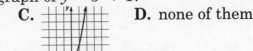   **D.** none of them

15. Which table of values displays exponential behavior?   15._____

   A.

x	0	1	2	3
y	0	1	32	243

   B.

x	0	1	2	3
y	1	5	25	125

   C.

x	0	1	2	3
y	0	5	10	15

   D. none of them

16. Solve $4^x = 2^{3x-6}$.   16._____

   A. $1\frac{1}{5}$ **B.** -6 **C.** 3   **D.** 6

17. If \$1000 is invested at an annual interest rate of 6% compounded monthly, which equation can you solve to find the value of the investment at the end of 2 years?   17._____

   A. $A = 1000(1.005)^{24}$ **B.** $A = 1000(1.06)^2$

   C. $A = 1000(1.005)^2$ **D.** $A = 1000(1.06)^{12}$

18. Suppose a printing press valued at \$100,000 depreciates 10% per year. After how many years will the value of the printing press be less than \$50,000?   18._____

   A. 5   **B.** 2   **C.** 7   **D.** 20

19. In 1995, the annual rate of inflation for consumer goods was about 2.5%. Suppose the inflation rate remains constant until the year 2000. What would a bag of groceries that cost \$25 in 1995 cost in 2000?   19._____

   A. \$28.29   **B.** \$37.50   **C.** \$76.29   **D.** \$67.50

20. In 1980, the population of Honolulu, Hawaii, was about 763,000. Since then, the population has been increasing at an average rate of 1.5% per year. What will be the population of Honolulu in 2030 if it continues to increase at the same rate?   20._____

   A. about 1,335,000   **B.** about 826,831,000

   C. about 358,000   **D.** about 1,606,000

Bonus Solve $x + 7 + \frac{3}{x} = 0$.   Bonus _____

1. What is an equation of the axis of symmetry of the graph of
   $y = 3x^2 + 18x - 7$?
   A. $x = 6$ **B.** $x = -3$ **C.** $x = 3$ **D.** $y = -3$

   1. _____

2. What are the coordinates of the vertex of the graph of
   $y = x^2 - 8x + 10$?
   A. $(4, -6)$ **B.** $(-4, -6)$ **C.** $(4, -16)$ **D.** $(-4, 26)$

   2. _____

3. Which of the following equations
   describes the graph at the right?
   A. $y = x^2 - 9$ **B.** $y = -x^2 - 4x - 5$
   C. $y = x^2 - 4x - 5$ **D.** none of them

   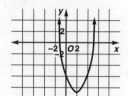

   3. _____

4. What are the coordinates of the vertex of the graph of $y = 16 - 4x^2$?
   State whether the vertex is a maximum or a minimum.
   A. $(2, 0)$; maximum   **B.** $(0, 16)$; minimum
   C. $(0, 16)$; maximum   **D.** $(2, 0)$; minimum

   4. _____

5. What equation would you use to graph $2x^2 + 3 = 7 - 5x$?
   A. $2x^2 + 3 = 0$ **B.** $0 = -2x^2 - 5x + 4$
   C. $y = 2x^2 + 3$ **D.** $y = 2x^2 + 5x - 4$

   5. _____

6. Estimate the roots of $x^2 - 2x - 5 = 0$ by graphing the related function.
   A. about 3.5 and about -1.5 **B.** $(1, -6)$
   C. about 3.5 and about -2.5 **D.** $(0, -5)$

   6. _____

7. What must be the value of c in the function $y = -x^2 + 4x + c$
   if its graph has a maximum point at $(2, 0)$?
   A. 4   **B.** 16   **C.** -2 **D.** -4

   7. _____

8. How many real roots does $n^2 - 5n - 6 = 0$ have?
   A. 0   **B.** 1   **C.** 2   **D.** cannot be
                                                             determined

   8. _____

9. What are the values of the coefficients a, b, and c in the
   equation $2x^2 + 5x = 14$?
   A. 2, 5, -14 **B.** 2, 5, 14   **C.** 2, 5, 0   **D.** $-2, -5, -14$

   9. _____

10. If $b^2 - 4ac = 0$, how many roots does the quadratic equation
    $ax^2 + bx + c = 0$ have?
    A. none   **B.** two   **C.** one   **D.** cannot be
                                                                     determined

    10. _____

11. What are the roots of $x^2 + 2x + 3 = 0$?
    A. 3 and -1 **B.** -3 and 1   **C.** -5 and 3   **D.** no real roots

    11. _____

12. Solve $2x^2 + 3x - 5 = 0$.

    A. $\varnothing$ **B.** $-2\frac{1}{2}, 1$ **C.** $-5, 1$ **D.** $2\frac{1}{2}, -1$

12. _____

13. What must be true if $y = a^x$ is an equation for an exponential function?

    A. $a > x$ **B.** $a > 0$ and $a \neq 1$
    C. $a > 1$ **D.** $x > 0$ and $x \neq 1$

13. _____

14. Which point is on the graph of $y = 2.5^x$?

    A. $(2, 6.25)$ **B.** $(0, 0)$ **C.** $(-2, -6.25)$ **D.** $(-1, -2.5)$

14. _____

15. Which table of values displays exponential behavior?

    A.

x	0	1	2	3
y	0	2	4	6

    B.

x	0	1	2	3
y	0	1	16	81

    C.

x	0	1	2	3
y	1	10	100	1,000

    D. none of them

15. _____

16. Which of the following is the graph of $y = 2^x - 2$?

    A.   **B.**   **C.**   **D.** none of them

16. _____

17. If the annual interest rate is 6% and interest is compounded monthly, what is the value of $\frac{r}{n}$ in the formula $A = P\left(1 + \frac{r}{n}\right)^{nt}$?

    A. 0.05   **B.** 0.5   **C.** 0.005   **D.** 5

17. _____

18. Suppose \$500 is invested at an annual interest rate of 8% compounded quarterly for 2 years. What is the final amount at the end of 2 years?

    A. \$583.20   **B.** \$585.83   **C.** \$541.22   **D.** \$520.20

18. _____

19. Which equation represents exponential decay?

    A. $y = 0.5(1.2)^x$ **B.** $y = 10(1.1)^x$
    C. $y = 100(0.95)^x$ **D.** $y = 0.1(1.02)^x$

19. _____

20. If $y = 10(2.5)^t$ represents the growth of bacteria, how many will there be at time $t = 6$?

    A. 2441   **B.** 244   **C.** 24   **D.** none

20. _____

Bonus Solve the equation $2^{x+1} = 4^{x-2}$.

Bonus _____

1. Find the equation of the axis of symmetry and the coordinates of the vertex of the graph of $y = -2x^2 - 8x - 5$.

1. _____

2. Find the equation of the axis of symmetry for the graph of $y = x^2 - 3x + 2$, and state whether the axis of symmetry contains a maximum point or a minimum point of the graph.

2. _____

3. Find the coordinates of the vertex of the graph of $y = -x^2 + 2$.

3. _____

4. The number of lines L that can be drawn between n points, if no three points are on the same line, is given by the formula $L = 0.5n^2 - 0.5n$. Graph the equation and tell how many points there must be if 66 lines can be drawn.

4. _____

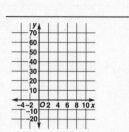

Solve each equation by graphing. If exact roots cannot be found, state the consecutive integers between which the roots lie.

5. $x^2 - 6x + 7 = 0$

5. _____

6. $x^2 + 2x + 3 = 0$

6. _____

7. Find a value of k for which the equation $x^2 + 5x = k$ will have one distinct root.

7. _____

8. Find two real numbers that have a difference of 2 and a product of 15.

8. _____

Solve using the quadratic formula.

9. $n^2 - 2n = 24$

9. _____

10. $3y^2 - 7y - 5 = 0$

10. _____

11. $2x^2 - 6x + 1 = 0$

11. _____

12. What is the value of $b^2 - 4ac$ for the equation $6x^2 - 5x - 4 = 0$? Tell whether the roots of the equation will be rational or irrational.

12. _____

13. Give the value of $4(0.2^{-3.1})$ to the nearest hundredth.

13. _____

14. Graph $y = 0.1(5)^x$.

14.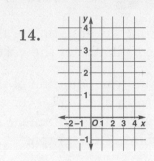

15. Determine if the data in the table below display exponential behavior. Write *yes* or *no*.

x	0	1	2	3	4	5	6
y	10	20	40	80	160	320	640

15. _____

16. Solve $27^{5x} = 3^{x^2}$.

16. _____

17. Compare the following investments.
$5000 for 10 years with an annual interest rate of 5% compounded monthly.
$5000 for 10 years with an annual interest rate of 6% compounded quarterly.
Which investment results in the greater final amount? How much greater?

17. _____

18. A $20,500 car depreciates in value at the rate of 15% per year. When will the car be worth less than $10,000?

18. _____

19. The population of Old Town is currently 275,000 and is declining at an annual rate of 1%. The population of New Town is 150,000 and is increasing at an annual rate of 2%. If the rates of decrease and increase remain constant, after how many years will the population of the two towns be about equal?

19. _____

20. One pension of $96,000 will increase at the annual rate of 2.8%. Another pension of the same amount will increase by $3000 per year. Which pension will be greater after 5 years?

20. _____

Bonus Graph the solution set of $y \geq x^2 - 2x - 3$.

Bonus

11

Chapter 11 Test, Form 2B

1. Find the equation of the axis of symmetry and the coordinates of the vertex of the graph of $y = -2x^2 + 4x - 5$.

1. _____

2. Find the equation of the axis of symmetry for the graph of $y = x^2 - 7x + 12$, and state whether the axis of symmetry contains a maximum point or a minimum point of the graph.

2. _____

3. Find the coordinates of the vertex of the graph of $y = 6x^2 - 14x$.

3. _____

4. The equation of the axis of symmetry of a parabola is $x = 3$. The point $(10, 0)$ is on the parabola. Name another point that is also on the parabola.

4. _____

5. For the graph shown, is the value of the coefficient of x^2 in the related quadratic equation positive or negative? How many real roots does the equation have?

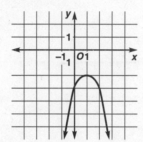

5. _____

6. _____

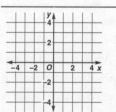

Solve each equation by graphing. If exact roots cannot be found, state the consecutive integers between which the roots lie.

6. $x^2 - 6x + 4 = 0$ 7. $x^2 - 4x + 5 = 0$

7. _____

8. $x^2 - 6x + 9 = 0$

8. _____

9. Suppose that the roots of a quadratic equation are given by $x = \dfrac{-5 \pm \sqrt{105}}{4}$. Approximate the roots of the equation to the nearest hundredth.

9. _____

Solve using the quadratic formula.

10. $y^2 - 9y + 8 = 0$ 10. _____

11. $3b^2 + 2b - 3 = 0$ 11. _____

12. $3x^2 = 10x$ 12. _____

13. Use a calculator to determine the value of $10(0.4^{-1.5})$ 13. _____
to the nearest hundredth.

14. What is the y-intercept of the graph of $y = 2.5 \cdot 10^x$?   14. _____

15. Graph $y = 0.4^x - 1$.   15.

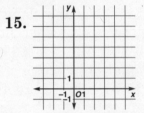

16. Solve $3^{2x + 5} = 9^{2x - 5}$.   16. _____

17. Suppose $500 is invested at an annual interest rate   17. _____
of 8% compounded semiannually. Write an equation
for finding the value of the investment at the end of
3 years.

18. A new car costing $16,500 depreciates 12% per year.   18. _____
What will be the value of the car after 10 years?

19. An oil painting that originally cost $2500 increases in   19. _____
value at an annual rate of 2%. What is the value of the
painting after 10 years?

20. In 1980, the population of Rochester, New York, was   20. _____
about 1,030,000. Since then, the population has been
increasing at an average rate of 0.25% per year. At this
rate of increase, what would be the approximate population
of Rochester in 2030?

Bonus Graph the solution set of $y \geq x^2 + 6x + 9$.   **Bonus**

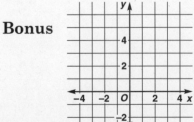

NAME_____ DATE _____

Chapter 11 Test, Form 2C

1. Find an equation of the axis of symmetry of the graph of $y = -4x^2 + 4x + 5$.

1. _____

2. Find the coordinates of the vertex of the graph of $y = 2x^2 - 10x - 3$, and state whether the vertex is a maximum or a minimum.

2. _____

Graph each equation.

3. $y = -x^2 + 3x + 10$

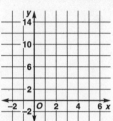

4. $y = \frac{1}{2}x^2 - 3x$

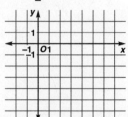

3. _____

4. _____

5. What is the related function you would use to solve $5x + 3 = 2x^2 - 5x$ by graphing?

5. _____

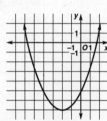

6. Estimate the roots of the equation whose related function is graphed at right.

6. _____

Solve each equation by graphing. If exact roots cannot be found, state the consecutive integers between which the roots lie.

7. $0.5x^2 - 2x + 1 = 0$

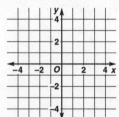

8. $-x^2 - 4x - 8 = 0$

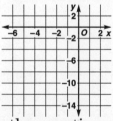

7. _____

8. _____

9. Give the values of a, b, and c in the equation $3x = 5 - 0.5x^2$.

9. _____

10. If $b^2 - 4ac < 0$, tell how many roots the quadratic equation $ax^2 + bx + c = 0$ has.

10. _____

Use the quadratic formula to solve each equation.

11. $3x^2 - 10x + 5 = 0$

11. _____

12. $-x^2 + 8x + 3 = 0$

12. _____

13. Solve $7^5 = 7^{2y+1}$.

13. _____

14. Determine if the data in the table display exponential behavior.

x	1	2	3	4	5	6
y	1	$\frac{1}{4}$	$\frac{1}{9}$	$\frac{1}{16}$	$\frac{1}{25}$	$\frac{1}{36}$

14. _____

Algebra 1

Graph each function and state the y-intercept.

15. $y = 3 \cdot 2^x$

15. _____

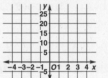

16. $y = (0.6)^x$

16. _____

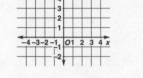

17. Suppose the annual interest rate is 7.5% and interest is compounded semiannually. Write an equation to find the total amount after 3 years on a $1000 investment.

17. _____

Determine the final amount for each investment.

18. $5000 invested for 5 years at an annual rate of 6% compounded quarterly

18. _____

19. $10,000 invested for 3 years at an annual rate of 7% compounded quarterly

19. _____

20. The population of Newburg was about 150,000 in 1990. If the population is decreasing at a rate of 0.3% per year, what will the population be in 2030?

20. _____

Bonus Solve the equation $5^{3x} = 5^{x^2 + 2}$.

Bonus _____

11

Chapter 11 Calculator-Based Test

Graph each equation. Make a sketch of the graph.

1. $y - 5 = 7x^2 - 22x + 5$

        1.

2. $y = 0.65x^2 + 10.13x - 41.25$

        2.

Solve each equation. Round answers to the nearest hundredth.

3. $5x^2 + 2x - 13 = 0$

        3. _____

4. $4x^2 - 5x = 17$

        4. _____

5. $0.8x^2 - 15 = 0$

        5. _____

6. $-x^2 + 22 = 18x$

        6. _____

Use the program ROOTS from your textbook to solve each equation. Round to the nearest thousandth.

7. $x^2 + 4x - 3 = 0$

        7. _____

8. $2x^2 + 98 = 28x$

        8. _____

9. $5x^2 - 11x + 9 = 0$

        9. _____

10. $3x^2 + 8x - 5 = 0$

        10. _____

Determine the value of each expression to the nearest hundredth.

11. $3^{2.1}$

        11. _____

12. $4.6^{1.6}$

        12. _____

13. $4^{-0.5}$

        13. _____

14. $20(0.75)^{-0.75}$

        14. _____

15. An investor deposits $2500 in a savings account that pays 6% interest compounded monthly. If the investor does not make any deposits or withdrawals, how much will be in the account after 3 years?

        15. _____

16. One hundred twenty grams of a radioactive substance decays at the rate of 15% per year. When would the remaining amount be less than half of the original amount?

        16. _____

11

Chapter 11 Performance Assessment

Instructions: *Demonstrate your knowledge by giving a clear, concise solution to each problem. Be sure to include all relevant drawings and justify your answers. You may show your solution in more than one way or investigate beyond the requirements of the problem.*

1. **a.** Write the equation of a quadratic function.

   b. Determine what the axis of symmetry and the maximum or minimum point of the graph of the equation would be without graphing the equation.

   c. Graph the function.

   d. Tell how the graph indicates the nature of the function's roots.

2. **a.** Write a word problem involving finding two real numbers that could be solved with the equation $x(9 - x) = 14$.

   b. Show how to solve the equation in part a by graphing.

3. Describe two real-life situations that could be represented by the graph shown below.

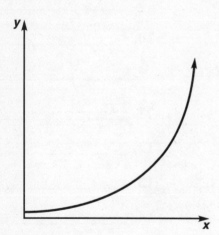

NAME_____ DATE _____

Chapter 11 Mid-Chapter Test (Lessons 11-1 through 11-3)

Write the equation of the axis of symmetry and find the coordinates of the vertex of the graph of each equation. State whether the vertex is a maximum or a minimum.

1. $y = x^2 - 2x - 8$

2. $y = x^2 - 3x + 2$

3. $y = -2x^2 + 4x + 3$

4. $y = x^2 + 5x + 4$

5. $y = 12 - 3x^2$

6. $y = x^2 + 6x + 5$

1. _____

2. _____

3. _____

4. _____

5. _____

6. _____

Graph each equation.

7. $y = x^2 - x - 6$

8. $y = -x^2 + 2x + 8$

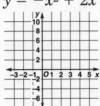

7. _____

8. _____

Solve each equation by graphing. If exact roots cannot be found, give the consecutive integers between which the roots lie.

9. $x^2 + 4x - 21 = 0$

10. $-x^2 - 6x - 9 = 0$

9. _____

10. _____

11. $x^2 - 4x + 1 = 0$

12. $-x^2 - 9 = 0$

11. _____

12. _____

State the values of a, b, and c for each quadratic equation. Then solve the equation. Approximate irrational roots to the nearest hundredth.

13. $x^2 - 5x + 1 = 0$

14. $-2x^2 + 18 = 7x$

15. $\frac{1}{2}x^2 + 2x = -10$

16. $-x^2 + x + 6 = 0$

13. _____

14. _____

15. _____

16. _____

Bonus The length and width of a rectangle that measures 6 in. by 8 in. are both increased by the same amount. The area of the new rectangle is twice the area of the original rectangle. How much was added to the dimensions of the original rectangle? Express your answer to the nearest hundredth of an inch.

Bonus _____

Chapter 11, Quiz A (Lessons 11-1 and 11-2)

In problems 1–4, use the quadratic function described by the equation $y = 2x^2 - 8x + 9$.

1. Find the equation of the axis of symmetry of the graph of the function.

    1._____

2. Find the coordinates of the vertex of the graph.

    2._____

3. Graph the function.

    3.

4. Find the roots of the equation $2x^2 - 8x + 9 = 0$ from the graph of $y = 2x^2 - 8x + 9$.

5. A ferry boat transports 600 people to an island each day for a fare of $16 per person. The owner wants to increase the price. She estimates that for each $1 increase in fare, 25 fewer people will use the ferry. What fare will maximize her income?

    4._____

    5._____

Chapter 11, Quiz B (Lesson 11-3)

Use the quadratic formula to solve each equation. Approximate irrational roots to the nearest hundredth.

1. $x^2 + 7x + 4 = 0$ 2. $m^2 - 8m + 6 = 0$

3. $4n^2 - 3n - 7 = 0$ 4. $2y^2 + 3 = -13y$

State the value of $b^2 - 4ac$ for each equation. Then determine the number and nature of the roots of each equation.

5. $x^2 - 7x - 5 = 0$ 6. $3y^2 - y + 14 = 0$

7. $12x^2 + 5x - 3 = 0$ 8. $4n^2 + 9 = 12n$

9. Can a rectangle with a perimeter of 36 meters have an area of 120 square meters?

10. Catalina is tossing pebbles into a lake. She tosses one pebble with an initial upward velocity v of 6 meters per second releasing it at an initial height h of 1 meter above the water level. In how many seconds will the pebble land in the lake? Use the formula $H = -4.9t^2 + vt + h$.

1._____

2._____

3._____

4._____

5._____

6._____

7._____

8._____

9._____

10._____

Chapter 11, Quiz C (Lesson 11-4)

1. Determine if the data in the table below displays exponential behavior. Write *yes* or *no*.

2. Graph the function $y = 1.8^x$.

x	y
-2	5
-1	-3
0	-1
1	1
2	3

3. Solve the equation $3^{x+2} = 3^{-3}$.

1. _____

2. _____
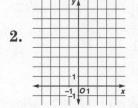

3. _____

Suppose B = 100 • 2⁴ᵗ represents the number of bacteria in a petri dish after t hours if you begin with 100 bacteria. Use this information for problems 4 and 5.

4. How many bacteria will there be after 2 hours?

4. _____

5. How long it will take for the number of bacteria to reach 1,000,000?

5. _____

Chapter 11, Quiz D (Lesson 11-5)

For problems 1–3, determine the final amount after 2 years.

1. $500 invested at 6% compounded quarterly

1. _____

2. $1500 invested at 5.5% compounded monthly

2. _____

3. $10,000 invested at 7.5% compounded daily

3. _____

The population of Atlanta, Georgia, was about 2,230,000 in 1980 and has been increasing at an annual rate of about 2.8%. The population of Detroit, Michigan, was about 5,300,000 in 1980 and has been decreasing at an annual rate of about 0.2%. Use this information for problems 4 and 5.

4. Estimate the population of each city in 2000.

4. _____

5. In what year will the populations of the two cities be about the same?

5. _____

Choose the best answer. Write A, B, C, or D.

1. If the product of a number and x is decreased by y, the result is z. Find the number in terms of x, y, and z.

   A. $\dfrac{z-y}{x}$ **B.** $\dfrac{z+y}{x}$ **C.** $\dfrac{y-z}{x}$ **D.** $z-y-x$

   1._____

2. Which of the following cannot be the average of 12, 6, 9, 8, 16, and x if $x > 7$?

   A. 7   **B.** 10   **C.** 12   **D.** 15

   2._____

3. How many fifths are there in $\dfrac{3}{8}$?

   A. $\dfrac{3}{40}$ **B.** $\dfrac{15}{8}$ **C.** $\dfrac{23}{40}$ **D.** $\dfrac{7}{40}$

   3._____

4. The midpoint of $\overline{RS}$ is M. If the coordinates of R are $(-2, 4)$ and the coordinates of M are $(4, -3)$, what are the coordinates of S?

   A. $\left(1, \dfrac{1}{2}\right)$ **B.** $\left(3, 3\dfrac{1}{2}\right)$ **C.** $(10, -10)$ **D.** $(8 - -5)$

   4._____

5. Which equation states that x is less than 3 units away from 2?

   A. $|x - 3| < 2$ **B.** $|x - 2| < 3$ **C.** $|x| < 3 - 2$ **D.** $|x - 3| > 2$

   5._____

6. The dimensions of a rectangle are $\dfrac{2x + 1}{6}$ and $\dfrac{3x + 2}{4}$. The perimeter of the rectangle is

   A. $\dfrac{5x + 3}{5}$.   **B.** $\dfrac{5x + 3}{6}$.   **C.** $\dfrac{13x + 8}{6}$.   **D.** $\dfrac{13x + 8}{12}$.

   6._____

7. If $2 + \dfrac{c}{6} = 4\dfrac{2}{3}$, then $c =$

   A. 4.   **B.** 8.   **C.** 12.   **D.** 16.

   7._____

8. If a line passes through $(0, -6)$ and has a slope of -3, what is the equation of the line?

   A. $y = -6x - 3$ **B.** $x = -6y - 3$
   C. $y = -3x - 6$ **D.** $x = -3y - 6$

   8._____

9. A line with a slope of -1 passes through points with coordinates $(2, 3)$ and $(5, y)$. Find the value of y.

   A. -6 **B.** 0   **C.** 3   **D.** 6

   9._____

10. A number plus two-thirds of itself is 20. Find the number.

    A. 4   **B.** 10   **C.** 12   **D.** 20

    10._____

Chapter 11 Cumulative Review

1. Evaluate $\frac{a+b}{a-b} + \frac{a^2-b^2}{a+b}$ if $a = 4$ and $b = 3$. (Lesson 1-3)

1. _____

2. Use a proportion to solve the following problem: If 16 inches of steel rod weighs 3 pounds, how long is a section of rod that weighs 5 pounds? (Lesson 4-2)

2. _____

3. Twenty-eight is what percent of 80? (Lesson 4-4)

3. _____

4. The sum of Nancy's age and John's age is 58. Nancy is 5 years older than Rufus. Rufus is 3 years younger than John. How old is John? (Lesson 2-9)

4. _____

5. Solve $10(a + 1) + 2a = 12 - (4a - 1)$. (Lesson 3-5)

5. _____

6. Two cars start at the same point and travel in the same direction on the same road. One travels 50 mi/h and the other 45 mi/h. After how many hours will they be 20 miles apart? (Lesson 4-7)

6. _____

7. Find the coordinates of the midpoint of a segment with endpoints $(3, -2)$ and $(-3, 9)$. (Lesson 6-7)

7. _____

8. Determine the value of r so that the line through $(1, 3)$ and $(6, r)$ has a slope of $-\frac{2}{5}$. (Lesson 6-1)

8. _____

9. Write an equation for the line that is perpendicular to the graph of $y - 3x = 2$ and passes through $(0, 6)$. (Lesson 6-6)

9. _____

Solve each inequality. (Lessons 7-2 and 7-3)

10. $4r > 2r - 18$

10. _____

11. $\frac{m}{-8} < -4$

11. _____

12. $9 - 4x \leq 21$

12. _____

13. $9a - 10 \geq -11a - 42$

13. _____

14. Solve the open sentence $|3m + 1| < 7$. Then graph its solution set. (Lesson 7-6)

14. _____

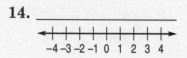

15. Five more than twice a number is greater than 53. Describe the number. (Lesson 7-3)

15. _____

16. Solve the system of equations $x + y = -5$ and $3x - 2y = 10$. (Lesson 8-4)

16. _____

17. Arrange the terms of $4x - 3 + 2x^2 + 3x^3$ so that the powers of x are in the descending order. (Lesson 9-4)

17. _____

18. Find $(4xy + 3x^2y - 5y^2) - (3y^2 - 5xy + 7x^2y)$. (Lesson 9-5)

18. _____

19. Simplify $(a^2 - 2)(3a^2 + 3)$. (Lesson 9-7)

19. _____

Factor each polynomial, if possible. (Lessons 10-2 and 10-3)

20. $12a^2b^2 - 16a^2b^3$

20. _____

21. $x^2 + 12x + 35$

21. _____

22. $2m^2 + 11m + 15$

22. _____

23. Use the quadratic formula to solve $x^2 + 3x + 1 = 0$. (Lesson 11-3)

23. _____

Solve each equation. (Lessons 11-2 and 11-3)

24. $2y^2 - 7y = 4$

24. _____

25. $r^2 + 5r - 3 = 0$

25. _____

Chapter 11 Answer Key

1. __B__

2. __C__

3. __D__

4. __B__

5. __B__

6. __A__

7. __B__

8. __A__

9. __D__

10. __A__

11. __B__

12. __C__

13. __A__

14. __A__

15. __D__

16. __B__

17. __C__

18. __A__

19. __C__

20. __D__

Bonus __-4, -1__

1. __B__

2. __A__

3. __C__

4. __A__

5. __C__

6. __A__

7. __C__

8. __C__

9. __C__

10. __D__

11. __A__

12. __D__

13. __C__

14. __C__

15. __B__

16. __D__

17. __A__

18. __C__

19. __A__

20. __D__

Bonus $\dfrac{-7 \pm \sqrt{37}}{2}$

 Algebra 1

Chapter 11 Answer Key

Form 1C

Page 285

1. __B__

2. __A__

3. __C__

4. __C__

5. __D__

6. __A__

7. __A__

8. __C__

9. __A__

10. __C__

11. __D__

Page 286

12. __B__

13. __B__

14. __A__

15. __C__

16. __C__

17. __C__

18. __B__

19. __C__

20. __A__

Bonus __$x = 5$__

Form 2A

Page 287

1. $x = -2$; $(-2, 3)$

2. $x = \dfrac{3}{2}$; minimum

3. $(0, 2)$

4. 12 points

5. $1 < x < 2$, $4 < x < 5$

6. no real roots

7. $-\dfrac{25}{4}$

8. $-3, -5$ or $3, 5$

9. $-4, 6$

10. $\dfrac{7 \pm \sqrt{109}}{6}$

11. $\dfrac{3 \pm \sqrt{7}}{2}$

12. 121; rational

13. 587.31

Page 288

14.

15. Yes

16. 0, 15

17. $8235.05; $9070.09; second investment; $835.04

18. between years 4 and 5

19. about 20 years

20. the second pension

Bonus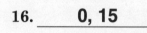

Chapter 11 Answer Key

Form 2B

1. $x = 1; (1, -3)$

2. $x = \frac{7}{2}$; minimum

3. $\left(\frac{7}{6}, -\frac{49}{6} \right)$

4. $(-4, 0)$

5. negative; none

6. $0 < x < 1, 5 < x < 6$

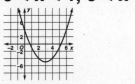

7. no real roots

8. 3

9. $-3.81, 1.31$

10. $1, 8$

11. $\dfrac{-1 \pm \sqrt{10}}{3}$

12. $0, \dfrac{10}{3}$

13. 39.53

14. 2.5

15.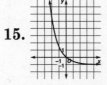

16. 7.5

17. $A = 500(1.04)^6$

18. $\$4595.27$

19. $\$3047.49$

20. about $1,167,000$

Bonus

            Algebra 1

Chapter 11 Answer Key

Form 2C

Page 291

1. $x = \frac{1}{2}$

2. $\left(2\frac{1}{2}, -15\frac{1}{2}\right)$; __minimum__

3.

4.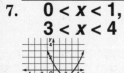

5. $y = 2x^2 - 10x - 3$

6. $-5\frac{3}{4}$ and $1\frac{3}{4}$

7. $0 < x < 1$, $3 < x < 4$

8. __no real roots__
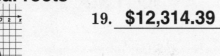

9. $0.5, 3, -5$

10. __no real roots__

11. $\dfrac{5 \pm \sqrt{10}}{3}$

12. $4 \pm \sqrt{19}$

13. 2

14. __no__

Page 292

15. __3__
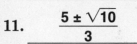

16. __1__

17. $A = 1000 (1.0375)^6$

18. $6734.28

19. $12,314.39

20. __about 133,000__

Bonus __{1, 2}__

Calculator-Based

Page 293

1. 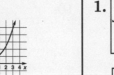 Yscl = 2

2. 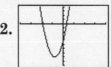 Xscl = 10 Yscl = 10

3. $-1.82, 1.42$

4. $-1.53, 2.78$

5. $-4.33, 4.33$

6. $-19.15, 1.15$

7. $0.646, -4.646$

8. 7

9. __no real roots__

10. $0.523, -3.189$

11. 10.05

12. 11.49

13. 0.5

14. 24.82

15. $2991.70

16. __between years 4 and 5__

Scoring Guide
Chapter 11
Performance Assessment

Level	Specific Criteria
3 Superior	• Shows thorough understanding of the concepts of *quadratic functions*, *roots of quadratic equations*, and *exponential functions*. • Uses appropriate strategies to solve problems. • Computations are correct. • Written explanations are exemplary. • Word problem is appropriate and makes sense. • Graphs are accurate and appropriate. • Goes beyond requirements of some or all problems.
2 Satisfactory, with Minor Flaws	• Shows understanding of the concepts of *quadratic functions*, *roots of quadratic equations*, and *exponential functions*. • Uses appropriate strategies to solve problems. • Computations are mostly correct. • Written explanations are effective. • Word problem is appropriate and makes sense. • Graphs are mostly accurate and appropriate. • Satisfies all requirements of problems.
1 Nearly Satisfactory, with Serious Flaws	• Shows understanding of most of the concepts of *quadratic functions*, *roots of quadratic equations*, and *exponential functions*. • May not use appropriate strategies to solve problems. • Computations are mostly correct. • Written explanations are satisfactory. • Word problem is mostly appropriate and sensible. • Graphs are mostly accurate and appropriate. • Satisfies most requirements of problems.
0 Unsatisfactory	• Shows little or no understanding of the concepts of *quadratic functions*, *roots of quadratic equations*, and *exponential functions*. • May not use appropriate strategies to solve problems. • Computations are incorrect. • Written explanations are not satisfactory. • Word problem is not appropriate or sensible. • Graphs are not accurate or appropriate. • Does not satisfy requirements of problems.

Chapter 11 Answer Key
Performance Assessment

Page 294

1. **a.** $y = x^2 - 4x$

   b. $\dfrac{-b}{2a} = \dfrac{4}{2}$, or 2

   $x = 2$ is the axis of symmetry.
   $(2, -4)$ is the minimum point.

   c.

   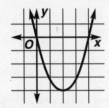

   d. The graph intersects the x-axis in two points. There are two real roots.

2. **a.** Sample answer: Find two real numbers whose sum is 9 and whose product is 14.

   b. Students' graphs should have x-intercepts at 2 and 7.

3. Situations should involve exponential growth.

Chapter 11 Answer Key

Mid-Chapter Test
Page 295

1. $x = 1$; $(1, -9)$; minimum

2. $x = \frac{3}{2}$; $\left(\frac{3}{2}, -\frac{1}{4}\right)$; minimum

3. $x = 1$; $(1, 5)$; maximum

4. $x = -\frac{5}{2}$; $\left(-\frac{5}{2}, -\frac{9}{4}\right)$; minimum

5. $x = 0$; $(0, 12)$; maximum

6. $x = -3$; $(-3, -4)$; minimum

7.   8.

9. $-7, 3$ 10. -3

11. $0 < x < 1, 3 < x < 4$

12. no real roots

13. $1, -5, 1$; $4.79, 0.21$

14. $-2, -7, 18$; $-5.22, 1.72$

15. $\frac{1}{2}, 2, 10$; no real roots

16. $-1, 1, 6$; $-2, 3$

Bonus   about 2.85 in.

Quiz A
Page 296

1. $x = 2$

2. $(2, 1)$

3.

4. no real roots

5. $20

Quiz B
Page 296

1. $\dfrac{-7 \pm \sqrt{33}}{2}$; $-0.63, -6.37$

2. $4 \pm \sqrt{10}$; $7.16, 0.84$

3. $-1, \dfrac{7}{4}$

4. $\dfrac{-13 \pm \sqrt{145}}{4}$; $-0.24, -6.26$

5. 69; 2 real, irrational roots

6. -167; no real roots

7. 169; 2 real, rational roots

8. 0; 1 real, rational root

9. no

10. 1.37 seconds

Quiz C
Page 297

1. no

2.

3. $x = -5$

4. 25,600

5. about 3.3 hours

Quiz D
Page 297

1. $563.25

2. $1674.00

3. $11,618.16

4. Atlanta: 3,874,000; Detroit: 5,092,000

5. 2009

Chapter 11 Answer Key

Standardized Test Practice
Page 298

1. __B__

2. __A__

3. __B__

4. __C__

5. __B__

6. __C__

7. __D__

8. __C__

9. __B__

10. __C__

Cumulative Review
Page 299

1. _____ 8 _____

2. $26\frac{2}{3}$ inches

3. _____ 35% _____

4. 28 years old

5. $\dfrac{3}{16}$

6. 4 hours

7. $\left(0, 3\frac{1}{2}\right)$

8. _____ 1 _____

9. $y = -\frac{1}{3}x + 6$

10. $r > -9$

11. $m > 32$

12. $x \geq -3$

13. $a \geq -\frac{8}{5}$

Page 300

14. $-\frac{8}{3} < m < 2$

15. $n > 24$

16. $(0, -5)$

17. $3x^3 + 2x^2 + 4x - 3$

18. $-4x^2y + 9xy - 8y^2$

19. $3a^4 - 3a^2 - 6$

20. $4a^2b^2(3 - 4b)$

21. $(x + 5)(x + 7)$

22. $(2m + 5)(m + 3)$

23. $\dfrac{-3 \pm \sqrt{5}}{2}$

24. $-\frac{1}{2}, 4$

25. $\dfrac{-5 \pm \sqrt{37}}{2}$

NAME_____ DATE _____

Chapter 12 Test, Form 1A

Write the letter for the correct answer in the blank at the right of each problem.

1. Simplify $\dfrac{y^2 + 2y - 24}{y^2 - 16}$.

    A. $\dfrac{3}{2}$ **B.** $\dfrac{y-3}{-1}$ **C.** $\dfrac{y-6}{y-4}$ **D.** $\dfrac{y+6}{y+4}$

1. _____

2. Simplify $\dfrac{3x^2 - 5x + 2}{x^2 - 3x + 2}$.

    A. $\dfrac{3x-2}{x-2}$ **B.** $\dfrac{3x+1}{x-1}$ **C.** $\dfrac{3x-5}{x-3}$ **D.** $\dfrac{2}{3}$

2. _____

3. Find $\dfrac{2n^2 y^3}{c^4} \cdot \dfrac{5nc}{14y^5}$.

    A. $\dfrac{5n^3}{7y^2 c^3}$ **B.** $\dfrac{n^3}{2y^2 c^3}$ **C.** $\dfrac{5n^2}{7y^2 c^4}$ **D.** $\dfrac{n^2}{2y^2 c^4}$

3. _____

4. What are the excluded values of x in the expression $\dfrac{x+7}{(x+3)(1-x)} \cdot \dfrac{3x-8}{5x+10}$?

    A. $x \neq -7, \dfrac{8}{3}, -3, -1, -2$ **B.** $x \neq -3, -1, -10$

    C. $x \neq 1, -2, -3, -7, 8$ **D.** $x \neq -2, 1, -3$

4. _____

5. Find $\dfrac{4m^2 n}{p^3} \div \dfrac{mn}{6p^4}$.

    A. $24mp$ **B.** $\dfrac{1}{24mp}$ **C.** $\dfrac{2m^3 n^2}{3p^7}$ **D.** $\dfrac{1}{10mp}$

5. _____

6. Find $\dfrac{v+y}{v-y} \div \dfrac{y+v}{y-v}$.

    A. 1 **B.** -1 **C.** $\dfrac{(v+y)^2}{(v-y)(v-y)}$ **D.** none of these

6. _____

7. In the long division $x - 2 \overline{)3x^3 + x^2 - 8x - 5}$, the remainder is

    A. 7.   **B.** -9.   **C.** -41.   **D.** none of these

7. _____

8. Find $\dfrac{x}{x-2} + \dfrac{5x}{x-2}$.

    A. -3 **B.** $\dfrac{5x^2}{x-2}$ **C.** $\dfrac{6x}{2x-4}$ **D.** $\dfrac{6x}{x-2}$

8. _____

9. Simplify $\left(\dfrac{45 \text{ miles}}{1 \text{ hour}} \cdot \dfrac{5280 \text{ feet}}{1 \text{ mile}} \div \dfrac{60 \text{ minutes}}{1 \text{ hour}} \right) \div \dfrac{60 \text{ seconds}}{1 \text{ minute}}$.

    A. $\dfrac{66 \text{ miles}}{1 \text{ hour}}$ **B.** $\dfrac{66 \text{ feet}}{1 \text{ second}}$ **C.** $\dfrac{855{,}360{,}000 \text{ feet}}{1 \text{ second}}$ **D.** $\dfrac{237{,}600 \text{ feet}}{1 \text{ second}}$

9. _____

10. Find $\dfrac{7}{6n} - \dfrac{6}{4n^2}$.

    A. $\dfrac{1}{12n^2}$ **B.** $\dfrac{7n-9}{6n^2}$ **C.** $\dfrac{28n-1}{4n^2}$ **D.** $\dfrac{1}{24n^3}$

10. _____

11. Find $\dfrac{x}{x-3} - \dfrac{4}{x^2 - 9}$.

    A. $\dfrac{x-4}{x-3}$ **B.** $\dfrac{x-4}{x^2-9}$ **C.** $\dfrac{(x+4)(x-1)}{(x+3)(x-3)}$ **D.** $\dfrac{(x+1)(x-1)}{(x+3)(x-3)}$

11. _____

12. Find $\dfrac{3m+2}{2m+3} + \dfrac{1}{3m+2}$.

    A. $\dfrac{9m^2 + 14m + 7}{(2m+3)(3m+2)}$ B. $\dfrac{3}{5}$

    C. $\dfrac{9m^2 + 12m + 5}{(2m+3)(3m+2)}$ D. $\dfrac{3(m+1)}{(2m+3)(3m+2)}$

12. _____

13. What is the simplest form of $\dfrac{\frac{3x+6}{5x-10}}{\frac{x^2-4}{15}}$?

    A. $9(x+2)^2$ B. $\dfrac{(x+2)^2}{25}$ C. $\dfrac{9}{(x-2)^2}$ D. 1

13. _____

14. Solve $\dfrac{1}{4x} + \dfrac{2}{3} = 5$.

    A. $\dfrac{52}{3}$ B. $\dfrac{3}{52}$ C. 4 D. $\dfrac{1}{4}$

14. _____

15. Solve $\dfrac{x}{x-2} - \dfrac{4}{x^2-2x} = \dfrac{1}{x}$.

    A. 2 B. -1 C. $-1, 2$ D. none of these

15. _____

16. What is the simplest form of $\dfrac{1}{1 + \dfrac{1}{1 + \frac{1}{2}}}$?

    A. $\dfrac{2}{3}$ B. $\dfrac{1}{3}$ C. $\dfrac{2}{5}$ D. $\dfrac{3}{5}$

16. _____

17. An airplane can fly at a rate of 540 mi/h in calm air. It can fly 2668 miles with the wind in the same time it can fly 2300 miles against the wind. If x represents the speed of the wind, which equation must be true?
    A. $2668(540 + x) = 2300(540 - x)$
    B. $2668(x + 540) = 2300(x - 540)$
    C. $2668(540 - x) = 2300(540 + x)$
    D. $2668(x - 540) = 2300(x + 540)$

17. _____

18. What is the value of k if $x - 5$ is a factor of $2x^2 + kx - 15$?
    A. -7 B. 7 C. 13 D. -13

18. _____

19. The ninth-grade class of Washington High School could form groups of 8, 12, or 15 students for photos. What is the least number of students in ninth grade?
    A. 480 B. 360 C. 1440 D. 120

19. _____

20. Given the formula $\dfrac{1}{R_T} = \dfrac{1}{R_1} + \dfrac{1}{R_2 + R_3}$ for the resistance of a circuit, what is the resistance R_2 if $R_T = 4.5$ ohms, $R_1 = 6$ ohms, and $R_3 = 9$ ohms?
    A. 27 ohms   B. 9 ohms   C. 3 ohms   D. 6 ohms

20. _____

Bonus $x - 4$ is a factor of $x^3 + x^2 - 14x - 24$. Find the other two factors.

Bonus _____

12 Chapter 12 Test, Form 1B

Write the letter for the correct answer in the blank at the right of each problem.

1. Simplify $\dfrac{4x - 4}{4x + 4}$.

   A. $x - 4$ **B.** $x + 4$ **C.** $\dfrac{x - 1}{x + 1}$ **D.** -1

   1. _____

2. Simplify $\dfrac{k^2 - 8k + 16}{k^2 - 16}$.

   A. $k - 4$ **B.** -1 **C.** $\dfrac{k - 4}{k + 4}$ **D.** $\dfrac{k + 4}{k - 4}$

   2. _____

3. What are the excluded values of x in $\dfrac{x - 3}{x^2 - 9}$?

   A. $x \neq 3$ **B.** $x \neq -3$ **C.** $x \neq 9$ **D.** $x \neq \pm 3$

   3. _____

4. What are the excluded values of n in $\dfrac{n^2 - 3n - 28}{n^2 + 3n - 4}$?

   A. $n \neq -1, 4$ **B.** $n \neq 1$ **C.** $n \neq -1$ **D.** $n \neq 1, -4$

   4. _____

5. Find $\dfrac{3a^2b}{b^2c^3} \cdot \dfrac{2bc^2}{15a}$.

   A. $\dfrac{ab}{3c}$ **B.** $\dfrac{2a^2b}{5c}$ **C.** $\dfrac{2a}{5c}$ **D.** $\dfrac{a^2}{3c^2}$

   5. _____

6. Find $\dfrac{(y + 2)^2}{8} \cdot \dfrac{72}{y^2 - 4}$.

   A. $\dfrac{9(y + 2)}{y - 2}$ **B.** $\dfrac{-9}{y + 2}$ **C.** $\dfrac{9}{y - 2}$ **D.** $\dfrac{-9}{8(y - 2)}$

   6. _____

7. Find $\dfrac{3}{x + 2} + \dfrac{2x}{x + 2}$.

   A. $\dfrac{5x}{x + 2}$ **B.** $\dfrac{2x + 3}{x + 2}$ **C.** $\dfrac{2x + 3}{2x + 4}$ **D.** $\dfrac{5x}{2x + 4}$

   7. _____

8. Find $\dfrac{u + t}{w - 6} + \dfrac{u + t}{6 - w}$.

   A. 0 **B.** $\dfrac{2t}{6 - w}$ **C.** $\dfrac{u + t}{w - 6}$ **D.** $\dfrac{2u + 2t}{w - 6}$

   8. _____

9. Find $\dfrac{16a^2 - 9w^2}{4a^2 - 3aw} \cdot \dfrac{a^2}{a + w}$.

   A. $\dfrac{4a - 3}{a + w}$ **B.** $\dfrac{a(4a + 3w)}{a + w}$

   C. $\dfrac{a^2(4a - 3w)}{(a + w)(2a - 3w)(2a + w)}$ **D.** a

   9. _____

10. Find $\dfrac{n^2 + 3n - 10}{n^2 + 6n + 8} \div \dfrac{n - 2}{n^2 + 2n}$.

    A. $\dfrac{n(n + 5)}{n + 4}$ **B.** $\dfrac{(n + 5)(n - 2)^2}{(n + 3)^3}$

    C. $\dfrac{n + 5}{n + 2}$ **D.** $\dfrac{n(n - 5)}{(n - 2)^2}$

    10. _____

11. Use long division to find the quotient $x + 3 \overline{)5x^2 - 9x + 20}$.

    A. $5x + 6 + \dfrac{38}{x + 3}$ **B.** $5x + 6 + \dfrac{2}{x + 3}$

    C. $5x - 24 + \dfrac{92}{x + 3}$ **D.** $5x - 24 + \dfrac{-52}{x + 3}$

    11. _____

12. What is the simplest form of $\dfrac{x - 11 + \dfrac{42}{x + 2}}{x - 5}$? 12._____

   A. $\dfrac{2x + 31}{(x - 5)(x + 2)}$ B. $\dfrac{x^2 + 20}{(x - 5)(x + 2)}$ C. $\dfrac{x^2 - 9x + 20}{x - 5}$ D. $\dfrac{x - 4}{x + 2}$

13. Solve $\dfrac{6}{y + 2} + \dfrac{1}{y} = 3$. 13._____

   A. $-\dfrac{2}{3}$ and 1 B. $\dfrac{2}{3}$ C. 1 D. $\dfrac{1}{7}$

14. Solve by making a list. In how many ways can the letters "C-A-T" 14._____
    be arranged to form a word? (A word is any arrangement of the
    letters.)
    A. 3 B. 4 C. 6 D. 1

15. Find $\dfrac{2x + 3}{x - 4} + \dfrac{8}{x + 1}$. 15._____

   A. $\dfrac{2x + 11}{x^2 - 3x - 4}$ B. $\dfrac{2x^2 + 5x + 12}{x^2 - 3x - 4}$ C. $\dfrac{10x - 9}{x + 1}$ D. $\dfrac{2x^2 + 13x - 29}{x^2 - 3x - 4}$

16. Find $\dfrac{10}{a - b} - \dfrac{6b}{a^2 - b^2}$. 16._____

   A. $\dfrac{4}{a - b}$ B. $\dfrac{10a - 6b}{a^2 - b^2}$ C. $\dfrac{4b}{a - b}$ D. $\dfrac{10a + 4b}{a^2 - b^2}$

17. Solve $\dfrac{5x}{3x + 1} - \dfrac{1}{9x + 3} = \dfrac{7}{6}$. 17._____

   A. 1 B. -1 C. $-\dfrac{9}{11}$ D. $\dfrac{9}{11}$

18. Solve $\dfrac{dn - n}{e} = f$ for n. 18._____

   A. $\dfrac{f - e}{d}$ B. $\dfrac{fe}{d - 1}$ C. $\dfrac{fe}{d}$ D. $\dfrac{f - e}{d - 1}$

19. Simplify $\dfrac{1}{1 + \dfrac{1}{1 - \frac{1}{2}}}$. 19._____

   A. $\dfrac{1}{3}$ B. $\dfrac{3}{5}$ C. $\dfrac{2}{3}$ D. $\dfrac{1}{2}$

20. The formula $\dfrac{1}{R_T} = \dfrac{1}{R_1} + \dfrac{1}{R_2} + \dfrac{1}{R_3}$ represents the total resistance 20._____
    of a circuit with 3 resistances connected in parallel. What is the
    resistance R_1 if $R_T = 2.5$ ohms, $R_2 = 10$ ohms, and $R_3 = 5$ ohms?
    A. 17.5 B. 2.5 C. 10 D. 7

Bonus Find the value of k so that $x + 1$ is a factor of Bonus _____
   $3x^3 - 2x^2 + x + k$.

12

Chapter 12 Test, Form 1C

Write the letter for the correct answer in the blank at the right of each problem.

1. Simplify $\dfrac{y^2 - y - 2}{y^2 + 4y + 3}$.

   A. $\dfrac{y + 2}{y - 3}$ **B.** $\dfrac{y - 2}{y + 3}$ **C.** $\dfrac{y + 2}{y + 3}$ **D.** $\dfrac{y - 2}{y - 3}$

   1. _____

2. Simplify $\dfrac{2m^2 - 5m - 3}{m^2 - 4m + 3}$.

   A. $\dfrac{m - 3}{m - 3}$ **B.** $\dfrac{2m - 1}{m - 1}$ **C.** $\dfrac{2m + 1}{m - 1}$ **D.** $2m + \dfrac{5}{4}$

   2. _____

3. Find $\dfrac{3m^2y^4}{2p^3} \cdot \dfrac{4p^4}{9my^6}$.

   A. $\dfrac{2mp}{3y^2}$ **B.** $\dfrac{2m^2y^2}{3p}$ **C.** $\dfrac{27m^3y^{10}}{8p^7}$ **D.** $\dfrac{2mp}{3y^{-2}}$

   3. _____

4. What are the excluded values of x in $\dfrac{x - 2}{x^2 - 4}$?

   A. $x \neq 4$ **B.** $x \neq 2$ **C.** $x \neq -2$ **D.** $x \neq 2, -2$

   4. _____

5. What are the excluded values of m in $\dfrac{2m^2 - m - 1}{m^2 + m - 2}$?

   A. $m \neq -2$ **B.** $m \neq 1$ **C.** $m \neq -2, 1$ **D.** $m \neq 2, -1$

   5. _____

6. Find $\dfrac{(x + 1)^2}{9} \cdot \dfrac{72}{x^2 - 1}$.

   A. $\dfrac{8(x + 1)}{x - 1}$ **B.** $\dfrac{8(x - 1)}{x + 1}$ **C.** $\dfrac{x + 1}{8(x - 1)}$ **D.** $\dfrac{x + 1}{x - 1}$

   6. _____

7. Find $\dfrac{4}{x + 1} + \dfrac{3x}{x + 1}$.

   A. $\dfrac{7x}{x + 1}$ **B.** $\dfrac{3x + 4}{2x + 2}$ **C.** $\dfrac{3x + 4}{x + 1}$ **D.** $\dfrac{7x}{2x + 2}$

   7. _____

8. Find $\dfrac{3}{x + 1} + \dfrac{2}{x + 3}$.

   A. $\dfrac{5x + 11}{(x + 1)(x + 3)}$ **B.** $\dfrac{5}{(x + 1)(x + 3)}$ **C.** $\dfrac{5x + 11}{2x + 4}$ **D.** $\dfrac{5}{2x + 4}$

   8. _____

9. Find $\dfrac{m^2}{8m^2 - 8n^2} \cdot \dfrac{m + n}{m^3 + m^2}$.

   A. 0 **B.** $\dfrac{1}{8(m - n)(m + 1)}$ **C.** $\dfrac{1}{8m(m - n)}$ **D.** $\dfrac{1}{(m - n)(m + 1)}$

   9. _____

10. Find $\dfrac{n^2 + 3n}{n^2 + 4n + 3} \div \dfrac{n^2 + 2n}{n + 1}$.

    A. 0 **B.** $\dfrac{1}{n - 2}$ **C.** $\dfrac{1}{n + 2}$ **D.** $\dfrac{n + 1}{n + 2}$

    10. _____

11. Use long division to find the quotient $x + 2 \overline{)8x^2 + 6x - 4}$.

    A. $8x - 10 + \dfrac{16}{x + 2}$ **B.** $8x - 10 - \dfrac{24}{x + 2}$

    C. $8x + 10 - \dfrac{24}{x + 2}$ **D.** $8x - 4 + \dfrac{4}{x + 2}$

    11. _____

12. What is the simplest form of $\dfrac{x + 1 + \dfrac{2}{x + 3}}{x - 4}$?   12._____

   A. $\dfrac{x + 5}{x + 3}$ **B.** $\dfrac{x^2 + 4x + 5}{(x + 3)(x - 4)}$

   C. $\dfrac{x^2 + 5}{(x + 3)(x - 4)}$ **D.** $\dfrac{x^2 + 4x + 5}{x - 4}$

13. Solve $\dfrac{1}{k + 1} + \dfrac{2}{k} = \dfrac{4}{3}$.   13._____

   A. 2 and $-\dfrac{3}{4}$ **B.** -1 and 2 **C.** 1   **D.** -2

14. A certain number of bowlers can be arranged in teams of   14._____
    4, 6, or 8. What can the smallest number of bowlers be?
    A. 192   **B.** 96   **C.** 48   **D.** 24

15. Find $\dfrac{x + 1}{x - 2} + \dfrac{4}{x + 1}$.   15._____

   A. $\dfrac{x - 7}{x - 2}$ **B.** $\dfrac{x + 5}{(x - 2)(x + 1)}$ **C.** $\dfrac{x^2 + 6x - 7}{(x - 2)(x + 1)}$ **D.** $\dfrac{4}{x - 2}$

16. Find $\dfrac{x - 1}{x + 2} - \dfrac{3}{x + 1}$.   16._____

   A. $\dfrac{x^2 - 3x - 7}{(x + 2)(x + 1)}$ **B.** $\dfrac{x - 4}{(x + 1)(x + 2)}$

   C. $\dfrac{-3}{x + 2}$ **D.** $\dfrac{x^2 - 3x + 5}{(x + 2)(x + 1)}$

17. Solve $\dfrac{1}{2x + 1} - \dfrac{1}{x} = -\dfrac{3}{10}$.   17._____

   A. -2 **B.** 2 and $-\dfrac{5}{6}$ **C.** no solution   **D.** 9

18. Solve $A = \dfrac{1}{2}h(x + y)$ for y.   18._____

   A. $\dfrac{2A - x}{h}$ **B.** $\dfrac{2A}{h} + x$ **C.** $\dfrac{2A + x}{h}$ **D.** $\dfrac{2A}{h} - x$

19. Simplify $\dfrac{1}{1 + \dfrac{1}{1 + \dfrac{1}{3}}}$.   19._____

   A. $\dfrac{4}{7}$ **B.** $\dfrac{7}{4}$ **C.** $\dfrac{3}{7}$ **D.** $\dfrac{7}{3}$

20. Given the formula $\dfrac{1}{R_r} = \dfrac{1}{R_1} + \dfrac{1}{R_2}$ for the resistance of a circuit,   20._____
    what is the resistance R_2 if $R_r = 5.0$ ohms and $R_1 = 10.0$ ohms?
    A. 2.5 ohms   **B.** 5 ohms   **C.** 10 ohms   **D.** 20 ohms

Bonus Find the value of k so that $x - 1$ is a factor of   **Bonus** _____
   $x^3 - 2x^2 + 3x + k$.

Perform the indicated operations. Write your answer in simplest form.

1. $\dfrac{y^2 - 12y + 35}{y^2 - 25}$

2. $\dfrac{5w^3y^2}{8v^4} \cdot \dfrac{12v^{11}w}{30y^9}$

3. $\dfrac{4n^2}{2n + 3} - \dfrac{9}{2n + 3}$

4. $\dfrac{\dfrac{6x + 30}{2x - 4}}{\dfrac{x^2 + 3x - 10}{4}}$

5. $\dfrac{n - 2}{w + 7} \div \dfrac{2 - n}{7 + w}$

6. $\dfrac{2n^2 - 9n + 4}{2n^2 - n} \cdot \dfrac{n^3}{n - 4}$

7. $\dfrac{9r^5u}{m^6} \div (3r^3m^2)$

8. $\dfrac{n}{n + 1} + \dfrac{3}{n}$

9. $\dfrac{2w}{w + 5} + \dfrac{3w}{5 + w}$

10. $\dfrac{3x^2 - 14x + 15}{7x^2 - 19x - 6} \div \dfrac{3x - 5}{7x + 2}$

11. $\dfrac{x - 9 + \dfrac{22}{x + 4}}{x + 2}$

12. $\dfrac{x^4 - 10x^2 + 9}{x^3 + 4x^2 + 3x}$

13. $\dfrac{5}{4v} + \dfrac{3}{2v^2}$

14. $\dfrac{5y}{y^2 - 36} - \dfrac{2}{y + 6}$

1. _____

2. _____

3. _____

4. _____

5. _____

6. _____

7. _____

8. _____

9. _____

10. _____

11. _____

12. _____

13. _____

14. _____

15. What are the excluded values of n in the expression $\dfrac{n + 5}{(8 - n)(n + 3)} \cdot \dfrac{n - 9}{2n - 3}$?

15. _____

16. Use long division to find the quotient
$(6x^2 - 16x - 5) \div (3x - 2)$.

16. _____

17. Solve by making a list.
In how many ways can Alex, Bob, Cora, and Debby be
seated around a table?

17. _____

Solve each equation.

18. $\dfrac{6}{5} + \dfrac{3}{2x} = \dfrac{7}{15}$

18. _____

19. $\dfrac{p^2}{p-3} + \dfrac{7}{3-p} = 9$

19. _____

20. $\dfrac{3}{x-1} - \dfrac{6}{x^2-1} = 1$

20. _____

21. The volume of a box is $2x^3 + 11x^2 + 18x + 9$. One
dimension of the box is $x + 1$. What are the other two
dimensions if they are polynomials in x with integer
coefficients?

21. _____

22. An airplane can fly at a rate of 560 mi/h in calm air. It
can fly 2400 miles with the wind in the same time it
can fly 2080 miles against the wind. If $x =$ the speed
of the wind in miles per hour, write an equation
involving x that represents this situation. Do not
solve the equation.

22. _____

23. Solve $v = \dfrac{ay}{n^2}$ for y.

23. _____

24. Given the formula $\dfrac{1}{R_T} = \dfrac{1}{R_1} + \dfrac{1}{R_2 + R_3}$ for the resistance
of a circuit, determine the resistance R_3 if $R_T = 3\dfrac{3}{7}$ ohms,
$R_1 = 6$ ohms, and $R_2 = 3$ ohms.

24. _____

25. Solve $Q = K\dfrac{(t_2 - t_1)aT}{d}$ for a.

25. _____

Bonus Find the constants k and c so that
$\dfrac{7x + 17}{x^2 + 4x + 3} = \dfrac{k}{x + 3} + \dfrac{c}{x + 1}$.

Bonus _____

Chapter 12 Test, Form 2B

Perform the indicated operations.

1. $\dfrac{a^2 - b^2}{a + b}$

2. $\dfrac{a^2 - 3a - 28}{a^2 + 3a - 4}$

3. $\dfrac{y^2 - 9}{4} \cdot \dfrac{8}{y + 3}$

4. $\dfrac{s^2 + 2s - 8}{s^2 + 3s - 10} \cdot \dfrac{s + 5}{s^2 - 16}$

5. $\dfrac{10 - 5x}{6 + 3x} \div \dfrac{5}{12 + 6x}$

6. $\dfrac{5m}{m + 1} \div \dfrac{25m^2}{m^2 + 2m + 1}$

7. $\dfrac{r}{r - 5} - \dfrac{5}{r - 5}$

8. $\dfrac{r^2}{r + s} - \dfrac{s^2}{r + s}$

9. $\dfrac{4n^2}{2n - 3} + \dfrac{9}{3 - 2n}$

10. $\dfrac{7}{6x^2r} + \dfrac{10}{3xr^2}$

11. $\dfrac{2a + 6}{a^2 + 6a + 9} + \dfrac{1}{a + 3}$

12. $\dfrac{8}{2a - 2b} - \dfrac{3b}{a^2 - b^2}$

13. $\dfrac{\dfrac{r^2 + r - 6}{r^2}}{\dfrac{r^2 + 3r}{r^2 + 2r}}$

14. $\dfrac{x - \dfrac{6}{x + 2}}{x + \dfrac{8}{x + 5}}$

15. What are the excluded values of y in the expression
$\dfrac{y^2 + y - 2}{y^2 - 2y - 15} \cdot \dfrac{y^2 - 5y + 5}{y^2 + 5y + 6}$?

16. Use long division to find the quotient
$(t^2 + 4t - 6) \div (t + 5)$.

1. _____

2. _____

3. _____

4. _____

5. _____

6. _____

7. _____

8. _____

9. _____

10. _____

11. _____

12. _____

13. _____

14. _____

15. _____

16. _____

17. Solve by making a tree diagram.
For dinner, you can choose spaghetti, tacos, or egg foo
yung. For a side dish, you can choose between a salad
or soup. Cake, pie, and ice cream are offered for dessert.
How many possible meals can you arrange?

17. _____

Solve each equation.

18. $\dfrac{a-3}{10} + \dfrac{a-5}{5} = \dfrac{1}{2}$

18. _____

19. $\dfrac{2}{x+2} = \dfrac{9}{8} - \dfrac{5x}{4x+8}$

19. _____

20. $\dfrac{2}{n-3} + \dfrac{2}{n+5} = \dfrac{5n-7}{n^2+2n-15}$

20. _____

21. Solve $\dfrac{y}{c} + \dfrac{n}{d} = 5$ for n.

21. _____

22. Simplify $\left[\left(\dfrac{45 \text{ miles}}{1 \text{ hour}} \cdot \dfrac{5280 \text{ feet}}{1 \text{ mile}}\right) \div \dfrac{60 \text{ minutes}}{1 \text{ hour}}\right] \div \dfrac{60 \text{ seconds}}{1 \text{ minute}}$.

22. _____

23. The volume of a box is $2x^3 + 11x^2 + 17x + 6$. One
dimension of the box is $x + 2$. What are the other two
dimensions if they are polynomials in x with integer
coefficients?

23. _____

24. An airplane can fly at a rate of 525 mi/h in still air. It
can fly 2800 miles with the wind in the same time that
it can fly 2450 miles against the wind. Find the rate of
the wind.

24. _____

25. Given the formula $\dfrac{1}{R_T} = \dfrac{1}{R_1} + \dfrac{1}{R_2 + R_3}$ for the resistance
of a circuit, determine the resistance R_2 if $R_T = 2$ ohms,
$R_1 = 3$ ohms, and $R_3 = 2\dfrac{3}{5}$ ohms.

25. _____

Bonus Cardiss can do a job in 4 hours. Rachel can do
the same job in 6 hours. Suppose that Rachel works
on the job for 2 hours and then is joined by Cardiss.
Find the time it will take both working together to
finish the job.

Bonus _____

Perform the indicated operations.

1. $\dfrac{x^2 - y^2}{x - y}$

1. _____

2. $\dfrac{k^2 + 2k - 15}{k^2 - 4k + 3}$

2. _____

3. $\dfrac{5}{m^2 - 4} \cdot \dfrac{m + 2}{10}$

3. _____

4. $\dfrac{r^2 + 2r - 3}{r^2 + 5r + 6} \cdot \dfrac{r + 2}{r^2 - 1}$

4. _____

5. $\dfrac{3x + 6}{2x - 2} \div \dfrac{7x - 14}{4x - 4}$

5. _____

6. $\dfrac{2x}{x + 3} \div \dfrac{8x^2}{x^2 + 5x + 6}$

6. _____

7. $\dfrac{v}{t + 6} + \dfrac{3}{t + 6}$

7. _____

8. $\dfrac{x^2}{x - 3} - \dfrac{9}{x - 3}$

8. _____

9. $\dfrac{x^2}{x - 2} + \dfrac{4}{2 - x}$

9. _____

10. $\dfrac{m}{2ab^2} + \dfrac{n}{4a^3b}$

10. _____

11. $\dfrac{w}{w^2 + 4w + 4} + \dfrac{2}{w + 2}$

11. _____

12. $\dfrac{1}{2r - 2s} - \dfrac{s}{r^2 - s^2}$

12. _____

13. $\dfrac{\dfrac{r^2 + 2r - 3}{r}}{\dfrac{r^2 + 3r}{r^2 - r}}$

13. _____

14. $\dfrac{x - \dfrac{1}{x + 3}}{x + \dfrac{2}{x + 3}}$

14. _____

15. What are the excluded values of x in the expression $\dfrac{x + 2}{x - 1} \cdot \dfrac{x - 1}{x + 3}$?

15. _____

16. Use long division to find the quotient $(x^2 - 8x + 9) \div (x - 2)$.

16. _____

17. Teresa has a collection of baseball cards. She can place the cards in groups of 15, 20, or 24 cards and have no cards left over. What is the least number of cards in Teresa's collection?

17._____

Solve each equation.

18. $\dfrac{b}{6} + \dfrac{b-1}{2} = \dfrac{1}{3}$

18._____

19. $\dfrac{1}{x+1} + \dfrac{2}{x-2} = \dfrac{9}{4}$

19._____

20. $\dfrac{2}{x-1} + \dfrac{2}{x+3} = \dfrac{3x+6}{x^2+2x-3}$

20._____

21. Solve $\dfrac{1}{j} + \dfrac{2}{k} = 1$ for k.

21._____

22. Simplify $\left[\left(\dfrac{30 \text{ miles}}{1 \text{ hour}} \cdot \dfrac{5280 \text{ feet}}{1 \text{ mile}}\right) \div \dfrac{60 \text{ minutes}}{1 \text{ hour}}\right] \div \dfrac{60 \text{ seconds}}{1 \text{ minute}}$.

22._____

23. The volume of a box is $2x^3 + 5x^2 + x - 2$. One dimension of the box is $x + 1$. What are the other two dimensions if they are polynomials in x with integer coefficients?

23._____

24. A boat can travel in still water at 20 miles per hour. It can travel downstream 120 miles in the same time it can travel 80 miles upstream. Find the speed of the river current.

24._____

25. Given the formula $\dfrac{1}{R_r} = \dfrac{1}{R_1} + \dfrac{1}{R_2}$ for the resistance of a circuit, determine R_1 when $R_r = 4$ ohms and $R_2 = 6$ ohms.

25._____

Bonus Allyn can do a job in 4 hours, while it would take Rex 6 hours to do the same job. How long will it take to complete the job if both work together?

Bonus _____

Simplify each expression. Verify your answer graphically.

1. $\dfrac{x^2 - 16}{x^2 + 8x + 16}$

1. _____

2. $\dfrac{5x + 10}{x^2 + 8x + 12}$

2. _____

3. $\dfrac{x^2 + 2x - 8}{x^2 - x - 20}$

3. _____

4. $\dfrac{3x^3 - 27x}{6x + 18}$

4. _____

Evaluate each expression for the given value.

5. $\dfrac{x^2 + 5x + 8}{x + 9}$; 2

5. _____

6. $\dfrac{16x^2 + 74x + 144}{35x - 3}$; 3

6. _____

Use the graphing calculator program POLYDIV from page 679 of your textbook to find the quotient and remainder of each division.

7. $(5x^2 - 4x + 3) \div (x - 4)$

7. _____

8. $(3x^2 - 4x - 7) \div (x + 1)$

8. _____

9. $(2x^2 + 15x - 13) \div (x + 8)$

9. _____

10. $(21x^2 - 17x - 13) \div (x - 7)$

10. _____

11. $(x^3 - 27) \div (x - 3)$

11. _____

12. $(3x^3 - 11x^2 + 5x - 8) \div (x + 4)$

12. _____

Use a graphing calculator for exercises 13–16.

13. Graph $y = \dfrac{x}{x - 2} - \dfrac{x + 4}{(x - 2)(x + 1)}$. Sketch the result.

13. _____

14. What are the excluded values of x in exercise 13?

14. _____

15. Graph $y = \dfrac{x + 2}{x + 1}$ on the same display used in exercise 13. Sketch the result and state the excluded values of x.

15. _____

16. Simplify $\dfrac{x}{x - 2} - \dfrac{x + 4}{(x - 2)(x + 1)}$. Explain how you got your answer.

16. _____

Chapter 12 Performance Assessment

Instructions: *Demonstrate your knowledge by giving a clear, concise solution to each problem. Be sure to include all relevant drawings and justify your answers. You may show your solution in more than one way or investigate beyond the requirements of the problem.*

1. The mechanical advantage (*M.A.*) of a machine is the ratio of the force (*R*) put out of the machine to the force (*r*) put in. A machine with a mechanical advantage of $\frac{4}{3}$ can lift a 4-pound weight with a force of only 3 pounds. The mechanical advantage of the pulley system at right is $M.A. = \frac{R}{r}$.

   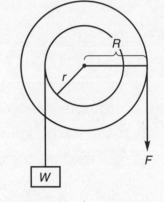

   a. If $R = \frac{3}{4}$ foot and $r = \frac{1}{2}$ foot, tell how you find the mechanical advantage. Explain each step.

   b. If the weight (*W*) that can be lifted by a force (*F*) is given by $W = \frac{R}{r} \cdot F$, what is the weight of an object that can be lifted with a force of 5.5 pounds? Show your work.

   c. If $R = 3x^2y$, $r = 2xy^2$, and $F = 6x^3$, find the weight that can be lifted by the pulley system. Show your work.

   d. Study the pulley system shown at the right. If the mechanical advantage of the complete system is equal to the product of the mechanical advantages of the two smaller pulley systems, *A* and *B*, what is the mechanical advantage of the complete system?

   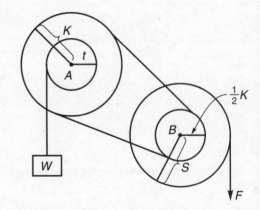

   e. Draw your own pulley system and determine the mechanical advantage.

2. The lens maker's formula is $\frac{1}{f} = (\mu - 1)\left(\frac{1}{r_1} - \frac{1}{r_2}\right)$, where *f* is the focal length, μ is the refractive index, and r_1 and r_2 are the radii as light encounters the curvature of the lens surface.

   a. Solve the equation for *f*. Show your work.

   b. Find the focal length of a lens if the refractive index is 1.5, $r_1 = 0.8$ inches, and $r_2 = -0.6$ inches.

12

Chapter 12 Mid-Chapter Test (Lessons 12-1 through 12-4)

Simplify. State the excluded values of the variable.

1. $\dfrac{4x^2y^2}{16yx^3}$

2. $\dfrac{x-3}{x^2-9}$

3. $\dfrac{6m-6n}{m^2-n^2}$

4. $\dfrac{a^2-3a-28}{a^2+3a-4}$

1. _____

2. _____

3. _____

4. _____

Perform the indicated operations.

5. $\dfrac{a^2b(2b)}{b^2c(a)}$

6. $\dfrac{y^2-9}{4}\cdot\dfrac{8}{y+3}$

7. $\dfrac{x^2-1}{2x-6}\cdot\dfrac{x^2-9}{3x-3}$

8. $\dfrac{y^2+y-2}{y^2-2y-15}\cdot\dfrac{y^2-6y+5}{y^2+5y+6}$

9. $\dfrac{rs^2}{t}\div\dfrac{r^2s}{t}$

10. $\dfrac{5m}{m+1}\div\dfrac{25m^2}{m^2+2m+1}$

11. $\dfrac{4a+12}{a^2-9}\div\dfrac{2a+6}{2a-6}$

12. $\dfrac{a^2-b^2}{a-b}\div\dfrac{2a+2b}{4a-4b}$

13. $\dfrac{3x^2-3y^2}{9}\div\dfrac{2x^2-2y^2}{3(x-y)^2}$

14. $\dfrac{2x^2-5x-3}{2x^2+9x+4}\cdot\dfrac{x^2+3x-4}{x^2-2x-24}$

15. $(x^3-x^2+6x+1)\div(x-3)$

16. $(4x^2-8x+10)\div(2x+1)$

17. $(x^3-5x^2+10x-8)\div(x-4)$

18. $(x^2-8x+10)\div(x+3)$

19. $(c^3-7c^2+11c-5)\div(c-5)$

20. $(2x^3-5x+1)\div(x+1)$

5. _____

6. _____

7. _____

8. _____

9. _____

10. _____

11. _____

12. _____

13. _____

14. _____

15. _____

16. _____

17. _____

18. _____

19. _____

20. _____

Bonus Find the value of k so that $x-5$ is a factor of
x^3-3x^2-6x-k.

Bonus _____

NAME _____ DATE _____

Chapter 12, Quiz A (Lessons 12-1 and 12-2)

Simplify. State the excluded values of the variables.

1. $\dfrac{4ab^2c}{32bc^4}$

2. $\dfrac{3x^2 - 6xy}{x^2 - 4y^2}$

3. $\dfrac{x^2 + x - 12}{60 - 5x - 5x^2}$

4. $\dfrac{x^4 - 13x^2 + 36}{x^2 + 5x + 6}$

Simplify. Assume that no denominator is equal to zero.

5. $\dfrac{5x}{3y^2} \cdot \dfrac{y}{15}$

6. $\dfrac{x + 2}{5x^2 + 15x} \cdot \dfrac{5x^3}{2x + 4}$

7. $\dfrac{x + 1}{3x - 1} \cdot \dfrac{9x^2 - 1}{x^2 + x}$

8. $\dfrac{r^3}{r^2 - 49} \cdot \dfrac{7 - r}{r}$

9. $\dfrac{3m^2n}{4m + 4n} \cdot \dfrac{3m + 3n}{9m^2n + 18mn^2}$

10. $\dfrac{x^2 - x - 12}{-x^2 + 3x + 4} \cdot \dfrac{x^2 - 1}{x^2 + 2x - 3}$

1. _____
2. _____
3. _____
4. _____
5. _____
6. _____
7. _____
8. _____
9. _____
10. _____

NAME _____ DATE _____

Chapter 12, Quiz B (Lessons 12-3 and 12-4)

Find each quotient.

1. $(5x^2 + 33x - 14) \div (x + 7)$

2. $(2x^2 - 15x + 31) \div (x - 3)$

3. $\dfrac{12a^3 - 8a^2 - a + 15}{3a + 1}$

4. $\dfrac{x^3 + 7x + 22}{x + 2}$

5. $\dfrac{xy^2}{wz^4} \div \dfrac{x^4y}{w^3z}$

6. $\dfrac{abc^2}{a^4bc^5} \div \dfrac{a^4bc^2}{abc^6}$

7. $\dfrac{x^2y^3}{v^2w^4} \div \dfrac{x^4y}{vw^3}$

8. $\dfrac{m^2 + 3m + 2}{m^3} \div \dfrac{m^2 + m - 2}{m^2}$

9. $\dfrac{m^2 + 5m + 6}{m + 4} \div \dfrac{m + 2}{m^2 + 5m + 4}$

10. $\dfrac{b^2 + 7b + 1}{b^2 + b - 2} \div \dfrac{2b^2 + 3b + 1}{b^2 + 2b - 3}$

1. _____
2. _____
3. _____
4. _____
5. _____
6. _____
7. _____
8. _____
9. _____
10. _____

Chapter 12, Quiz C (Lessons 12-5 and 12-6)

Find each sum or difference.

1. $\dfrac{y}{8} + \dfrac{5y}{8}$

2. $\dfrac{x+9}{4} - \dfrac{x-3}{4}$

3. $\dfrac{a}{2b^2} - \dfrac{6}{2b^2}$

4. $\dfrac{x^2+16}{x+4} + \dfrac{8x}{x+4}$

5. $\dfrac{x^2+15}{x+5} + \dfrac{8x}{x+5}$

6. $\dfrac{2}{r-s} + \dfrac{3r}{s-r}$

7. $\dfrac{5b}{3a^2c} - \dfrac{4}{3c^2}$

8. $\dfrac{x-2}{x+2} + \dfrac{x+2}{x-2}$

9. $\dfrac{2}{x^2-1} + \dfrac{1}{x+1}$

10. $\dfrac{7}{x^2+3x+2} - \dfrac{3}{x^2+4x+3}$

1. _____

2. _____

3. _____

4. _____

5. _____

6. _____

7. _____

8. _____

9. _____

10. _____

Chapter 12, Quiz D (Lessons 12-7 and 12-8)

Solve each equation.

1. $\dfrac{m-5}{m} - \dfrac{3}{2m} = \dfrac{1}{4}$

2. $\dfrac{2}{x+2} + \dfrac{5}{3x} = \dfrac{4}{x}$

3. Solve $\dfrac{n}{v} + \dfrac{1}{u} = \dfrac{n-1}{r}$ for u.

1. _____

2. _____

3. _____

Simplify.

4. $\dfrac{\dfrac{x^2y}{5n^3}}{\dfrac{x^3y^5}{15n}}$

5. $\dfrac{x - \dfrac{x+4}{x-3}}{\dfrac{x+4}{x-3} + x}$

4. _____

5. _____

Choose the best answer. Write A, B, C, or D.

1. If $x + 3 = y$, then $(x - y)^5 =$
   A. -243.   B. -15.   C. 15.   D. 243.

   1._____

2. What is the average of $3c - 2$, $2c + 6$, and $c + 2$?
   A. $\dfrac{2c + 1}{3}$ B. $2c + 2$ C. $\dfrac{2c + 2}{3}$ D. $2c + 6$

   2._____

3. If $a + t = 7$ and $a^2 - t^2 = 35$, find $a - t$.
   A. $\dfrac{1}{5}$ B. 5 C. 28 D. 42

   3._____

4. If $mn = 30$ and $m^2 + n^2 = 109$, find $(m + n)^2$.
   A. 49 B. 79 C. 139 D. 169

   4._____

5. Joshua spent one-third of his money on a shirt and then spent two-thirds of what was left on a pair of slacks. What part of his money did he have left?
   A. none   B. $\dfrac{2}{9}$ C. $\dfrac{4}{9}$ D. $\dfrac{2}{3}$

   5._____

6. If $\dfrac{x}{4}$, $\dfrac{x}{5}$, and $\dfrac{x}{8}$ are integers, x could be
   A. 20.   B. 30.   C. 32.   D. 40.

   6._____

7. If d is a negative integer and $d^2 - 12d = a$, a could be
   A. -28.   B. -10.   C. 0.   D. 28.

   7._____

8. If $(24)(y)(9) = 27$, then $y =$
   A. $\dfrac{1}{3}$.   B. $\dfrac{1}{6}$.   C. $\dfrac{1}{8}$.   D. $\dfrac{1}{9}$.

   8._____

9. If Carlota can type a word every 1.5 seconds, how many words can she type in $1\dfrac{1}{2}$ hours?
   A. 36 B. 40 C. 360 D. 3600

   9._____

10. The difference of the squares of the least and greatest of three consecutive positive integers is 88. If x is the smallest of the three integers, which equation must be true?
    A. $4x + 4 = 88$ B. $8x + 16 = 88$
    C. $(x + 2)^2 - x^2 = 88$ D. $x^2 - (x + 4)^2 = 88$

    10._____

Chapter 12 Cumulative Review

1. State the property shown in $3 + 2 = 3 + 2$. (Lesson 1-6)

1. _____

2. Simplify $6x^2 + 9x^2 + 4x + 6x$. (Lesson 1-1)

2. _____

3. Find $-2.349 + 1.456$. (Lesson 2-5)

3. _____

4. Use substitution to solve the system of equations $x + y = 2$ and $2x - y = 1$. (Lesson 8-2)

4. _____

5. Use elimination to solve the system of equations $2x + 2y = -4$ and $7x + 4y = 1$. (Lesson 8-4)

5. _____

Use the data 50, 46, 68, 62, 59, 74, 60, 70, and 64 for exercises 6–10. (Lessons 3-7, 5-7, and 7-7)

6. Find the mean to the nearest tenth.

6. _____

7. Find the median.

7. _____

8. Find the lower quartile.

8. _____

9. Find the upper quartile.

9. _____

10. Make a box-and-whisker plot for the data.

10.

Simplify. (Lessons 9-1 and 9-2)

11. $(-4x^5y^3)(2xy^2)$

11. _____

12. $\left(\frac{2}{3}c^2d^3\right)^4$

12. _____

13. $\frac{21hk^3j}{-14h^5kj^8}$

13. _____

14. Find $(2x^2y - 3xy + 4y^3) - (4xy - 3y^3 + x^2y)$. (Lesson 9-5)

14. _____

15. Find $(3m - 2n)(3m + 2n)$. (Lesson 9-8)

15. _____

Factor each polynomial, if possible. (Lessons 10-2 and 10-3)

16. $12c - 8d - 15rc + 10rd$

16. _____

17. $3a^2 - 13a + 12$

17. _____

Solve each equation. (Lessons 10-6 and 11-4)

18. $(x + 3)(x - 4) = 0$

18. _____

19. $4r^2 - 7r + 3 = 0$

19. _____

20. $3^{5y + 4} = 3^y$

20. _____

21. $4^{x - 1} = 2^x$

21. _____

22. Simplify $\dfrac{2x^2 + 3x + 1}{4x^2 + 4x + 1}$. (Lesson 12-1)

22. _____

23. Simplify $\dfrac{4x^2 - 8x - 5}{2x^2 + x - 15}$. (Lesson 12-1)

23. _____

24. Find $\dfrac{a^3}{a - b} \cdot \dfrac{a^2 - b^2}{a}$. (Lesson 12-2)

24. _____

25. Find $(2x^2 + 3x - 5) \div (x - 3)$. (Lesson 12-4)

25. _____

26. Find $\dfrac{2}{3k - 1} + \dfrac{k}{k + 3}$. (Lesson 12-6)

26. _____

27. Find $\dfrac{c^2}{c^2 - 4} - \dfrac{5c + 14}{c^2 - 4}$. (Lesson 12-5)

27. _____

28. Simplify $\dfrac{z - \dfrac{3}{z - 2}}{z - \dfrac{6}{z - 1}}$. (Lesson 12-7)

28. _____

29. Solve $wx - w = \dfrac{x}{y}$ for w. (Lesson 12-8)

29. _____

30. Find three consecutive even integers such that the difference of the squares of the least and the greatest is 96. (Lesson 10-4)

30. _____

31. The length of a rectangular lot is 10 feet less than 3 times its width. The perimeter of the lot is 620 feet. Find the dimensions of the lot. (Lesson 3-3)

31. _____

32. Carlos paid $37.98 for some compact discs. This included $5\frac{1}{2}$% sales tax. What did the CDs cost without the tax? (Lesson 4-5)

32. _____

33. Find the dimensions of the rectangle whose width is 8 cm less than its length and whose area is 20 cm². (Lesson 11-3)

33. _____

Chapter 12 Answer Key

1. __D__

2. __A__

3. __A__

4. __D__

5. __A__

6. __B__

7. __A__

8. __D__

9. __B__

10. __B__

11. __C__

12. __A__

13. __C__

14. __B__

15. __B__

16. __D__

17. __C__

18. __A__

19. __D__

20. __B__

Bonus __$(x + 2)$ and $(x + 3)$__

1. __C__

2. __C__

3. __D__

4. __D__

5. __C__

6. __A__

7. __B__

8. __A__

9. __B__

10. __A__

11. __C__

12. __D__

13. __A__

14. __C__

15. __D__

16. __D__

17. __A__

18. __B__

19. __A__

20. __C__

Bonus __6__

Chapter 12 Answer Key

Form 1C

Page 313

1. __B__

2. __C__

3. __A__

4. __D__

5. __C__

6. __A__

7. __C__

8. __A__

9. __B__

10. __C__

11. __A__

Page 314

12. __B__

13. __A__

14. __D__

15. __C__

16. __A__

17. __B__

18. __D__

19. __A__

20. __C__

Bonus __−2__

Form 2A

Page 315

1. $\dfrac{y-7}{y+5}$

2. $\dfrac{v^7 w^4}{4y^7}$

3. $2n-3$

4. $\dfrac{12}{(x-2)^2}$

5. -1

6. n^2

7. $\dfrac{3r^2 u}{m^8}$

8. $\dfrac{n^2+3n+3}{n(n+1)}$

9. $\dfrac{5w}{w+5}$

10. 1

11. $\dfrac{x-7}{x+4}$

12. $\dfrac{(x-3)(x-1)}{x}$

13. $\dfrac{5v+6}{4v^2}$

14. $\dfrac{3y+12}{(y+6)(y-6)}$

15. $8,\ -3,\ \dfrac{3}{2}$

Page 316

16. $2x-4-\dfrac{13}{3x-2}$

17. __6 ways__

18. $-\dfrac{45}{22}$

19. __4, 5__

20. __2__

21. $2x+3,\ x+3$

22. $\dfrac{2400}{560+x}=\dfrac{2080}{560-x}$

23. $y=\dfrac{n^2 v}{a}$

24. __5 ohms__

25. $a=\dfrac{Qd}{KT(t_2-t_1)}$

Bonus $k=2,\ c=5$

Chapter 12 Answer Key

Form 2B

Page 317

1. $a - b$

2. $\dfrac{a - 7}{a - 1}$

3. $2y - 6$

4. $\dfrac{1}{s - 4}$

5. $4 - 2x$

6. $\dfrac{m + 1}{5m}$

7. 1

8. $r - s$

9. $2n + 3$

10. $\dfrac{7r + 20x}{6x^2 r^2}$

11. $\dfrac{3}{a + 3}$

12. $\dfrac{4a + b}{a^2 - b^2}$

13. $\dfrac{r^2 - 4}{r^2}$

14. $\dfrac{(x + 5)(x^2 + 2x - 6)}{(x + 2)(x^2 + 5x + 8)}$

15. $y \neq 5, -3, -2$

16. $t - 1 - \dfrac{1}{t + 5}$

Page 318

17. **18 meals**

18. **6**

19. **2**

20. **11**

21. $n = \dfrac{5cd - dy}{c}$

22. **66 ft/sec**

23. $x + 3, 2x + 1$

24. **35 mi/h**

25. $3\frac{2}{5}$ **ohms**

Bonus $1\frac{3}{5}$ **h**

Chapter 12 Answer Key

Page 319

1. $x + y$

2. $\dfrac{k + 5}{k - 1}$

3. $\dfrac{1}{2(m - 2)}$

4. $\dfrac{1}{r + 1}$

5. $\dfrac{6x + 12}{7x - 14}$

6. $\dfrac{x + 2}{4x}$

7. $\dfrac{v + 3}{t + 6}$

8. $x + 3$

9. $x + 2$

10. $\dfrac{2ma^2 + nb}{4a^3b^2}$

11. $\dfrac{3w + 4}{(w + 2)^2}$

12. $\dfrac{1}{2(r + s)}$

13. $\dfrac{r^2 - 2r + 1}{r}$

14. $\dfrac{x^2 + 3x - 1}{x^2 + 3x + 2}$

15. $1, -3$

16. $x - 6 - \dfrac{3}{x - 2}$

Page 320

17. **120 cards**

18. $\dfrac{5}{4}$

19. $3, -\dfrac{2}{3}$

20. 2

21. $k = \dfrac{2j}{j - 1}$

22. **44 ft/sec**

23. $x + 2, 2x - 1$

24. **4 mi/h**

25. **12 ohms**

Bonus   **2.4 h**

Page 321

1. $\dfrac{x - 4}{x + 4}$

2. $\dfrac{5}{x + 6}$

3. $\dfrac{x - 2}{x - 5}$

4. $\dfrac{x(x - 3)}{2}$

5. 2

6. 5

7. $5x + 16 \text{ R67}$

8. $3x - 7 \text{ RO}$

9. $2x - 1 \text{ R}-5$

10. $21x + 130 \text{ R897}$

11. $x^2 + 3x + 9 \text{ RO}$

12. $3x^2 - 23x + 97 \text{ R}-396$

13. **See students' graphs.**

14. $2, -1$

15. **See students' graphs; -1.**

16. $\dfrac{x + 2}{x + 1}$; the graphs of $y = \dfrac{x - \dfrac{x + 4}{x + 1}}{x - 2}$ and $y = \dfrac{x + 2}{x + 1}$ are the same (except for the excluded values).

Scoring Guide
Chapter 12
Performance Assessment

Level	Specific Criteria
3 Superior	• Shows thorough understanding of the concepts of *simplifying rational expressions, multiplying rational expressions*, and *solving rational equations*. • Uses appropriate strategies to solve problems. • Computations are correct. • Written explanations are exemplary. • Diagrams are accurate and appropriate. • Goes beyond requirements of some or all problems.
2 Satisfactory, with Minor Flaws	• Shows understanding of the concepts of *simplifying rational expressions, multiplying rational expressions*, and *solving rational equations*. • Uses appropriate strategies to solve problems. • Computations are mostly correct. • Written explanations are effective. • Diagrams are mostly accurate and appropriate. • Satisfies all requirements of problems.
1 Nearly Satisfactory, with Serious Flaws	• Shows understanding of most of the concepts of *simplifying rational expressions, multiplying rational expressions*, and *solving rational equations*. • May not use appropriate strategies to solve problems. • Computations are mostly correct. • Written explanations are satisfactory. • Diagrams are mostly accurate and appropriate. • Satisfies most requirements of problems.
0 Unsatisfactory	• Shows little or no understanding of the concepts of *simplifying rational expressions, multiplying rational expressions*, and *solving rational equations*. • May not use appropriate strategies to solve problems. • Computations are incorrect. • Written explanations are not satisfactory. • Diagrams are not accurate or appropriate. • Does not satisfy requirements of problems.

Chapter 12 Answer Key
Performance Assessment

Page 322

1. a. $M.A. = \dfrac{R}{r}$

$\qquad = \dfrac{\frac{3}{4}}{\frac{1}{2}}$ Substitute for R and r.

$\qquad = \dfrac{3}{4} \cdot \dfrac{2}{1}$ Invert and multiply.

$\qquad = \dfrac{3}{2}$ Simplify.

b. $\quad W = \dfrac{R}{r} \cdot F$

$\qquad = \dfrac{3}{2}(5.5)$

$\qquad = \dfrac{16.5}{2}$

$\qquad = 8.25 \text{ or } 8\dfrac{1}{4}$

c. $\quad W = \dfrac{R}{r} \cdot F$

$\qquad = \dfrac{3x^2y}{2xy^2} \cdot 6x^3$

$\qquad = \dfrac{18x^5y}{2xy^2}$

$\qquad = \dfrac{9x^4}{y}$

d. $M.A. = \dfrac{R_1}{r_1} \cdot \dfrac{R_2}{r_2}$

$\qquad = \dfrac{S}{\frac{1}{2}K} \cdot \dfrac{K}{t}$

$\qquad = S \cdot \dfrac{2}{K} \cdot \dfrac{K}{t} \text{ or } \dfrac{2S}{t}$

e. $M.A. = \dfrac{10}{2} = 5$

2. a. $\quad \dfrac{1}{f} = (\mu - 1)\left(\dfrac{1}{r_1} - \dfrac{1}{r_2}\right)$

$\qquad \dfrac{1}{f} = (\mu - 1)\left(\dfrac{r_2 - r_1}{r_1 r_2}\right)$

$\qquad f = \dfrac{r_1 r_2}{(\mu - 1)(r_2 - r_1)}$

b. $\quad f = \dfrac{0.8(-0.6)}{0.5(-0.6 - 0.8)} = 0.7 \text{ inches}$

Chapter 12 Answer Key

Mid-Chapter Test
Page 323

1. $\dfrac{y}{4x}$; $x, y \neq 0$

2. $\dfrac{1}{x+3}$; $x \neq \pm 3$

3. $\dfrac{6}{m+n}$; $m \neq \pm n$

4. $\dfrac{a-7}{a-1}$; $a \neq 1$; $a \neq -4$

5. $\dfrac{2a}{c}$

6. $2(y-3)$

7. $\dfrac{x^2+4x+3}{6}$

8. $\dfrac{y^2-2y+1}{y^2+6y+9}$

9. $\dfrac{s}{r}$

10. $\dfrac{m+1}{5m}$

11. $\dfrac{4}{a+3}$

12. $2a-2b$

13. $\dfrac{(x-y)^2}{2}$

14. $\dfrac{(x-3)(x-1)}{(x-6)(x+4)}$

15. $x^2+2x+12+\dfrac{37}{x-3}$

16. $2x-5+\dfrac{15}{2x+1}$

17. $x^2-x+6+\dfrac{16}{x-4}$

18. $x-11+\dfrac{43}{x+3}$

19. c^2-2c+1

20. $2x^2-2x-3+\dfrac{4}{x+1}$

Bonus 20

Quiz A
Page 324

1. $\dfrac{ab}{8c^3}$; $b, c \neq 0$

2. $\dfrac{3x}{x+2y}$; $x \neq \pm 2y$

3. $-\dfrac{1}{5}$; $x \neq -4, 3$

4. $(x-2)(x-3)$; $x \neq -2, -3$

5. $\dfrac{x}{9y}$

6. $\dfrac{x^2}{2(x+3)}$

7. $\dfrac{3x+1}{x}$

8. $\dfrac{-r^2}{r+7}$

9. $\dfrac{m}{4(m+2n)}$

10. -1

Quiz B
Page 324

1. $5x-2$

2. $2x-9+\dfrac{4}{x-3}$

3. $4a^2-4a+1+\dfrac{14}{3a+1}$

4. $x^2-2x+11$

5. $\dfrac{yw^2}{x^3z^3}$

6. $\dfrac{c}{a^6}$

7. $\dfrac{y^2}{vwx^2}$

8. $\dfrac{m+1}{m(m-1)}$

9. m^2+4m+3

10. $\dfrac{(b+3)(b^2+7b+1)}{(b+2)(b+1)(2b+1)}$

Quiz C
Page 325

1. $\dfrac{3y}{4}$

2. 3

3. $\dfrac{a-6}{2b^2}$

4. $x+4$

5. $x+3$

6. $\dfrac{2-3r}{r-s}$

7. $\dfrac{5bc-4a^2}{3a^2c^2}$

8. $\dfrac{2x^2+8}{x^2-4}$

9. $\dfrac{1}{x-1}$

10. $\dfrac{4x+15}{(x+2)(x+1)(x+3)}$

Quiz D
Page 325

1. $\dfrac{26}{3}$

2. -14

3. $u=\dfrac{rv}{nv-v-nr}$

4. $\dfrac{3}{n^2xy^4}$

5. $\dfrac{x^2-4x-4}{x^2-2x+4}$

Chapter 12 Answer Key

Standardized Test Practice Page 326	Cumulative Review Page 327	Page 328
1. **A**	1. **reflexive**	18. **−3, 4**
2. **B**	2. $15x^2 + 10x$	19. $\frac{3}{4}, 1$
3. **B**	3. **−0.893**	20. **−1**
4. **D**	4. **(1, 1)**	21. **2**
5. **B**	5. **(3, −5)**	22. $\frac{x+1}{2x+1}$
	6. **61.4**	23. $\frac{2x+1}{x+3}$
	7. **62**	24. $a^2(a+b)$
	8. **54.5**	25. $2x + 9 + \frac{22}{x-3}$
6. **D**	9. **69**	26. $\frac{3k^2 + k + 6}{(3k-1)(k+3)}$
	10.	27. $\frac{c-7}{c-2}$
7. **D**	11. $-8x^6y^5$	28. $\frac{(z+1)(z-1)}{(z+2)(z-2)}$
8. **C**	12. $\frac{16}{81}c^8d^{12}$	29. $w = \frac{x}{y(x-1)}$
	13. $-\frac{3k^2}{2h^4j^7}$	30. **10, 12, and 14**
9. **D**	14. $x^2y - 7xy + 7y^3$	31. **80 ft by 230 ft**
	15. $9m^2 - 4n^2$	32. **$36**
10. **C**	16. $(4 - 5r)(3c - 2d)$	33. **2 cm and 10 cm**
	17. $(3a - 4)(a - 3)$	

13

Chapter 13 Test, Form 1A

Write the letter for the correct answer in the blank at the right of each problem.

1. The legs of a right triangle have lengths of a and b. The hypotenuse has a length of c. If $a = \sqrt{8}$ and $c = 9$, then what is the length of b?
   A. $\sqrt{17}$ B. $\sqrt{89}$ C. $\sqrt{73}$ D. 1

   1. _____

2. Which of the following are measures of three sides of a right triangle?
   A. 4, 7, 8   B. 10, 15, 20   C. 3, 7, 9   D. 9, 12, 15

   2. _____

3. What is the length of the diagonal of a rectangle whose length is 7 ft and whose width is $3\sqrt{2}$ ft?
   A. $\sqrt{31}$ ft   B. $\sqrt{67}$ ft   C. $21\sqrt{2}$ ft   D. 20 ft

   3. _____

4. Simplify $\sqrt{252}$.
   A. $7\sqrt{6}$ B. $7\sqrt{36}$ C. $6\sqrt{7}$ D. $36\sqrt{7}$

   4. _____

5. Simplify $\sqrt{18n^3y^2}$.
   A. $3n|y|\sqrt{2n}$ B. $2|n|y\sqrt{3n}$ C. $3|n|y\sqrt{2n}$ D. $2n|y|\sqrt{3n}$

   5. _____

6. Simplify $\dfrac{\sqrt{5n^6}}{\sqrt{3y^5}}$.
   A. $\dfrac{n^3\sqrt{3y}}{15|y^3|}$ B. $\dfrac{n^3\sqrt{15y}}{3|y^3|}$ C. $\dfrac{|n^3|\sqrt{15y}}{3y^3}$ D. $\dfrac{|n^3|\sqrt{3y}}{15y^3}$

   6. _____

7. Simplify $\dfrac{3}{4-\sqrt{13}}$.
   A. $\dfrac{\sqrt{13}}{-3}$ B. $\dfrac{12+3\sqrt{13}}{29}$ C. $4+\sqrt{13}$ D. $\dfrac{12-3\sqrt{13}}{29}$

   7. _____

8. Simplify $4\sqrt{13} - \sqrt{13}$.
   A. $3\sqrt{13}$ B. -52 C. 4 D. $-4\sqrt{13}$

   8. _____

9. Simplify $3\sqrt{32} - 2\sqrt{18} + \sqrt{54}$.
   A. $4\sqrt{2} - 3\sqrt{6}$ B. $2\sqrt{6} + 6\sqrt{3}$
   C. $2\sqrt{6} - 6\sqrt{3}$ D. $6\sqrt{2} + 3\sqrt{6}$

   9. _____

10. Which expression *cannot* be simplified?
    A. $5\sqrt{8} + 2\sqrt{18}$ B. $2\sqrt{112} + \sqrt{63}$
    C. $3\sqrt{55} - 4\sqrt{65}$ D. $2\sqrt{45} + 4\sqrt{20}$

    10. _____

11. Simplify $\sqrt{14} - \sqrt{\frac{2}{7}}$.

    A. $\frac{6\sqrt{14}}{7}$ **B.** $\frac{2\sqrt{7}}{7}$ **C.** $\frac{8\sqrt{14}}{7}$ **D.** $7\sqrt{2}$

11. _____

12. Solve $\sqrt{3n + 1} + 3 = 7$.

    A. $\{13\}$ **B.** $\left\{\frac{1}{3}\right\}$ **C.** $\left\{-1, \frac{1}{3}\right\}$ **D.** $\{5\}$

12. _____

13. Solve $\sqrt{12x^2 - 75} = 3x$.

    A. $\{5, -5\}$ **B.** $\{-5\}$ **C.** $\{5\}$ **D.** no solution

13. _____

14. Which equation has no real solution?

    A. $\sqrt{6x} - 8 = -6$ **B.** $\sqrt{6x} - 8 = 6$
    C. $\sqrt{6x - 8} = -6$ **D.** $\sqrt{6x - 8} = 6$

14. _____

15. What is the distance between $(-2, 7)$ and $(-3, -4)$?

    A. $\sqrt{29}$ **B.** $\sqrt{82}$ **C.** $\sqrt{34}$ **D.** $\sqrt{122}$

15. _____

16. The distance between $(n, 5)$ and $(2, -8)$ is $\sqrt{185}$. If the two possible values for n are added together, then what is the result?

    A. 4   **B.** -4 **C.** 2   **D.** -2

16. _____

17. What is the distance between the origin and $(-7, 5)$?

    A. $\sqrt{24}$ **B.** 12   **C.** $\sqrt{74}$ **D.** $\sqrt{34}$

17. _____

18. What value of c makes $x^2 - 5x + c$ a perfect square?

    A. $-\frac{5}{2}$ **B.** $\frac{25}{2}$ **C.** $\frac{25}{4}$ **D.** -5

18. _____

19. If $2n^2 - 6n = 3$ is to be solved by completing the square, what would be the best thing to do first?

    A. Add $6n$ to each side.   **B.** Divide each side by 2.
    C. Add 9 to each side.   **D.** Subtract 3 from each side.

19. _____

20. Solve $y^2 + 8y = 2$.

    A. $-4 \pm \sqrt{10}$ **B.** $-4 \pm 3\sqrt{2}$ **C.** $4 \pm 3\sqrt{2}$ **D.** $4 \pm \sqrt{10}$

20. _____

    Bonus   Solve $8 - 3x = \sqrt{4x^2 + 20} + 8$.   Bonus _____

Write the letter for the correct answer in the blank at the right of each problem.

1. What is the measure of the hypotenuse of a right triangle with side $a = \sqrt{6}$ and side $b = 8$?
   A. $\sqrt{58}$ B. $\sqrt{70}$ C. $\sqrt{14}$ D. 2

   1. _____

2. Which of the following are the measures of three sides of a right triangle?
   A. 6, 8, 10   B. 5, 9, 11   C. 11, 13, 16   D. 3, 8, 12

   2. _____

3. What is the length of the diagonal of a rectangle with a length of 12 m and width of 5 m?
   A. 169 m   B. 13 m   C. $\sqrt{17}$ m   D. $\sqrt{119}$ m

   3. _____

4. Simplify $\sqrt{96}$.
   A. $6\sqrt{4}$ B. $6\sqrt{16}$ C. $16\sqrt{6}$ D. $4\sqrt{6}$

   4. _____

5. Simplify $\sqrt{28x^2y^3}$.
   A. $7x|y|\sqrt{2y}$ B. $2x|y|\sqrt{7y}$ C. $2|x|y\sqrt{7y}$ D. $7|x|y\sqrt{2y}$

   5. _____

6. Simplify $\sqrt{\dfrac{18}{40}}$.
   A. $\dfrac{\sqrt{3}}{2}$ B. $\dfrac{3\sqrt{20}}{20}$ C. $\dfrac{3\sqrt{5}}{10}$ D. $\dfrac{\sqrt{45}}{10}$

   6. _____

7. Simplify $\dfrac{5}{4 + \sqrt{6}}$.
   A. $\dfrac{4 - \sqrt{6}}{2}$ B. $\dfrac{20 - 5\sqrt{6}}{22}$ C. $\dfrac{20 + 5\sqrt{6}}{22}$ D. $\dfrac{-\sqrt{6}}{2}$

   7. _____

8. Simplify $5\sqrt{7} - \sqrt{7}$.
   A. $4\sqrt{7}$ B. -35 C. 5   D. $-5\sqrt{7}$

   8. _____

9. Which expression cannot be simplified?
   A. $5\sqrt{8} + 6\sqrt{2}$ B. $5\sqrt{10} + 3\sqrt{5}$
   C. $7\sqrt{48} + \sqrt{108}$ D. $\sqrt{52} + \sqrt{13}$

   9. _____

10. Simplify $\sqrt{18} - \sqrt{54} + 2\sqrt{50}$.
    A. $13\sqrt{2} - 3\sqrt{6}$ B. $-4\sqrt{3} + 4\sqrt{5}$
    C. $-4\sqrt{3} - 4\sqrt{5}$ D. $8\sqrt{2} - 3\sqrt{6}$

    10. _____

11. Simplify $\sqrt{15} + \sqrt{\dfrac{3}{5}}$.

    A. $\dfrac{2\sqrt{15}}{5}$ B. $\dfrac{6\sqrt{15}}{5}$ C. $2\sqrt{3}$ D. $\dfrac{\sqrt{15}}{5}$

11. _____

12. Solve $\sqrt{3x-2} = 4$.

    A. $\{12\}$ B. $\{6\}$ C. $\left\{\dfrac{2}{3}\right\}$ D. $\left\{\dfrac{3}{2}\right\}$

12. _____

13. Solve $\sqrt{3a+28} = a$.

    A. $\{-4\}$ B. $\{7\}$ C. $\{7, -4\}$ D. no solution

13. _____

14. Solve $\sqrt{5n-1} - n = 1$.

    A. $\{1, 2\}$ B. $\{-1, -2\}$ C. $\left\{\dfrac{1}{4}\right\}$ D. $\{1\}$

14. _____

15. What is the distance between $(-3, 4)$ and $(2, 7)$?

    A. $\sqrt{34}$ B. $\sqrt{74}$ C. $2\sqrt{30}$ D. $\sqrt{10}$

15. _____

16. The distance between $(n, 4)$ and $(-2, 7)$ is $\sqrt{73}$. What is one possible value for n?

    A. -6 B. 10 C. 8 D. -10

16. _____

17. What is the distance between the origin and $(-6, 8)$?

    A. 10 B. 2 C. 14 D. $\sqrt{28}$

17. _____

18. What value of c makes $y^2 - y + c$ a perfect square?

    A. $\dfrac{1}{2}$ B. $-\dfrac{1}{2}$ C. $\dfrac{1}{4}$ D. $-\dfrac{1}{4}$

18. _____

19. If $b^2 + 6b - 10 = 0$ is to be solved by completing the square, what would be the best thing to do first?

    A. Divide each side by 8.   B. Add 10 to each side.

    C. Subtract 8 from each side.   D. Add 2 to each side.

19. _____

20. Solve $d^2 - 6d + 4 = 0$.

    A. $3 \pm \sqrt{5}$ B. $6 \pm 2\sqrt{5}$ C. $\dfrac{-6 \pm \sqrt{5}}{2}$ D. $\dfrac{3 \pm 2\sqrt{5}}{2}$

20. _____

Bonus Simplify $\sqrt{4x^2 + 12x + 9}$.

Bonus _____

13

Chapter 13 Test, Form 1C

Write the letter for the correct answer in the blank at the right of each problem.

1. What is the measure of the hypotenuse of a right triangle with side $a = \sqrt{3}$ and $b = 4$?
   A. 5   **B.** $\sqrt{11}$ **C.** $\sqrt{19}$ **D.** $\sqrt{13}$

1. _____

2. Which of the following are the measures of three sides of a right triangle?
   A. 4, 5, 6   **B.** 3, 4, 5   **C.** 5, 11, 12   **D.** 4, 8, 12

2. _____

3. What is the length of the diagonal of a rectangle with a length of 8 m and a width of 6 m?
   A. 10 m   **B.** 14 m   **C.** 48 m   **D.** 100 m

3. _____

4. Simplify $\sqrt{72}$.
   A. $2\sqrt{18}$ **B.** $3\sqrt{8}$ **C.** $6\sqrt{2}$ **D.** $36\sqrt{2}$

4. _____

5. Simplify $\sqrt{20x^3y^2}$.
   A. $5x|y|\sqrt{2x}$ **B.** $2x|y|\sqrt{5x}$ **C.** $2|x|y\sqrt{5x}$ **D.** $5|x|y\sqrt{2x}$

5. _____

6. Simplify $\sqrt{\dfrac{12}{28}}$.
   A. $\sqrt{\dfrac{3}{7}}$ **B.** $\dfrac{\sqrt{21}}{7}$ **C.** $\dfrac{\sqrt{10}}{7}$ **D.** $\dfrac{\sqrt{84}}{14}$

6. _____

7. Simplify $\dfrac{3}{5 - \sqrt{2}}$.
   A. $\dfrac{15 + 3\sqrt{2}}{23}$ **B.** $\dfrac{15 - 3\sqrt{2}}{23}$ **C.** $15 + 3\sqrt{2}$ **D.** $\dfrac{15 + 3\sqrt{2}}{3}$

7. _____

8. Simplify $6\sqrt{5} - 2\sqrt{5}$.
   A. 4   **B.** -12 **C.** $-12\sqrt{5}$ **D.** $4\sqrt{5}$

8. _____

9. Which expression cannot be simplified?
   A. $3\sqrt{8} + 4\sqrt{2}$ **B.** $3\sqrt{11} - 7\sqrt{5}$
   C. $\sqrt{50} - \sqrt{24}$ **D.** $2\sqrt{12} + 5\sqrt{14}$

9. _____

10. Simplify $3\sqrt{12} + \sqrt{27} - 2\sqrt{20}$.
    A. $14\sqrt{3} - 4\sqrt{5}$ **B.** $3\sqrt{3} - \sqrt{2}$
    C. $9\sqrt{3} - 4\sqrt{5}$ **D.** $21\sqrt{3} - 8\sqrt{5}$

10. _____

11. Simplify $\sqrt{3} + \sqrt{\frac{1}{3}}$.

   A. $\frac{\sqrt{3}}{3}$ B. $\frac{2\sqrt{3}}{3}$ C. $\frac{4\sqrt{3}}{3}$ D. $2\sqrt{3}$

11. _____

12. Solve $\sqrt{2x - 5} = 3$.

   A. $\{4\}$ B. $\{7\}$ C. $\{-8\}$ D. $\left\{\frac{11}{2}\right\}$

12. _____

13. Solve $\sqrt{2x + 8} = x$.

   A. $\{4, -2\}$ B. $\{4\}$ C. $\{-2\}$ D. no solution

13. _____

14. Solve $\sqrt{2x + 3} = x + 2$.

   A. $\{-1\}$ B. $\{1\}$ C. $\left\{\frac{-3}{2}, -2\right\}$ D. no solution

14. _____

15. What is the distance between $(-2, 3)$ and $(3, 5)$?

   A. $\sqrt{7}$ B. $\sqrt{29}$ C. $\sqrt{5}$ D. $\sqrt{65}$

15. _____

16. The distance between $(4, 2)$ and $(n, 6)$ is 5. What is one possible value for n?

   A. 3   B. 5   C. 7   D. -1

16. _____

17. What is the distance from the origin to $(5, -1)$?

   A. 4   B. 6   C. $2\sqrt{6}$ D. $\sqrt{26}$

17. _____

18. What value of c makes $x^2 + 10x + c$ a perfect square?

   A. 100   B. 25   C. 10   D. 5

18. _____

19. If $x^2 - 8x - 3 = 0$ is to be solved by completing the square, what would be the best thing to do first?

   A. Add 3 to both sides.   B. Add $8x$ to both sides.
   C. Add 16 to both sides.   C. Divide each side by -8.

19. _____

20. Solve $x^2 - 8x = 5$.

   A. $4 \pm \sqrt{21}$ B. $4 \pm \sqrt{13}$ C. $-4 \pm \sqrt{21}$ D. $-4 \pm \sqrt{13}$

20. _____

Bonus Simplify $\sqrt{4x^2 + 4x + 1}$.

Bonus _____

13

Chapter 13 Test, Form 2A

1. Find the length of the hypotenuse of a right triangle if side $a = \sqrt{5}$ and side $b = 6$.

1. _____

2. Find the width of a rectangle with a diagonal of 12 cm and a length of 10 cm.

2. _____

3. Two buildings are separated by a 3-ft alleyway. Fatima wants to use a 16-ft ladder to reach a window in the wall of one of these buildings. If she places the foot of the ladder against the base of the other building, how far up the wall will the top of the ladder reach?

3. _____

Simplify. Leave in radical form and use absolute values when necessary.

4. $\sqrt{378}$

4. _____

5. $\sqrt{21n^6 y^{11}}$

5. _____

6. $\sqrt{\dfrac{5x^4}{4n^5}}$

6. _____

7. $\dfrac{\sqrt{8}}{2\sqrt{5} + \sqrt{6}}$

7. _____

8. $7\sqrt{6} + 8\sqrt{3} - \sqrt{6}$

8. _____

9. $5\sqrt{12} + 6\sqrt{\dfrac{1}{3}} - 3\sqrt{48}$

9. _____

10. $2\sqrt{20} - \sqrt{50} + 3\sqrt{45}$

10. _____

11. $(2\sqrt{6} + 7\sqrt{3})(2\sqrt{6} - 7\sqrt{3})$

11. _____

Solve each equation. Check the solutions.

12. $\sqrt{3n - 2} + 6 = 10$

12. _____

13. $\sqrt{\dfrac{n}{3}} + 12 = 7$

13. _____

14. $3 + \sqrt{x - 1} = x$

14. _____

15. Find the distance between $(-4, 6)$ and $(5, 3)$.

15. _____

16. The distance between $(a, 4)$ and $(-3, -2)$ is $\sqrt{61}$. Find the two possible values for a.

16. _____

17. Find the distance from the origin to $(-9, 5)$.

17. _____

Solve by completing the square.

18. $x^2 - 14x - 5 = 0$

18. _____

19. $2x^2 + x - 3 = 0$

19. _____

20. Find the value for c that makes $x^2 - \dfrac{1}{4}x + c$ a perfect square.

20. _____

Bonus Simplify $\sqrt{\dfrac{2}{3}} - \sqrt{\dfrac{3}{2}}$.

Bonus _____

NAME_____ DATE_____

Chapter 13 Test, Form 2B

1. Use the Pythagorean theorem to find the hypotenuse of a right triangle if side $a = 6$ and side $b = 10$.

1. _____

2. Find the width of a rectangle with a diagonal of 25 cm and a length of 24 cm.

2. _____

3. A rope from the top of a mast on a sailboat is attached to a point on the deck 5 feet from the base of the mast. If the rope is 13 feet long, how high is the mast?

3. _____

Simplify. Leave in radical form and use absolute value symbols when necessary.

4. $\sqrt{24}$

4. _____

5. $\sqrt{75y^4w^3}$

5. _____

6. $\dfrac{\sqrt{14}}{\sqrt{45}}$

6. _____

7. $\dfrac{6}{6 - \sqrt{11}}$

7. _____

8. $3\sqrt{11} + 2\sqrt{11}$

8. _____

9. $\sqrt{20} + 2\sqrt{45}$

9. _____

10. $\sqrt{14} + \sqrt{\dfrac{2}{7}}$

10. _____

11. $\sqrt{6}(\sqrt{30} + 4\sqrt{10})$

11. _____

Solve each equation. Check the solutions.

12. $\sqrt{x-8} = x - 10$

12. _____

13. $\sqrt{\dfrac{9a}{3}} - 4 = 0$

13. _____

14. $\sqrt{m} = 2\sqrt{3}$

14. _____

15. Find the distance between $(0, -4)$ and $(5, 2)$.

15. _____

16. The distance between $(3, 5)$ and $(7, a)$ is 5. Find the two possible values for a.

16. _____

17. Find the distance from the origin to $(5, -4)$.

17. _____

Solve by completing the square.

18. $r^2 + 18r + 9 = 0$

18. _____

19. $b^2 + 8b + 10 = 0$

19. _____

20. Find the value for c that makes $x^2 + 3x + c$ a perfect square.

20. _____

Bonus For what values of x is $\sqrt{7x - 4}$ a real number?   **Bonus** _____

1. Use the Pythagorean theorem to find the hypotenuse of a right triangle if side $a = 4$ and side $b = 7$.

1. _____

2. Find the width of a rectangle with a diagonal of 17 cm and a length of 15 cm.

2. _____

3. A 10-ft ladder leans against the side of a house. The top of the ladder rests 8 ft above the ground. How far from the house is the base of the ladder?

3. _____

Simplify. Leave in radical form and use absolute value symbols when necessary.

4. $\sqrt{40}$

4. _____

5. $\sqrt{50x^3y^2}$

5. _____

6. $\dfrac{\sqrt{6}}{\sqrt{18}}$

6. _____

7. $\dfrac{5}{\sqrt{10} - 3}$

7. _____

8. $4\sqrt{7} + 3\sqrt{7}$

8. _____

9. $2\sqrt{24} + \sqrt{54}$

9. _____

10. $\sqrt{10} + \sqrt{\dfrac{2}{5}}$

10. _____

11. $\sqrt{6}(\sqrt{2} - 3\sqrt{3})$

11. _____

Solve each equation. Check the solutions.

12. $\sqrt{\frac{4x}{3}} - 2 = 0$

12. _____

13. $\sqrt{7x - 3} = 5$

13. _____

14. $\sqrt{2x - 3} = x - 3$

14. _____

15. Find the distance between $(-3, 0)$ and $(2, 7)$.

15. _____

16. The distance between $(2, 1)$ and $(n, 4)$ is 5. Find the two possible values for n.

16. _____

17. Find the distance from the origin to $(6, -8)$.

17. _____

Solve by completing the square.

18. $m^2 + 8m - 3 = 0$

18. _____

19. $x^2 - 12x + 25 = 0$

19. _____

20. Find the value for c that makes $x^2 + 7x + c$ a perfect square.

20. _____

Bonus Simplify $\sqrt{\frac{1}{4}} - \sqrt{\frac{1}{2}}$.

Bonus _____

13

Chapter 13 Calculator-Based Test

For a right triangle with legs a and b and hypotenuse c, find the length of the missing side, to the nearest hundredth.

1. $a = 24.1$ and $b = 32.3$

1. _____

2. $a = 10.8$ and $c = 16.5$

2. _____

3. $c = \sqrt{23}$ and $b = 1.6$

3. _____

4. $a = 96$ and $c = 204$

4. _____

5. $b = \sqrt{29}$ and $c = 31$

5. _____

6. $a = \sqrt{7}$ and $c = \sqrt{151}$

6. _____

7. The voltage required for a circuit is given by $V = \sqrt{PR}$, where P is the power in watts and R is the resistance in ohms. Find the number of volts needed to light a 120-watt bulb with a resistance of 144 ohms.

7. _____

Compare the expressions. Use <, = , or >.

8. $\sqrt{\dfrac{5}{6}}$ _____ $\dfrac{\sqrt{30}}{6}$

8. _____

9. $\dfrac{3}{\sqrt{11}}$ _____ $\dfrac{6}{\sqrt{22}}$

9. _____

10. $\dfrac{2}{\sqrt{6} - \sqrt{2}}$ _____ $\dfrac{1}{2}(\sqrt{6} + \sqrt{2})$

10. _____

Simplify.

11. $8\sqrt{3} - 3\sqrt{75}$

11. _____

12. $7\sqrt{98} + 5\sqrt{32} - 2\sqrt{75}$

12. _____

13. $6\sqrt{5} - 4\sqrt{6} + \sqrt{28}$

13. _____

Find the distance between each pair of points, to the nearest hundredth.

14. $(14, -11)$ and $(-13, -4)$

14. _____

15. $(-4, -9)$ and $(5, 15)$

15. _____

16. Two bicycle riders start out from the same point. One rides west, 5 mi/h faster than the other rider heading south. After 2 hours, they are 45 mi apart. To the nearest tenth, find the rate of the rider heading south.

16. _____

Chapter 13 Performance Assessment

Instructions: *Demonstrate your knowledge by giving a clear, concise solution to each problem. Be sure to include all relevant drawings and justify your answers. You may show your solution in more than one way or investigate beyond the requirements of the problem.*

1. Mrs. Raines is having a sprinkler system installed in her flower bed. The diagram below shows the location of sprinklers A, B, C, and D. The water source S is in the center of the bed.

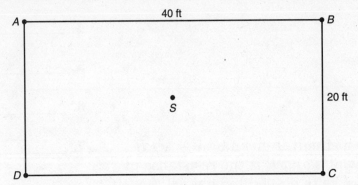

a. How much pipe would be required to hook each sprinkler directly to the water source? Explain your answer.

b. Do you think she could save pipe by running pipe from S to A, from A to B, from B to C, and from C to D? Explain your answer.

c. Would running pipe from A to B and from C to D before connecting the midpoint of each line to the water source S save pipe? Justify your answer.

d. If A is connected to D and B is connected to C and the midpoints of these two lines connected to the water source, would Mrs. Raines save pipe over the arrangement in part c? Why?

e. Would the arrangement in part d save pipe over the arrangement in part a? Justify your answer.

f. What other considerations might Mrs. Raines consider in choosing the hook-up arrangement?

g. Find the pipe arrangement that would use the least pipe for a square of side a feet. Justify your answer.

2. Solve $8\sqrt{4z^2 - 43} = 40$. Justify each step in your solution.

Chapter 13 Mid-Chapter Test (Lessons 13-1 through 13-3)

If c is the measure of the hypotenuse of a right triangle, find each missing measure.

1. $a = 6$, $b = 10$, $c = ?$ 1. _____

2. $b = \sqrt{5}$, $c = 6$, $a = ?$ 2. _____

3. $a = 5$, $c = 13$, $b = ?$ 3. _____

The measures of three sides of a triangle are given. Determine whether each triangle is a right triangle.

4. 13, 17, 21   4. _____

5. 10, 24, 26   5. _____

6. Find the length of the diagonal of a rectangle   6. _____
   whose length is 8 ft and whose width is $3\sqrt{8}$ ft.

7. A 12-ft rope attached to the top of the mast of a sailboat   7. _____
   is fastened to a point on the deck 4 ft from the base of the
   mast. What is the height of the mast?

Simplify. Leave in radical form and use absolute value symbols when necessary.

8. $\sqrt{288}$ 9. $\sqrt{18x^6y^3}$ 8. _____

                                                    9. _____

10. $(x - 2\sqrt{5})^2$ 11. $(4\sqrt{3} + 5)(4\sqrt{3} - 5)$ 10. _____

                                                    11. _____

12. $\dfrac{10}{\sqrt{8}}$ 13. $\dfrac{6}{5 - \sqrt{3}}$ 12. _____

                                                    13. _____

14. $6\sqrt{5} - 2\sqrt{10} + \sqrt{5}$ 14. _____

15. $5\sqrt{12} - \frac{4}{3}\sqrt{27} + \sqrt{\frac{1}{3}}$ 15. _____

16. $3\sqrt{50} - 2\sqrt{72} + \sqrt{24}$ 16. _____

Bonus   The area of a square is 72 m². Find the length   **Bonus** _____
   of the diagonal of the square.

If c is the measure of the hypotenuse of a right triangle, find each missing measure. Round answers to the nearest hundredth.

1. $a = 12$, $b = 5$, $c = ?$ 2. $b = 3$, $c = 15$, $a = ?$

1. _____

2. _____

3. The measures of the three sides of a triangle are 11, 60, and 61. Determine whether this triangle is a right triangle.

3. _____

Simplify. Leave in radical form and use absolute value symbols when necessary.

4. $\sqrt{8x^2y}$ 5. $\sqrt{5} \cdot \sqrt{30}$

4. _____

5. _____

6. $\dfrac{\sqrt{32}}{\sqrt{6}}$ 7. $\sqrt{\dfrac{54x}{x^5}}$

6. _____

7. _____

8. $\dfrac{3}{4 + \sqrt{2}}$ 9. $\sqrt{72}$

8. _____

9. _____

10. $(3\sqrt{7} + 5\sqrt{2})(3\sqrt{7} - 5\sqrt{2})$

10. _____

Simplify. Then use a calculator to verify your answer.

1. $6\sqrt{45} + 2\sqrt{80}$ 2. $5\sqrt{6} - 4\sqrt{10} - \sqrt{6} + 12\sqrt{10}$

1. _____

2. _____

3. $\sqrt{15} - \sqrt{\dfrac{3}{5}}$ 4. $2\sqrt{27} + \sqrt{18} - 4\sqrt{75}$

3. _____

4. _____

5. The width of a rectangle is $2\sqrt{18}$. The length is $5\sqrt{2} - 2\sqrt{3}$. Find the exact measures of the perimeter and area, in simplest form.

5. _____

Chapter 13, Quiz C (Lessons 13-4 and 13-5)

Solve each equation. Check the solution.

1. $\sqrt{7y} = 14$ 2. $\sqrt{2x + 9} + 6 = 10$

   1. _____

   2. _____

3. $\sqrt{4a} = 3\sqrt{2}$ 4. $\sqrt{c + 2} = c - 4$

   3. _____

   4. _____

5. $\sqrt{\dfrac{3a}{5}} - 6 = 0$

   5. _____

Find the distance between each pair of points whose coordinates are given. Express answers in simplest form and as decimal approximations rounded to the nearest hundredth.

6. $(4, -6), (7, -10)$ 7. $(0, 7), (-5, 13)$

   6. _____

   7. _____

8. Find a if the distance between the points with coordinates $(-2, 3)$ and $(5, a)$ is $\sqrt{50}$.

   8. _____

9. Find two numbers with a geometric mean of $\sqrt{30}$ if one number is 7 more than twice the other.

   9. _____

10. Find the perimeter of the triangle with vertices $A(-2, 3)$, $B(1, -1)$, and $C(3, 3)$.

   10. _____

Chapter 13, Quiz D (Lesson 13-6)

1. Find the value of c that makes $x^2 + 9x + c$ a perfect square.

   1. _____

2. Find the value of c that makes $x^2 - 12x + c$ a perfect square.

   2. _____

Solve each equation by completing the square. Leave irrational roots in simplest radical form.

3. $w^2 + 8w - 20 = 0$

   3. _____

4. $x^2 - 6x + 3 = 0$

   4. _____

5. $x^2 - 3x + 1 = 0$

   5. _____

Choose the best answer. Write A, B, C, or D.

1. What is the sum of the product of $4m$ and $2n$ and the difference of $4m$ and $2n$?
   A. $8m$
   B. $16m^2 - 4n^2$
   C. $8mn + 4m - 2n$
   D. $10mn$

   1._____

2. In a classroom, the number of seats in each row is two more than the number of rows. If there are 48 seats in all, find the number of rows.
   A. 4
   B. 5
   C. 6
   D. 7

   2._____

3. If $r^2 = 6$ then what is a possible value of $(2r - 1)^2$?
   A. 1
   B. $23 - 4\sqrt{6}$
   C. $25 - 4\sqrt{6}$
   D. 25

   3._____

4. Kevin chooses three numbers such that when he adds them in pairs the sums are 27, 31, and 34. Which of the following is the greatest number?
   A. 19
   B. 28
   C. 30
   D. 35

   4._____

5. It takes 3 hours for 2 men to wallpaper a room. How many hours would it take 3 men, working at the same rate, to wallpaper the same room?
   A. $\frac{1}{2}$
   B. 2
   C. 6
   D. 9

   5._____

6. How many cartons are needed to pack 300 glasses if each carton has 4 rows and each row holds 4 glasses?
   A. 16
   B. 17
   C. 18
   D. 19

   6._____

7. If $3y - \frac{2}{3} = \frac{3}{5}$, then $\frac{2}{3} - 3y =$
   A. $\frac{5}{3}$.
   B. $-\frac{3}{5}$.
   C. $\frac{2}{5}$.
   D. $-\frac{2}{5}$.

   7._____

8. If $m = 5 - (n - 1)^2$, which of the following values of n gives the greatest value of m?
   A. 1
   B. 2
   C. 3
   D. 4

   8._____

9. If the sum of three consecutive even integers is 42, what is the sum of the next three consecutive even integers?
   A. 12
   B. 54
   C. 57
   D. 60

   9._____

10. How many miles can a car traveling 55 mi/h travel in $\frac{2}{5}$ of a minute?
    A. $\frac{11}{30}$
    B. $2\frac{7}{24}$
    C. 22
    D. $137\frac{1}{2}$

    10._____

13

Chapter 13 Cumulative Review

1. Write a mathematical expression for the product of 8 and the square of a number. (Lesson 1-1)

1. _____

2. State the property shown in $(ab)c = a(bc)$. (Lesson 1-8)

2. _____

3. Find $-\frac{2}{3} + \frac{3}{4}$. (Lesson 2-5)

3. _____

4. Simplify $-5(4) + (-6)(-2)$. (Lesson 2-6)

4. _____

5. Solve $4y - 5 = 7y + 6$. (Lesson 3-5)

5. _____

6. Find three consecutive odd integers such that 8 more than twice the first integer is equal to 19 less than three times the third integer. (Lesson 3-3)

6. _____

7. A student answered 34 out of 40 questions correctly. What percent were answered correctly? (Lesson 4-4)

7. _____

8. Marvella has 23 coins in nickels, dimes, and quarters. If she has twice as many nickels as dimes and has $2.45 in all, how many of each does she have? (Lesson 4-7)

8. _____

9. Where on the coordinate plane does the point $(0, -3)$ lie? (Lesson 5-1)

9. _____

10. If $f(x) = \frac{1}{2}x^2 + 3x - 1$, find $f(-2)$. (Lesson 5-5)

10. _____

11. Write an equation in slope-intercept form for the line passing through $(-2, 1)$ with a slope of 4. (Lesson 6-4)

11. _____

12. Write an equation in standard form for the line that passes through $(0, -2)$ and is perpendicular to the line $x - 4y = 8$. (Lesson 6-6)

12. _____

13. Solve $10y - 3(y + 4) \le 0$. (Lesson 7-3)

13. _____.

14. Graph $3y - x \le 3$. (Lesson 7-8)

14.

Solve each system of equations. (Lesson 8-4)

15. $x + 3y = 6$
$5x - 4y = 11$

15. _____

16. $4x - 5y = 23$
$5x + 6y = -8$

16. _____

17. Find $(4x^2 - 2x + 3) + (6x^2 + x - 2)$. (Lesson 9-5)

17. _____

18. Simplify $(2a + 3)(3a - 7)$. (Lesson 9-7)

18. _____.

19. Solve $6z^2 + 5z = 21$. (Lesson 10-6)

19. _____

20. The length of a rectangle is 9 cm more than its width. The area of the rectangle is 136 cm². What are its dimensions? (Lesson 11-3)

20. _____

21. Solve $3^{2-x} = 3^x$. (Lesson 11-4)

21. _____

22. Use the quadratic formula to solve $4n^2 - 5n - 3 = 0$. (Lesson 11-3)

22. _____

23. Simplify $\dfrac{m^2 - 1}{2 - m - m^2}$. (Lesson 12-1)

23. _____

24. Find $\dfrac{a^2 - 4}{a} \div \dfrac{a^2 - 3a + 2}{a^2}$. (Lesson 12-3)

24. _____

25. Find $\dfrac{1}{m + 2} - \dfrac{1}{m - 2}$. (Lesson 12-6)

25. _____

26. Solve $\dfrac{7}{x^2 - 5x} + \dfrac{3}{5 - x} = \dfrac{4}{x}$. (Lesson 12-8)

26. _____

Simplify.

27. $\pm\sqrt{\dfrac{144}{25}}$ (Lesson 13-2)

27. _____

28. $\sqrt{12x^2y}$ (Lesson 13-2)

28. _____

29. $\dfrac{\sqrt{40}}{\sqrt{7}}$ (Lesson 13-2)

29. _____

30. $\sqrt{20} - \sqrt{45} + \sqrt{72}$ (Lesson 13-3)

30. _____

31. $\dfrac{2}{1 + \sqrt{3}}$ (Lesson 13-3)

31. _____

32. Solve and check $\sqrt{3x + 1} = 5$. (Lesson 13-4)

32. _____

33. Find the distance between $(5, -6)$ and $(2, 3)$. (Lesson 13-5)

33. _____

Chapter 13 Answer Key

1. __C__   11. __A__

2. __D__   12. __D__

3. __B__   13. __C__

4. __C__   14. __A__

5. __A__   15. __D__

6. __C__   16. __A__

7. __C__   17. __C__

8. __A__   18. __C__

9. __D__   19. __B__

10. __C__   20. __B__

1. __B__   11. __B__

2. __A__   12. __B__

3. __B__   13. __B__

4. __D__   14. __A__

5. __C__   15. __A__

6. __C__   16. __D__

7. __A__   17. __A__

8. __A__   18. __C__

9. __B__   19. __B__

10. __A__   20. __A__

Bonus __−2__

Bonus $|2x + 3|$

Chapter 13 Answer Key

Form 1C — Page 341

1. C
2. B
3. A
4. C
5. B
6. B
7. A
8. D
9. B
10. C

Page 342

11. C
12. B
13. B
14. A
15. B
16. C
17. D
18. B
19. A
20. A

Bonus $|2x + 1|$

Form 2A — Page 343

1. $\sqrt{41}$
2. $2\sqrt{11}$ cm, or ≈ 6.6 cm
3. $\sqrt{247}$, or ≈ 15.7 ft
4. $3\sqrt{42}$
5. $|n^3|y^5\sqrt{21y}$
6. $\dfrac{x^2\sqrt{5n}}{2n^3}$
7. $\dfrac{2\sqrt{10} - 2\sqrt{3}}{7}$
8. $6\sqrt{6} + 8\sqrt{3}$
9. 0
10. $13\sqrt{5} - 5\sqrt{2}$
11. -123

Page 344

12. 6
13. no solution
14. 5
15. $3\sqrt{10}$
16. $2, -8$
17. $\sqrt{106}$
18. $7 \pm 3\sqrt{6}$
19. $-\dfrac{3}{2}, 1$
20. $\dfrac{1}{64}$

Bonus $-\dfrac{\sqrt{6}}{6}$

Chapter 13 Answer Key

Form 2B

1. $2\sqrt{34}$, or 11.66

2. 7 cm

3. 12 ft

4. $2\sqrt{6}$

5. $5y^2w\sqrt{3w}$

6. $\dfrac{\sqrt{70}}{15}$

7. $\dfrac{36 + 6\sqrt{11}}{25}$

8. $5\sqrt{11}$

9. $8\sqrt{5}$

10. $\dfrac{8}{7}\sqrt{14}$

11. $6\sqrt{5} + 8\sqrt{15}$

12. 12

13. $\dfrac{16}{3}$

14. 12

15. $\sqrt{61}$, or 7.81

16. 2, 8

17. $\sqrt{41}$

18. $-9 \pm 6\sqrt{2}$

19. $-4 \pm \sqrt{6}$

20. $\dfrac{9}{4}$

Bonus $x \geq \dfrac{4}{7}$

Chapter 13 Answer Key

Calculator-Based
Page 349

Form 2C — Page 347

1. $\sqrt{65}$

2. 8 cm

3. 6 ft

4. $2\sqrt{10}$

5. $5x|y|\sqrt{2x}$

6. $\dfrac{\sqrt{3}}{3}$

7. $5\sqrt{10} + 15$

8. $7\sqrt{7}$

9. $7\sqrt{6}$

10. $\dfrac{6}{5}\sqrt{10}$

11. $2\sqrt{3} - 9\sqrt{2}$

Page 348

12. 3

13. 4

14. 6

15. $\sqrt{74}$

16. $-2, 6$

17. 10

18. $-4 \pm \sqrt{19}$

19. $6 \pm \sqrt{11}$

20. $\dfrac{49}{4}$

Bonus $\dfrac{1 - \sqrt{2}}{2}$

Calculator-Based — Page 349

1. 40.30

2. 12.47

3. 4.52

4. 180

5. 30.53

6. 12

7. ≈ 131.45 volts

8. $=$

9. $<$

10. $=$

11. -12.12

12. ≈ 80.26

13. ≈ 8.91

14. 27.89

15. 25.63

16. 13.2 mi/h

Scoring Guide
Chapter 13
Performance Assessment

Level	Specific Criteria
3 Superior	• Shows thorough understanding of the concepts of *finding square roots, using the Pythagorean theorem, simplifying radical expressions*, and *solving radical equations*. • Uses appropriate strategies to solve problems. • Computations are correct. • Written explanations are exemplary. • Diagrams are accurate and appropriate. • Goes beyond requirements of some or all problems.
2 Satisfactory, with Minor Flaws	• Shows understanding of the concepts of *finding square roots, using the Pythagorean theorem, simplifying radical expressions*, and *solving radical equations*. • Uses appropriate strategies to solve problems. • Computations are mostly correct. • Written explanations are effective. • Diagrams are mostly accurate and appropriate. • Satisfies all requirements of problems.
1 Nearly Satisfactory, with Serious Flaws	• Shows understanding of most of the concepts of *finding square roots, using the Pythagorean theorem, simplifying radical expressions*, and *solving radical equations*. • May not use appropriate strategies to solve problems. • Computations are mostly correct. • Written explanations are satisfactory. • Diagrams are mostly accurate and appropriate. • Satisfies most requirements of problems.
0 Unsatisfactory	• Shows little or no understanding of the concepts of *finding square roots, using the Pythagorean theorem, simplifying radical expressions*, and *solving radical equations*. • May not use appropriate strategies to solve problems. • Computations are incorrect. • Written explanations are not satisfactory. • Diagrams are not accurate or appropriate. • Does not satisfy requirements of problems.

Chapter 13 Answer Key
Performance Assessment

Page 350

1. a. $4\sqrt{10^2 + 20^2} = 40\sqrt{5}$, or about 89.5 ft

b. no; $10\sqrt{5} + 80 + 20 > 89.5$ ft

c. no; $80 + 20 > 89.5$ ft

d. yes; $40 + 40 < 100$ ft

e. yes; $40 + 40 < 89.5$ ft

f. She should consider whether she would like individual shutoffs centralized near the source. Are the trees or shrubs in the way?

g.

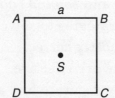

Source to corners

$\overline{AC} \perp \overline{BD}$, since they are diagonals of a square. Also $\overline{AS}, \overline{BS}, \overline{CS}$, and $\overline{DS}$ are all equal in length. Each right triangle formed is a $45°-45°-90°$ triangle. Let $x =$ the length of a leg of the right triangle. Find a value for x in terms of a.

$\frac{x}{a} = \frac{1}{\sqrt{2}}$ $x = \frac{a}{\sqrt{2}}$, or $\frac{a\sqrt{2}}{2}$

The total pipe length would be $4 \cdot \frac{a\sqrt{2}}{2}$, or $2a\sqrt{2}$.

Justification: For A to B and D to C, connected to the source at their midpoints, the total pipe length would be $3a$. Since $2.8a < 3a$, the source to the corners uses less pipe.

2. $8\sqrt{4z^2 - 43} = 40$

$64(4z^2 - 43) = 1600$	Square each side.
$4z^2 - 43 = 25$	Division property
$4z^2 = 68$	Addition property
$z^2 = 17$	Division property
$z = \pm\sqrt{17}$	Take square root of each side.

Chapter 13 Answer Key

Mid-Chapter Test
Page 351

1. $2\sqrt{34}$, 11.66

2. $\sqrt{31}$, 5.57

3. 12

4. no

5. yes

6. $2\sqrt{34}$, or 11.66, ft

7. $8\sqrt{2}$, or 11.31, ft

8. $12\sqrt{2}$

9. $3\,|x^3 y|\,\sqrt{2y}$

10. $x^2 - 4\sqrt{5}x + 20$

11. 23

12. $\frac{5}{2}\sqrt{2}$

13. $\frac{15 + 3\sqrt{3}}{11}$

14. $7\sqrt{5} - 2\sqrt{10}$

15. $\frac{19}{3}\sqrt{3}$

16. $3\sqrt{2} + 2\sqrt{6}$

Bonus   12 m

Quiz A
Page 352

1. 13

2. 14.70

3. yes

4. $2\,|x|\,\sqrt{2y}$

5. $5\sqrt{6}$

6. $\frac{4\sqrt{3}}{3}$

7. $\frac{3\sqrt{6}}{x^2}$

8. $\frac{12 - 3\sqrt{2}}{14}$

9. $6\sqrt{2}$

10. 13

Quiz B
Page 352

1. $26\sqrt{5}$; 58.14

2. $4\sqrt{6} + 8\sqrt{10}$; 35.10

3. $\frac{4\sqrt{15}}{5}$; 3.10

4. $3\sqrt{2} - 14\sqrt{3}$; -20.01

5. $P = 22\sqrt{2} - 4\sqrt{3}$; $A = 60 - 12\sqrt{6}$

Quiz C
Page 353

1. 28

2. $\frac{7}{2}$

3. $\frac{9}{2}$

4. 7

5. 60

6. 5

7. $\sqrt{61}$, 7.81

8. 2, 4

9. $\frac{5}{2}$, 12; -6, -5

10. $10 + 2\sqrt{5}$

Quiz D
Page 353

1. $\frac{81}{4}$

2. 36

3. -10, 2

4. $3 \pm \sqrt{6}$

5. $\frac{3 \pm \sqrt{5}}{2}$

Chapter 13 Answer Key

<table>
<tr><td>

Standardized Test Practice
Page 354

1.   **C**

2.   **C**

3.   **C**

4.   **A**

5.   **B**

6.   **D**

7.   **B**

8.   **A**

9.   **D**

10.   **A**

</td><td>

Cumulative Review
Page 355

1. $8x^2$

2. **associative of mult.**

3. $\dfrac{1}{12}$

4. -8

5. $-\dfrac{11}{3}$

6. **15, 17, and 19**

7. **85%**

8. **12 nickels; 6 dimes; 5 quarters**

9. **on the y-axis**

10. -5

11. $y = 4x + 9$

12. $4x + y = -2$

13. $y \le \dfrac{12}{7}$

14.

15. $(3, 1)$

16. $(2, -3)$

17. $10x^2 - x + 1$

</td><td>

Page 356

18. $6a^2 - 5a - 21$

19. $-\dfrac{7}{3}, \dfrac{3}{2}$

20. **8 cm by 17 cm**

21. 1

22. $\dfrac{5 \pm \sqrt{73}}{8}$

23. $-\dfrac{m+1}{m+2}$

24. $\dfrac{a(a+2)}{a-1}$

25. $-\dfrac{4}{m^2-4}$

26. $\dfrac{27}{7}$

27. $\pm\dfrac{12}{5}$

28. $2\,|x|\,\sqrt{3y}$

29. $\dfrac{2\sqrt{70}}{7}$

30. $-\sqrt{5} + 6\sqrt{2}$

31. $-1 + \sqrt{3}$

32. 8

33. $3\sqrt{10}$

</td></tr>
</table>

NAME_____ DATE _____

Placement Test

Write the letter for the correct answer in the blank at the right of each problem.

1. Which of the following is an algebraic expression for the verbal expression *7 less than three times a number*?
   A. $7 - 3x$ **B.** $3x - 7$ **C.** $7 < 3x$ **D.** none of these

   1. _____

2. What is the next number in the sequence 2, 5, 10, 17, 26, $\cdots$?
   A. 11   **B.** 35   **C.** 37   **D.** 50

   2. _____

3. Evaluate the expression $\dfrac{5y + 2 - 3x}{x^2 - 3y}$ when $x = 3$ and $y = 2$.
   A. 1   **B.** 0   **C.** $\dfrac{11}{3}$ **D.** undefined

   3. _____

4. What property is illustrated by $(5x)y = 5(xy)$?
   A. commutative property of multiplication
   B. distributive property
   C. multiplicative identity property
   D. associative property of multiplication

   4. _____

5. What was the price of one share of company X's stock on Wednesday?
   A. $9.57   **B.** $8.76
   C. $876   **D.** $87.60

   Price of One Share of Company X's Stock

   5. _____

6. Evaluate $9 + (-4) + (-11) + 3$.
   A. 27   **B.** -9 **C.** -3 **D.** none of these

   6. _____

7. Evaluate $\dfrac{3x - 4y}{x^2 - y^3}$ when $x = -2$ and $y = -4$.
   A. $\dfrac{5}{34}$ **B.** $\dfrac{1}{6}$ **C.** $\dfrac{-11}{34}$ **D.** none of these

   7. _____

8. Evaluate $-3^2 + 12 \div (-6) \cdot 2$.
   A. -13 **B.** -10 **C.** -7 **D.** 5

   8. _____

9. Which of the following is the graph of $x \le 2$?
   A.   **B.**

   C.   **D.**

   9. _____

10. Which equation represents *the sum of three times a number and 5 is 14?*
   A. $3(x + 5) = 14$ **B.** $3x + 5 = 14$ **C.** $3x - 5 = 14$ **D.** $3(x - 5) = 14$

   10. _____

11. Solve $n + 17 = 8$.
    A. 25   **B.** 9   **C.** -9 **D.** -25

11. _____

12. Solve $-3x = -21$.
    A. 63   **B.** 7   **C.** -7 **D.** -63

12. _____

13. Solve $6x - 7 = -4$.
    A. 2   **B.** $\frac{1}{2}$ **C.** $\frac{-11}{6}$ **D.** none of these

13. _____

14. Solve $7n - 11 = 12n + 19$.
    A. 6   **B.** $\frac{8}{5}$ **C.** $\frac{-8}{5}$ **D.** none of these

14. _____

15. Solve $a + ny = n$ for n.
    A. $n = \frac{a}{y}$ **B.** $n = \frac{a}{1-y}$ **C.** $n = \frac{1-a}{y}$ **D.** $n = \frac{a}{1+y}$

15. _____

16. Solve the proportion $\frac{x+6}{3} = \frac{8}{5}$.
    A. $\frac{-6}{5}$ **B.** $\frac{18}{5}$ **C.** 2   **D.** none of these

16. _____

17. Eight is what percent of 20?
    A. $\frac{2}{5}$%   **B.** 8%   **C.** 20%   **D.** 40%

17. _____

18. What is the percent increase from 8 to 10?
    A. 2%   **B.** 20%   **C.** 25%   **D.** 125%

18. _____

19. Maria has $1.05 in dimes and nickels. She has 6 more nickels than dimes. How many nickels does Maria have?
    A. 5   **B.** 7   **C.** 9   **D.** 11

19. _____

20. If y varies directly as x and $y = 6$ when $x = 12$, find y when $x = 40$.
    A. 20   **B.** 80   **C.** 72   **D.** none of these

20. _____

Placement Test (continued)

Write the answer in the blank at the right of each problem.

21. Write an algebraic expression for *six less than a number*.   21. _____

22. Draw the next figure in the following pattern.   22. _____

23. What property is illustrated by $(3 \cdot 4) \cdot 5 = 5 \cdot (3 \cdot 4)$?   23. _____

24. Name the property illustrated by the following statement.   24. _____
If $3 + 4 = 7$ and $7 = 6 + 1$, then $3 + 4 = 6 + 1$.

25. What does the entry   25. _____
$23 \mid 8$ represent in the
stem-and-leaf plot?

Stem	Leaf
21	3 5 6 6
22	4 4 9
23	2 8 *21|3 = 213*

26. Evaluate $2^3 + 24 \div 6 \cdot 2 - 2$.   26. _____

27. What property is illustrated by $12x + 15 = 3(4x + 5)$?   27. _____

28. On four carries, a football player gained 5 yards, lost   28. _____
3 yards, gained 2 yards, and lost 1 yard. What was the
player's net gain or loss?

29. Evaluate $-15 + 7 + (-11) + 18$.   29. _____

30. Evaluate $\dfrac{-2}{3} + \dfrac{3}{4} - \dfrac{1}{2}$.   30. _____

31. Evaluate $4 \cdot \dfrac{-3}{5} \div \dfrac{-9}{10}$.   31. _____

32. Graph $x > -2$.   32.

33. Between what two consecutive integers is $-\sqrt{30}$?   33. _____

34. Translate the sentence below into an equation.   34. _____
The product of 5 and 3 more than a number is 35.

35. Solve $m - 12 = -4$.   35. _____

36. Solve $\dfrac{t}{-5} = 8$.   36. _____

37. Solve $9y + 14 = -22$.   37. _____

38. Solve $4x + 11 = 7x - 10$.   38. _____

39. Solve $5(2w + 3) = 6w - 2(w - 6)$.   39. _____

40. Solve $3x + 5 = n + xy$ for x.   40. _____

41. The length of a rectangle is 5 cm longer than its width. The perimeter of the rectangle is 50 cm. Find the length of the rectangle.   41. _____

42. Solve $\dfrac{1}{3}x + \dfrac{3}{4} = \dfrac{5}{6}x - \dfrac{1}{2}$.   42. _____

43. Solve the proportion $\dfrac{5}{2x - 1} = \dfrac{3}{x}$.   43. _____

44. Ten is 40% of what number?   44. _____

45. A student answered 34 out of 40 questions correctly. What percent was answered correctly?   45. _____

46. A movie theater increased ticket prices for matinees from $4.00 to $4.50. What percent of increase is this?   46. _____

47. A shirt that regularly cost $25.00 is marked 30% off. What is the sale price of the item?   47. _____

48. If y varies inversely as x and $y = 8$ when $x = 12$, find x when $y = 4$.   48. _____

49. Chocolate chip cookies sell for $0.50 each and oatmeal cookies sell for $0.35 each. On Monday morning, the bakery sold 20 cookies and received $8.80. How many chocolate chip cookies were sold?   49. _____

50. Rose starts to print out a long document on a printer that prints at a rate of 3 pages per minute. Twenty minutes later, Daisy starts to print out the same document on a printer that prints at a rate of 5 pages per minute. How long will it take Daisy's printer to catch up with Rose's printer?   50. _____

First Semester Test

Write the letter for the correct answer in the blank at the right of each problem.

1. Evaluate $a(b^2 - 5) \div (a + b)$ when $a = 7$ and $b = 4$.   1. _____
   A. 2   **B.** 7   **C.** 5   **D.** 10

2. State the property illustrated by $3 \cdot 1 = 3$.   2. _____
   A. substitution property   **B.** reflexive property
   C. commutative property of multiplication
   D. multiplicative identity property

3. Simplify $10y + 4y^2 - 6y$.   3. _____
   A. $4(y^2 + 1)$ **B.** $4y + 4y^2$ **C.** $8y^2$ **D.** $4y + 1$

4. Evaluate $6(-12) + (-3)(-8)$.   4. _____
   A. 18   **B.** -30 **C.** 96   **D.** -48

5. Evaluate $-\frac{2}{3} - \left(-\frac{1}{2}\right)$.   5. _____
   A. $-\frac{1}{6}$ **B.** $\frac{1}{6}$ **C.** $-\frac{7}{6}$ **D.** $\frac{7}{6}$

6. Solve $m + 12 = 19$.   6. _____
   A. 31   **B.** -31 **C.** 7   **D.** -7

7. Find the median of the data listed below.   7. _____
   18, 21, 15, 18, 25, 22, 18, 19
   A. 19.5   **B.** 18.5   **C.** 18   **D.** no median

8. Solve $6(x + 5) = -2(x - 3)$.   8. _____
   A. 1   **B.** -1 **C.** 3   **D.** -3

9. What is 16% of 13?   9. _____
   A. 2.08   **B.** 20.8   **C.** 208   **D.** 81.25

10. A road rises 50 feet vertically over a horizontal distance of   10. _____
    200 feet. What is the angle of elevation of the road?
    A. about 14°   **B.** about 76°   **C.** about 22°   **D.** about 68°

11. How many liters of water must be added to 5 liters
of a 30% acid solution to obtain a 20% acid solution?
A. 2 liters   **B.** 2.5 liters   **C.** 5 liters   **D.** 7.5 liters

11. _____

12. What inequality is graphed below?

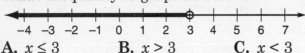

A. $x \le 3$ **B.** $x > 3$ **C.** $x < 3$ **D.** $x \ge 3$

12. _____

13. Solve $-6p \ge 42$.
A. $p \le 7$ **B.** $p \ge -7$ **C.** $p \le -7$ **D.** $p \ge 7$

13. _____

14. Solve $8 - 4m > 16$.
A. $m > 2$ **B.** $m > -2$ **C.** $m < 2$ **D.** $m < -2$

14. _____

15. Simplify $\frac{1}{2}(8x - 4y) - 3(2x - 3y)$.
A. $2x - 7y$ **B.** $3x - y$ **C.** $-2x + 7y$ **D.** $3x - 7y$

15. _____

16. Solve $y = 4x + 1$ if the domain is $\{0, 1, 2\}$.
A. $\left\{\left(-\frac{1}{4}, 0\right), (0, 1), \left(\frac{1}{4}, 2\right)\right\}$ **B.** $\{(1, 0), (5, 1), (9, 2)\}$
C. $\{(0, 1), (1, 5), (2, 9)\}$ **D.** $\left\{\left(0, -\frac{1}{4}\right), (1, 0), \left(2, \frac{1}{4}\right)\right\}$

16. _____

17. Given $f(x) = x^2 + 10x - 6$, determine the value of $f(-3)$.
A. 33   **B.** -45 **C.** -8 **D.** -27

17. _____

18. Determine the slope of the line passing through
$(-4, -2)$ and $(5, 1)$.
A. 1   **B.** -1 **C.** 3   **D.** $\frac{1}{3}$

18. _____

19. Which equation has a graph that is a horizontal line?
A. $x + y = 0$ **B.** $y = x$ **C.** $y = -2$ **D.** $x = 4$

19. _____

20. Write an equation in slope-intercept form for the line that is
parallel to the graph of $3y - 6x = 4$ and passes through $(4, 0)$.
A. $y = 2x - 8$ **B.** $2y = -x$ **C.** $y = 2x + 4$ **D.** $y = -2x + 8$

20. _____

First Semester Test (continued)

Write the answer in the blank at the right of each problem.

21. Write a mathematical expression for 5 more than twice the cube of a number.

21. _____

22. Simplify $6x + 3 - x + 2x$.

22. _____

23. What property is illustrated by $(x + 5) + 7 = 7 + (x + 5)$?

23. _____

24. Make a stem-and-leaf plot of the data listed below.
4300, 5800, 4700, 5200, 5500, 4800, 5200

24.

Stem	Leaf

25. What is the range of the data in question 24?

25. _____

26. Evaluate $31 + (-78)$.

26. _____

27. Evaluate $|-2.3 + (-4)|$.

27. _____

28. Find $\begin{bmatrix} -3 & 1 \\ 0 & 6 \end{bmatrix} + \begin{bmatrix} 2 & 4 \\ -1 & 5 \end{bmatrix}$.

28. _____

29. Evaluate $\dfrac{-56}{-8}$.

29. _____

30. Solve $3y = -42$.

30. _____

31. Find three consecutive integers whose sum is 81.

31. _____

32. Solve $\dfrac{2}{5} = \dfrac{x + 5}{10}$.

32. _____

33. Solve $\dfrac{4}{5}z < -\dfrac{1}{3}$.

33. _____

34. Graph the solution set of $-3 \le x < 2$.

34.

35. Kellie is 5 years younger than Renée. The sum of their ages is 39. What are their ages?

35. _____

36. Maria scored 16 points in one basketball game and 20 points in a second game. By what percent did her scoring increase?

36. _____

37. State the domain and range for the relation {(2, 3), (−4, 6), (7, 9), (1, 3)} and state whether or not this relation is a function.

37. _____

38. Name the quadrant in which point $B(-2, 5)$ is located.

38. _____

39. If $f(x) = 2x^2 + x - 3$, find $f(-2)$.

39. _____

40. Solve $\frac{2d - 5}{3} = 7$.

40. _____

41. Solve $3x - (x - 3) > -7$.

41. _____

42. Bob leaves the campground at the same time as Jane. Bob drives 4 mi/h faster than Jane. After 2 hours of driving in opposite directions, they are 116 miles apart. How fast is Bob driving?

42. _____

43. Find the slope, y-intercept, and x-intercept for the graph of $3x - 4y = 8$.

43. _____

44. Graph the equation $3y - 2x = 1$ on the coordinate plane provided.

44.

45. Determine the value of r so that the line through (2, 3) and $(r, -3)$ is perpendicular to the graph of $y = -\frac{1}{6}x + 3$.

45. _____

46. Write an equation in slope-intercept form of the line through (4, 5) with a slope of $\frac{1}{2}$.

46. _____

47. If the odds in favor of an event are 3 : 7, what is the probability of the event occurring?

47. _____

48. Make a box-and-whisker plot for the data below.
40, 31, 50, 49, 17, 46, 43, 55, 48, 24, 52

48. _____

49. Triangles ABC and DEF are similar. If $b = 6$, $c = 2$, $d = 3$, and $e = 4$, find the measures of a and f.

49. _____

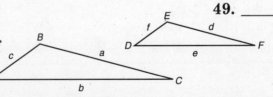

50. Solve the right triangle ABC in which the measure of angle B is 45°, $b = 6$, and angle C is a right angle.

50. _____

NAME_____ DATE _____

Second Semester Test

Write the letter for the correct answer in the blank at the right of each problem.

1. Solve the system of equations $y = 2x + 5$ and $3x - 2y = 10$.
   A. $(-5, -5)$ B. $(-20, -35)$ C. $(10, -20)$ D. none of these

   1. _____

2. Which system has infinitely many solutions?
   A. $x - y = 0$ B. $y = 3x + 8$ C. $3y = 2x - 4$ D. $2x - y = 8$
      $x + y = 0$ $y = 3x + 10$ $6y = 4x - 8$ $2x + y = 8$

   2. _____

3. Simplify $(3p^2a)^3$.
   A. $3p^5a^3$ B. $3pa^2$ C. $27p^6a^3$ D. $27p^5a^4$

   3. _____

4. Express 0.0000618 in scientific notation.
   A. 6.18×10^{-5} B. 6.18×10^5 C. 618×10^7 D. 6.18×10^{-4}

   4. _____

5. Multiply $(4x - 3)(x + 5)$.
   A. $4x^2 - 15$ B. $4x^2 + 6x - 15$
   C. $4x^2 + 17x - 15$ D. none of these

   5. _____

6. Find the prime factorization of 90.
   A. $5 \cdot 3^2 \cdot 2^2$ B. $5 \cdot 3 \cdot 3 \cdot 2$ C. $10 \cdot 3^2 \cdot 1$ D. $10 \cdot 3 \cdot 3 \cdot 2$

   6. _____

7. Factor $c^2 - 36$.
   A. $(c + 6)(c + 6)$ B. $(c - 6)(c - 6)$
   C. $(c + 6)(c - 6)$ D. prime

   7. _____

8. Solve $(2x + 1)(x - 8) = 0$.
   A. $\left\{-\dfrac{1}{2}, 8\right\}$ B. $\left\{\dfrac{1}{2}, -8\right\}$ C. $\left\{-\dfrac{1}{2}, -8\right\}$ D. $\left\{\dfrac{1}{2}, 8\right\}$

   8. _____

9. Simplify $\dfrac{2m^2}{6m^3 - 4m^2}$.
   A. $3m - 2$ B. $\dfrac{1}{3m + 2}$ C. $\dfrac{1}{3m - 2}$ D. $\dfrac{2}{6m - 4}$

   9. _____

10. Simplify $\dfrac{3x}{x + 4} - \dfrac{x + 5}{x + 4}$.
    A. $\dfrac{2x + 5}{2x + 8}$ B. $\dfrac{2x + 5}{x + 4}$ C. $\dfrac{2x - 5}{2x + 8}$ D. $\dfrac{2x - 5}{x + 4}$

    10. _____

11. Simplify $\dfrac{n^2 - 10n + 25}{n^3} \cdot \dfrac{n}{3n - 15}$

    A. $\dfrac{n-5}{3n^2}$ **B.** $\dfrac{(n+5)^2}{3n^2(n-5)}$ **C.** $\dfrac{n^2(n-5)}{3}$ **D.** none of these

11. _____

12. A two-digit number is 3 more than 3 times the sum of its digits. The tens digit is 6 less than the units digit. If t = the tens digit and u = the units digit, which system must be true?

    A. $t - u = 6$
         $10t + u = 3t + u - 3$

    B. $t = u - 6$
         $10t + u = 3t + u - 3$

    C. $t - u = 6$
         $10t + u = 3(t + u) - 3$

    D. $t = u - 6$
         $10t + u = 3(t + u) + 3$

12. _____

13. Simplify $\sqrt{50x^7y^4}$.

    A. $5x^3y^2\sqrt{2x}$ **B.** $5x^3y\sqrt{10x}$ **C.** $2x^3y^2\sqrt{5x}$ **D.** $2x^3y^2\sqrt{5x}$

13. _____

14. Simplify $\sqrt{6} \cdot \sqrt{18}$.

    A. $3\sqrt{54}$ **B.** $6\sqrt{3}$ **C.** $3\sqrt{6}$ **D.** $9\sqrt{2}$

14. _____

15. Solve $\sqrt{4m - 1} + 3 = 0$.

    A. 2.5   **B.** 1   **C.** -2 **D.** no solution

15. _____

16. What value of c makes $x^2 + 9x + c$ a perfect trinomial square?

    A. $\dfrac{9}{2}$ **B.** $\dfrac{81}{2}$ **C.** $\dfrac{81}{4}$ **D.** 9

16. _____

17. Solve $3x^2 + 2x - 7 = 0$.

    A. $\dfrac{-1 \pm 2\sqrt{22}}{3}$ **B.** $\dfrac{-2 \pm \sqrt{22}}{6}$ **C.** $\dfrac{-1 \pm \sqrt{22}}{3}$ **D.** $\dfrac{-1 \pm 2\sqrt{22}}{3}$

17. _____

18. Solve $x^2 = 4x - 10$.

    A. $2 \pm 2\sqrt{14}$ **B.** $2 \pm \sqrt{6}$ **C.** $-4, 8$ **D.** no real solution

18. _____

19. Solve $5^{3x-1} = 25^{2x+1}$.

    A. 2   **B.** -3 **C.** $\dfrac{3}{4}$ **D.** no solution

19. _____

20. Melanie can do a job in 4 hours. Kim can do the same job in 6 hours. If they work together, how long will it take to complete the job?

    A. 2.4 hours   **B.** 4.2 hours   **C.** 5 hours   **D.** 2.5 hours

20. _____

Write the answer in the blank at the right of each problem.

21. Solve the system of equations $6x - 3y = 11$ and $6x + 3y = 17$.

21. _____

22. Solve the system of equations $3x + 5y = 22$ and $4x + 3y = 11$.

22. _____

23. The sum of the digits of a two-digit number is 7. The number is 10 times its tens digit. Find the number.

23. _____

24. Solve the system of equations $y = 3x - 5$ and $12x - 4y = 5$.

24. _____

25. Solve the system of inequalities $y < x$ and $y \geq x - 4$ by graphing.

25.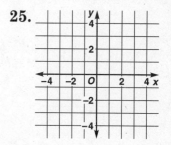

26. Simplify $(3a^2b^3)(-6ab^6)$.

26. _____

27. Simplify $\dfrac{-3a^2bc^5}{12a^6b^2c}$.

27. _____

28. Simplify $(7x^2 - 4xy + 6y^2) - (5x^2 - 10xy - 4y^2)$.

28. _____

29. Simplify $(2a - 4)(2a + 4)$.

29. _____

30. Simplify $(x + 3y)^2$.

30. _____

31. Factor $m^2 + 18m + 81$.

31. _____

32. Solve $k^2 + 7k = 0$.

32. _____

33. Factor $3t^2 - 21t + 18$.

33. _____

34. Solve $x^2 + 11x + 28 = 0$.

34. _____

35. Six times a number subtracted from the number squared is 40. Find the number.

35. _____

36. Find the equation of the axis of symmetry and the vertex of the graph of $y = 3x^2 - 4x + 5$.

36. _____

37. Solve the equation $25x^2 - 30x + 9 = 0$ by using the quadratic formula.

37. _____

38. Find a quadratic equation whose roots are -6 and 1.

38. _____

39. Solve $2x^2 - 3x - 1 = 0$.

39. _____

40. Solve $4^{x^2} = 64^{2x-3}$.

40. _____

41. Simplify $\dfrac{m-3}{m+4} \div \dfrac{m^2 - 4m + 3}{m^2 - 16}$.

41. _____

42. Simplify $\dfrac{2x-1}{x-1} + \dfrac{2-x}{x-1}$.

42. _____

43. Simplify $\dfrac{2y+4}{y+1} + \dfrac{3y}{4y+4}$.

43. _____

44. Solve $\dfrac{3x}{5} + \dfrac{x}{10} = 1$.

44. _____

45. Solve $\dfrac{4}{a-2} - \dfrac{6}{a+2} = 0$.

45. _____

46. Simplify $\sqrt{\dfrac{5}{3}}$.

46. _____

47. Simplify $7\sqrt{28} + 3\sqrt{63}$.

47. _____

48. Solve $\sqrt{3y} = 10$.

48. _____

49. Determine whether 5, 7, and 9 could be the measures of the sides of a right triangle.

49. _____

50. Find the distance between $(-2, 6)$ and $(1, 3)$.

50. _____

Final Test

Write the letter for the correct answer in the blank at the right of each problem.

1. Evaluate $4(2 + 3 \cdot 5) - 3^2$.
   A. 46   B. 59   C. 111   D. 14

   1. _____

2. Find the value of $-|a - w|$ if $a = -15$ and $w = -8$.
   A. 23   B. -23 C. 7   D. -7

   2. _____

3. Solve $6r + 5 = 7r$.
   A. 5   B. 7   C. -5 D. -7

   3. _____

4. A number decreased by -14 is 20. What is the number?
   A. 34   B. -34 C. 6   D. -6

   4. _____

5. Solve $6(x + 1) - 4 = 3x + 2$.
   A. 0   B. -1
   C. no solutions   D. The equation is an identity.

   5. _____

6. If y varies directly as x and $y = 14$ when $x = 8$, find x when $y = 21$.
   A. $\frac{294}{8}$ B. $\frac{112}{21}$ C. $\frac{168}{14}$ D. $\frac{14}{168}$

   6. _____

7. Seventeen is what percent of 25?
   A. 68%   B. 14.7%   C. 1.47%   D. 32%

   7. _____

8. Which open sentence is graphed?

   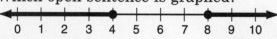

   A. $4 \le x \ge 8$ B. $4 \ge x \le 8$
   C. $x \ge 4$ or $x \le 8$ D. $x \le 4$ or $x \ge 8$

   8. _____

9. The sum of three times a number and 6 is at least 3. What is the number?
   A. -1 or greater   B. 3 or greater
   C. -3 or less   D. 1 or less

   9. _____

10. Simplify $(7x^2 - 4x + 6) - (2x^2 + 3x - 10)$.
    A. $5x^2 - x - 6$ B. $5x^2 - 7x + 16$
    C. $5x^2 - 7x - 4$ D. $5x^2 - x - 4$

    10. _____

11. Simplify $(3x - 4)(2x + 1)$.   11. _____
    A. $6x^2 - 4$ B. $-8x + 3$ C. $-8x - 4$ D. $6x^2 - 5x - 4$

12. Factor $6a^2b + 8a^3b^2$.   12. _____
    A. $2a^2b(3 + 4ab)$ B. $2ab(3a + 4a^2b)$
    C. $2a^2(3b + 4ab^2)$ D. $6a^2b(2ab)$

13. Factor $4y^2 - 6y - 4$.   13. _____
    A. $(4y + 2)(y - 2)$ B. $(y + 2)(2y - 4)$
    C. $2(y + 1)(y - 2)$ D. $2(2y + 1)(y - 2)$

14. The product of two consecutive even integers is 168.   14. _____
    If x is the smaller number, which equation must be true?
    A. $x(x + 1) = 168$ B. $x(x + 2) = 168$
    C. $x(x + 4) = 168$ D. $(x + 2)(x + 4) = 168$

15. Simplify $x - \dfrac{10}{x + 4}$.   15. _____
    A. $\dfrac{x - 10}{x + 4}$ B. $\dfrac{x - 6}{x + 4}$ C. $\dfrac{-10x}{x + 4}$ D. $\dfrac{x^2 + 4x - 10}{x + 4}$

16. Solve $\dfrac{3}{x - 4} + \dfrac{x}{x + 4} = 1$.   16. _____
    A. -28 B. 28 C. $-\dfrac{4}{7}$ D. $\dfrac{4}{7}$

17. Given $f(x) = 3x^2 - 4x$, determine $f(-5)$.   17. _____
    A. 55 B. -5 C. 95 D. 35

18. Solve $y = 3x + 2$ if the domain is $\{2, 3, -4\}$.   18. _____
    A. $\{(2, 8), (3, 11), (-4, -10)\}$ B. $\{(8, 2), (11, 3), (-10, -4)\}$
    C. $\left\{(2, 0), \left(3, \frac{1}{3}\right), (-4, -2)\right\}$ D. $\left\{(0, 2), \left(\frac{1}{3}, 3\right), (-2, -4)\right\}$

19. What is the x-intercept of the graph of $2x + 5y = 20$?   19. _____
    A. 4 B. $\dfrac{1}{3}$ C. 10 D. 2

20. What are the coordinates of the midpoint of the line   20. _____
    segment whose endpoints are $(-4, -7)$ and $(2, 1)$?
    A. $(1, 3)$ B. $(3, 4)$ C. $(-3, -4)$ D. $(-1, -3)$

21. Solve the system of equations $x = 4 - y$ and $3x - 2y = 8$.

 A. $\left(\dfrac{16}{5}, \dfrac{4}{5}\right)$ **B.** $(6, -2)$ **C.** $\left(\dfrac{16}{3}, -\dfrac{4}{3}\right)$ **D.** none of these

21._____

22. Solve the system of equations $2x - y = 10$.
$$3x + y = 15$$

 A. $(5, 0)$ **B.** $(0, 5)$ **C.** $(-5, 0)$ **D.** none of these

22._____

23. Simplify $\sqrt{72m^3n^4}$.

 A. $6m\,|\,n^2\,|\,\sqrt{2m}$ **B.** $6mn^2\sqrt{2m}$
 C. $2\,|\,m\,|\,n^2\sqrt{6m}$ **D.** $2mn^2\sqrt{6m}$

23._____

24. Simplify $2\sqrt{90} - \sqrt{40}$.

 A. $4\sqrt{10}$ **B.** $6\sqrt{10} - 4\sqrt{10}$
 C. $8\sqrt{5}$ **D.** $3\sqrt{10}$

24._____

25. Solve $\sqrt{4p + 1} - 7 = 0$.

 A. 2 **B.** 9 **C.** 12 **D.** $\dfrac{3}{2}$

25._____

26. What is the equation of the axis of symmetry of the graph of $y = 2x^2 - 6x + 1$?

 A. $x = \dfrac{3}{2}$ **B.** $x = -\dfrac{3}{2}$ **C.** $x = 3$ **D.** $x = -3$

26._____

27. Solve $x^2 + 6x - 10 = 0$.

 A. $-3 \pm 6\sqrt{10}$ **B.** $-1, -5$ **C.** $-3 \pm \sqrt{19}$ **D.** none of these

27._____

28. Which of the following is a quadratic equation whose roots are -3 and 5?

 A. $x^2 + 2x + 15 = 0$ **B.** $x^2 - 2x - 15 = 0$
 C. $x^2 - 2x + 15 = 0$ **D.** $x^2 - 15x - 2 = 0$

28._____

29. Find the mean and median of the data in the stem-and-leaf plot.

Stem	Leaf
8	1 9
9	2 3 8
10	1 9
11	2 4 8 9
12	5 7 $10|1 = 101$

 A. mean = 106, median = 109   **B.** mean = 109, median = 106
 C. mean = 106, median = 101   **D.** mean = 109, median = 101

29._____

30. The diagonal of a rectangle is 14 cm long and makes an angle of 35° with a side of the rectangle. Find the length and width of the rectangle to the nearest tenth of a centimeter.

 A. 9.8 cm by 10 cm   **B.** 8.0 cm by 16.1 cm
 C. 8.0 cm by 11.5 cm   **D.** 11.5 cm by 18.1 cm

30._____

Write the answer in the blank at the right of each problem.

31. Write the fractions $\frac{5}{13}$, $\frac{23}{51}$, and $\frac{11}{30}$ in order from least to greatest.

31. _____

32. Determine which is the better buy, 3.0 liters of soda at \$2.49 or 2.0 liters of soda at \$1.89.

32. _____

33. State the property illustrated by $4 + 1 = 1 + 4$.

33. _____

34. Write the following verbal sentence as an equation. The sum of y and the cube of n is 6 less than the square of v.

34. _____

35. Write the next two terms in the sequence $2, 6, 5, 15, 14, 42, \cdots$.

35. _____

36. State the property illustrated by the following sentence. If $mx + b = y$, then $y = mx + b$.

36. _____

37. Find $\begin{bmatrix} 3.5 & -8 \\ 2.7 & -5 \end{bmatrix} - \begin{bmatrix} 2.3 & 6 \\ 1.25 & -5 \end{bmatrix}$.

37. _____

38. Solve $\frac{x-6}{2} = 8$.

38. _____

39. An \$80 jacket is on sale for 30% off. What is the sale price?

39. _____

40. Write the equation for the relation $\{(-1, -2), (0, 1), (1, 4), (2, 7), (3, 10)\}$. Is this relation a function?

40. _____

41. If $f(x) = 4x^2 + 5x - 1$, find $f(-3)$.

41. _____

42. Determine the slope of the line passing through $(5, -6)$ and $(3, -6)$.

42. _____

43. Write an equation in slope-intercept form of the line that passes through $(4, 8)$ and $(2, -10)$.

43. _____

44. Write an equation in slope-intercept form of the line that is parallel to the graph of $3y - 4x = 1$ and passes through $(0, 6)$.

44. _____

45. Solve $4z + 6 \le 10z - 2$.

45. _____

46. Solve $\frac{x}{-2} - 4 \geq -5$. Graph the solution set.

46. _____

47. Graph the solution set of $3 < x$ or $x \leq -2$.

47. _____

48. Graph the inequality $y \leq 1$.

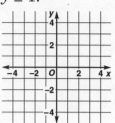

49. Graph the system of equations $y = 3x - 1$ and $y = 3x + 1$. Then determine the number of solutions.

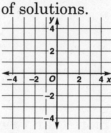

48. _____

49. _____

50. Solve the system of equations $2x - 4y = 26$ and $3x + 2y = 15$.

50. _____

51. The sum of the digits of a two-digit number is 12. If the units digit is 3 times the tens digit, find the number.

51. _____

52. Simplify $(-3x^5y^3)^2(2xy^4)^3$.

52. _____

53. Simplify $\frac{25m^3n^5p}{-5m^6n^2p^3}$.

53. _____

54. Write the expression below as a single number in scientific notation. $\frac{6 \times 10^{-5}}{3 \times 10^4}$

54. _____

55. Simplify $(7x^2 - 4x + 6) - (2x^2 + 3x - 10)$.

55. _____

56. Factor $4x^2 - 49y^2$.

56. _____

57. Solve $m^2 - 11m + 18 = 0$.

57. _____

58. Solve $5x^2 - 6x + 1 = 0$.

58. _____

59. Find the complement of an angle whose measure is $38°$.

59. _____

60. If the probability of an event is $\frac{7}{10}$, what are the odds against the event?

60. _____

Final Test (continued)

61. Find the mean, median, and mode(s) of the data
    listed below.
    16, 23, 2, 6, 14, 19, 16, 6, 8, 10

61. _____

62. Find the interquartile range of the data in
    question 61.

62. _____

63. Triangles ABC and DEF are similar. If $a = 4$, $b = 7$,
    $c = 6$, and $d = 3$, find the measures of e and f.

63. _____

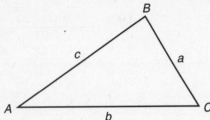

64. The length of a rectangle is 2 feet more than twice the
    width. The perimeter is 34 feet. Find the dimensions
    of the rectangle.

64. _____

65. Find the equation of the axis of symmetry and the
    vertex of the graph of $y = 4x^2 - 3x + 2$.

65. _____

66. Solve $3x^2 - 5x - 4 = 0$.

66. _____

67. Find the value of c so that $x^2 - x + c$ is a perfect
    square trinomial.

67. _____

68. Simplify $\dfrac{x^2 - 1}{x^2 + 2x + 1} \cdot \dfrac{x^2 - 4}{x^2 + x - 2}$.

68. _____

69. Simplify $\dfrac{10x}{5x + 3} + \dfrac{6}{10x + 6}$.

69. _____

70. Simplify $\dfrac{3 - x}{x^2 + x - 12}$.

70. _____

71. Simplify $5\sqrt{6} \cdot 3\sqrt{6}$.

71. _____

72. Simplify $3\sqrt{45} - \sqrt{50}$.

72. _____

73. Simplify $\dfrac{4}{3 + \sqrt{2}}$.

73. _____

74. Find the distance between $(1, 5)$ and $(-3, 9)$.

74. _____

75. Fred can paint a fence by himself in 6 hours. Working
    together with his neighbor Barney, Fred can paint the
    fence in 2 hours. How long would it take Barney to paint
    the fence by himself?

75. _____

Placement Test Answer Key

Page 365

1. __B__

2. __C__

3. __A__

4. __D__

5. __B__

6. __C__

7. __A__

8. __A__

9. __D__

10. __B__

Page 366

11. __C__

12. __B__

13. __B__

14. __D__

15. __B__

16. __A__

17. __D__

18. __C__

19. __D__

20. __A__

Placement Test Answer Key

21. _____ $x - 6$ _____

22.

23. **commutative prop. of mult.**

24. **transitive prop. of equality**

25. _____ **238** _____

26. _____ **14** _____

27. **distributive prop.**

28. **gain of 3 yards**

29. _____ **−1** _____

30. $-\dfrac{5}{12}$

31. $\dfrac{8}{3}$

32.

33. **−6 and −5**

34. **5(x + 3) = 35**

35. _____ **8** _____

36. _____ **−40** _____

37. _____ **−4** _____

38. _____ **7** _____

39. $-\dfrac{1}{2}$

40. $\dfrac{n-5}{3-y}$

41. _____ **15 cm** _____

42. $\dfrac{5}{2}$

43. _____ **3** _____

44. _____ **25** _____

45. _____ **85%** _____

46. _____ **12.5%** _____

47. _____ **$17.50** _____

48. _____ **24** _____

49. _____ **12** _____

50. _____ **3 hours** _____

First Semester Test Answer Key

1. __B__   11. __B__

2. __D__   12. __C__

3. __B__   13. __C__

4. __D__   14. __D__

5. __A__   15. __C__

6. __C__   16. __C__

7. __B__   17. __D__

8. __D__   18. __D__

9. __A__   19. __C__

10. __A__   20. __A__

                                       Algebra 1

First Semester Test Answer Key

Page 371

Page 372

21. $2n^3 + 5$

36. 25%

22. $7x + 3$

37. $D = \{-4, 2, 1, 7\};$
$R = \{3, 6, 9\};$ yes

23. commutative prop. of add.

24.

Stem	Leaf
4	3 7 8
5	2 2 5 8

$5|2 = 5200$

38. Quadrant II

39. 3

25. 1500

40. 13

26. -47

41. $x > -5$

27. 6.3

42. 31 mi/h

43. $\frac{3}{4}; -2; \frac{8}{3}$

28. $\begin{bmatrix} -1 & 5 \\ -1 & 11 \end{bmatrix}$

44.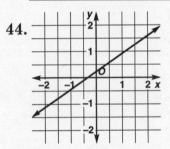

29. 7

30. -14

45. 1

31. 26, 27, 28

46. $y = \frac{1}{2}x + 3$

32. -1

47. $\frac{3}{10}$

33. $z < -\frac{5}{12}$

48.

34.

49. $a = 4\frac{1}{2}; f = \frac{4}{3}$

35. Kellie: 17, Renée: 22

50. $m\angle A = 45°; a = 6; c = 6\sqrt{2},$
or about 8.5

Second Semester Test Answer Key

Page 373

1. __B__

2. __C__

3. __C__

4. __A__

5. __C__

6. __B__

7. __C__

8. __A__

9. __C__

10. __D__

Page 374

11. __A__

12. __D__

13. __A__

14. __B__

15. __D__

16. __C__

17. __C__

18. __D__

19. __B__

20. __A__

Second Semester Test Answer Key

21. $\left(2\frac{1}{3}, 1\right)$

22. $(-1, 5)$

23. 70

24. no solution

25.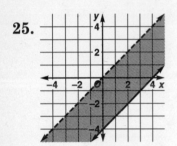

26. $-18a^3b^9$

27. $-\dfrac{c^4}{4a^4b}$

28. $2x^2 + 6xy + 10y^2$

29. $4a^2 - 16$

30. $x^2 + 6xy + 9y^2$

31. $(m + 9)^2$

32. $0, -7$

33. $3(t - 1)(t - 6)$

34. $-7, -4$

35. 10 or -4

36. $x = \dfrac{2}{3}; \left(\dfrac{2}{3}, \dfrac{11}{3}\right)$

37. $\dfrac{3}{5}$

38. $x^2 + 5x - 6 = 0$

39. $\dfrac{3 \pm \sqrt{17}}{4}$

40. 3

41. $\dfrac{m - 4}{m - 1}$

42. $\dfrac{x + 1}{x - 1}$

43. $\dfrac{11y + 16}{4(y + 1)}$

44. $\dfrac{10}{7}$

45. 10

46. $\dfrac{\sqrt{15}}{3}$

47. $23\sqrt{7}$

48. $33\frac{1}{3}$

49. no

50. $3\sqrt{2}$

Algebra 1

Final Test Answer Key

Page 377	Page 378	Page 379
1. __B__	11. __D__	21 __A__
2. __D__	12. __A__	22. __A__
3. __A__	13. __D__	23. __B__
4. __C__	14. __B__	24. __A__
5. __A__	15. __D__	25. __C__
6. __C__	16. __B__	26. __A__
7. __A__	17. __C__	27. __C__
8. __D__	18. __A__	28. __B__
9. __A__	19. __C__	29. __A__
10. __B__	20. __D__	30. __C__

Final Test Answer Key

Page 380

31. $\dfrac{11}{30}, \dfrac{5}{13}, \dfrac{23}{51}$

32. 3.0 liters at $2.49

33. commutative prop. of add.

34. $y + n^3 = v^2 - 6$

35. 41, 123

36. symmetric prop.

37. $\begin{bmatrix} 1.2 & -14 \\ 1.45 & 0 \end{bmatrix}$

38. 22

39. $56

40. $y = 3x + 1$; yes

41. 20

42. 0

43. $y = 9x - 28$

44. $y = \dfrac{4}{3}x + 6$

45. $z \geq \dfrac{4}{3}$

46. $x \leq 2$

47.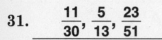

48. See students' graphs.

49. See students' graphs; no solutions.

50. $(7, -3)$

51. 39

52. $72x^{13}y^{18}$

53. $\dfrac{-5n^3}{m^3 p^2}$

54. 2×10^{-9}

55. $5x^2 - 7x + 16$

56. $(2x - 7y)(2x + 7y)$

57. 2, 9

58. $\dfrac{1}{5}, 1$

59. 52°

60. 3 : 7

Page 382

61. mean: 12; median: 12; modes: 6 and 16

62. 10

63. $e = 5.25$; $f = 4.5$

64. 5 ft by 12 ft

65. $x = \dfrac{3}{8}; \left(\dfrac{3}{8}, \dfrac{23}{16} \right)$

66. $\dfrac{5 \pm \sqrt{73}}{6}$

67. $\dfrac{1}{4}$

68. $\dfrac{x - 2}{x + 1}$

69. $\dfrac{10x + 3}{5x + 3}$

70. $\dfrac{-1}{x + 4}$

71. 90

72. $9\sqrt{5} - 5\sqrt{2}$

73. $\dfrac{12 - 4\sqrt{2}}{7}$

74. $4\sqrt{2}$

75. 3 hours

How to Use Mathematics Learning Assessment

Nearly all school districts and many states use standardized tests for grouping students and diagnosing, evaluating, and comparing their progress. Traditionally, these tests have taken the form of multiple-choice tests. But as the curriculum begins to emphasize the development of mathematical power, new methods of standardized testing can reinforce its development by providing thoughtful problem-solving situations and opportunities for students to construct their own responses, instead of choosing a single answer. So, many state and national tests now include:

- enhanced multiple-choice questions,
- constructed-response questions, and
- open-ended problems.

Some programs may eventually include portfolios and investigations in their assessment. Even college admissions tests are shifting to a more open-ended format.

In order to help you prepare your students for the new generation of standardized tests, the Mathematics Learning Assessment part of this Assessment and Evaluation Masters contains three Practice Tests, each designed as follows:

Section One | 7 enhanced multiple-choice questions
Section Two | 4 constructed-response questions
Section Three | 2 open-ended problems

Each test has a Scoring Guide for the open-ended problems and Sample Answers for all of the questions.

In addition, **Additional Practice** is included for enhanced multiple-choice, constructed-response, and open-ended problems. You may wish to have your students take one or two Practice Tests. Depending on the results, they may need to use these additional practice problems for concentration on one or more types of questions.

Examples of enhanced multiple-choice questions, constructed-response questions, open-ended problems, and a scoring guide may be found on the following pages.

Enhanced Multiple-Choice Questions

Enhanced multiple-choice questions are similar to traditional multiple-choice questions in that both have a single correct answer. But instead of testing computational facts, enhanced multiple-choice questions test a problem-solving or application situation. Since computational facts are not tested, you may want to allow students to use a calculator when taking each test.

A sample enhanced multiple-choice question follows.

The line plot shows the heights in inches of the Washington Middle School girls' basketball team. Which sentence best describes the data?

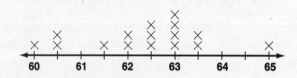

A. The range is 6 inches.
B. Most of the players are 63 inches tall.
C. There are 8 players.
D. Most of the players are between 62 and 64 inches tall.

The answer is **D**.

Constructed-Response Questions

Constructed-response questions are similar to "short answer" questions. Students are usually required to perform a calculation and write an answer or to examine a situation and tell why one alternative or another is correct. The questions also may require students to draw a graph or chart. While these questions do not require extensive amounts of problem solving, they do move beyond the selection of an answer from a list, as in the multiple-choice format. Each answer may be scored as either receiving credit or not receiving credit.

A sample student-constructed response question follows.

What are the next two terms in the sequence 2, 5, 10, 17, ...?

The answer is **26, 37**.

Open-Ended Problems

Perhaps the greatest change in standardized testing comes with the inclusion of open-ended problems. These questions not only require students to construct their own responses, but, in contrast to constructed-response questions, also require students to demonstrate their mathematical reasoning and problem-solving abilities and to communicate effectively. Open-ended questions encourage students to solve problems in a variety of ways, which highlight the development of mathematical power in the classroom.

A sample open-ended problem follows.

> **Mike knows that half of the students from his class are recommended for algebra. Also, half are recommended for a foreign language. Mike thinks that this adds up to 100 percent, so he will surely be recommended for one or the other class. Explain why Mike may be wrong. If possible, use a diagram in your explanation.**

In this case, the student's response reveals his or her ability to describe a situation in which two groups can each be half of the total, but not be mutually exclusive. The mathematical language used helps to assess student's mathematical knowledge. The student may show his or her understanding with a Venn diagram. Open-ended problems are usually evaluated using a scoring guide.

How to Use a Scoring Guide

Open-ended problems involve understanding of mathematical concepts and procedures; they are thought-provoking and seldom have a single answer. The evaluation of such tasks involves the professional judgement of a trained teacher and is generally holistic rather than analytical. Holistic evaluation means to judge a work as a whole. Some have indicated that such an evaluation should be one's first impression of the complete piece of work. In contrast, analytic evaluation means to judge the work in parts before combining these judgments to arrive at an overall assessment. By scoring holistically, the evaluator is free to respond to the student's complete thinking and communicating processes.

The first step in evaluating an open-ended problem is to establish a system for documenting student performance. A scoring guide, like the one shown on the following page, establishes the criteria for judging the work. Students should know what constitutes each level of performance. Thus, specific performance criteria as provided on the scoring guide should accompany each open-ended problem when given to a student.

For your convenience, a scoring guide is provided with each Practice Test in Mathematics Learning Assessment. The guide uses a four-point scale ranging from superior to unsatisfactory. The scale can be easily modified to add additional points for finer judgments. You may want to modify the sample guide on the following page for use with the open-ended practice problems which begin on page 461.

When students have completed the open-ended problems, their work is compared to the specific scoring guide and scored holistically according to the level that best describes the work. To help you understand what kind of work is expected on the open-ended problems, there are four samples of student work beginning on page 427. The problems are taken from the Practice Tests.

Sample Scoring Guide

Level	Criteria
3 Superior	• Shows thorough understanding of the concepts. • Uses appropriate strategies. • Computations are correct. • Written explanations are exemplary. • Diagrams are accurate and appropriate. • Goes beyond requirements of the problems.
2 Satisfactory, with Minor Flaws	• Shows understanding of the concepts. • Uses appropriate strategies. • Computations are mostly correct. • Written explanations are effective. • Diagrams are mostly accurate and appropriate. • Satisfies all requirements of the problems.
1 Nearly Satisfactory, with Serious Flaws	• Shows understanding of most of the concepts. • May not use appropriate strategies. • Computations are mostly correct. • Written explanations are satisfactory. • Diagrams are mostly accurate and appropriate. • Satisfies most requirements of the problems.
0 Unsatisfactory	• Shows little or no understanding of the concepts. • May not use appropriate strategies. • Computations are incorrect. • Written explanations are not satisfactory. • Diagrams are not accurate or appropriate. • Does not satisfy requirements of problems.

Practice Test 1

Section One

There are seven multiple-choice questions in this section. Work the problem in the area marked "Scratch work." Circle the letter of the correct answer.

1. The sum of five consecutive integers is always divisible by

    A. 2   **B.** 4   **C.** 5   **D.** 10

Scratch work

2. If the radius of a circle is tripled, then the area is multiplied by

    A. 3   **B.** 6   **C.** 9   **D.** 27

Scratch work

Practice Test 1
(continued)

3. If $8x + 10y$ represents the perimeter of a rectangle and $x + 3y$ represents its width, its length is represented by

   A. $3x + 2y$ **B.** $7x + 7y$ **C.** $6x + 4y$ **D.** $3.5x + 3.5y$

Scratch work

4. In a random sample of 150 students, 60 ride the bus to school, 54 ride in car pools, and 36 walk. If 800 students are enrolled next year, about how many will need bus transportation?

   A. 60   **B.** 80   **C.** 160   **D.** 320

Scratch work

GO ON TO NEXT PAGE

Practice Test 1
(continued)

5. Three straight lines intersect at the same point.

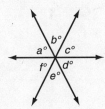

$a° + b° =$

A. $b° + f°$ **B.** $e° + d°$ **C.** $f° + d°$ **D.** $c° + e°$

Scratch work

6. In the sequence 2, 6, 11, 17, 24, ..., the eighth term is

A. 41   **B.** 45   **C.** 51   **D.** 62

Scratch work

GO ON TO NEXT PAGE

Practice Test 1
(continued)

7. What is the value of $(x - y)^3$ if $y = x + 3$?

   A. −27   **B.** −9   **C.** 27   **D.** 9

Scratch work

GO ON TO NEXT PAGE

Practice Test 1
(continued)

Section Two

This section contains four questions for which you will provide short answers.
Work the problem in the area marked "Scratch work."

8. In the figure below, $ABCD$ is a square with sides 2 inches long. M and N are the midpoints of sides $\overline{AB}$ and $\overline{BC}$, respectively. What is the ratio of the area of triangle MND to the area of square $ABCD$?

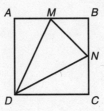

Scratch work

9. The graph at the right shows the height of a ball thrown in the air with respect to time. Describe what is happening at point A in terms of height.

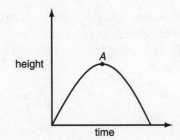

Scratch work

GO ON TO NEXT PAGE

Practice Test 1
(continued)

10. Find the slope of the line that contains the points $A(5, 3)$ and $B(-1, 1)$.

Scratch work

11. The chart below lists the number and type of chocolates found in two boxes of candy. A milk chocolate is chosen at random. Then a dark chocolate is chosen at random. Find the probability that a milk chocolate with nuts and a dark chocolate with nuts will be chosen.

Boxes	Nuts	Fruits	Plain
Milk chocolate	4	6	2
Dark chocolate	2	6	6

Scratch work

GO ON TO NEXT PAGE

Practice Test 1
(continued)

Section Three

This section contains two open-ended problems. Demonstrate your knowledge by giving a clear, concise solution to each problem.

Your score on these problems will depend on how well you
- *can explain your reasoning.*
- *show your understanding of the mathematics in an organized manner.*
- *use charts, graphs, and diagrams in your explanation.*
- *show the solution in more than one way or relate it to other situations.*
- *investigate beyond the requirements of the problems.*

12. Develop a plan for estimating the height of your school building without directly measuring it.

GO ON TO NEXT PAGE

Practice Test 1
(continued)

13. Anthropologists study the origin and development of the human race. Their work is based on the scientific method. They gather data, represent it in a meaningful form, and then look for patterns.

The *humerus* is the long bone of the upper arm. The scatter plot below shows the length of the humerus and the height of twelve adult males in a study. The graph suggests that, the longer the humerus is, the greater the height. Suppose that an anthropologist believes that the relationship is linear. She might draw a line on the graph, as shown below.

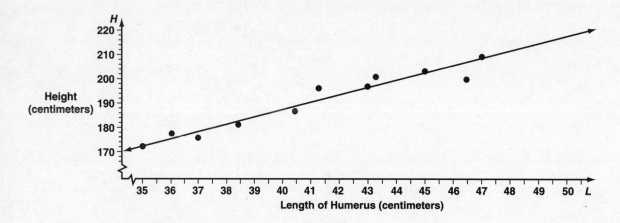

A. Estimate the slope of the line using two ordered pairs from the graph.

B. Find an equation for the line.

C. An anthropologist knows that the length of the humerus of an adult male is 50 centimeters. Find an estimate of the man's height.

END OF TEST
You may go back and work more or check your answers.

Practice Test 1

Scoring Guide

Level	Criteria
3 Superior	• Shows thorough understanding of the concepts of *similar figures, slope,* and *finding the equation of a line.* • Uses appropriate strategies to evaluate and model expressions. • Computations are correct. • Written explanations are exemplary. • Diagrams are accurate and appropriate. • Goes beyond requirements of the problems.
2 Satisfactory, with Minor Flaws	• Shows understanding of the concepts of *similar figures, slope,* and *finding the equation of a line.* • Uses appropriate strategies to evaluate and model expressions. • Computations are mostly correct. • Written explanations are effective. • Diagrams are mostly accurate and appropriate. • Satisfies all requirements of the problems.
1 Nearly Satisfactory, with Serious Flaws	• Shows understanding of most of the concepts of *similar figures, slope,* and *finding the equation of a line.* • May not use appropriate strategies to evaluate and model expressions. • Computations are mostly correct. • Written explanations are satisfactory. • Diagrams are mostly accurate and appropriate. • Satisfies most requirements of the problems.
0 Unsatisfactory	• Shows little or no understanding of the concepts of *similar figures, slope,* and *finding the equation of a line.* • May not use appropriate strategies to evaluate and model expressions. • Computations are incorrect. • Written explanations are not satisfactory. • Diagrams are not accurate or appropriate. • Does not satisfy requirements of problems.

Practice Test 1

Solutions

Section One

1. C

2. C

3. A

4. D

5. B

6. C

7. A

Section Two

8. 3 to 8

9. Point A represents the highest point the ball reaches before falling.

10. $\dfrac{1}{3}$

11. $\dfrac{1}{18}$

Section Three

This section contains two open-ended problems which allow for alternate solutions, differing explanations, and expressions of personal opinion. What follows are sample solutions that will often vary greatly from correct responses by students. The rubric provided with each unit will usually be a better scoring guide than direct comparison of student answers with answers given here.

12. On a sunny day, measure the shadow cast by a meter-stick. At the same time, measure the shadow cast by the school building. Solve the following proportion to find the height of the school in meters.

$$\frac{shadow\ of\ meter\ stick}{1\ meter} = \frac{shadow\ of\ school}{height\ of\ school}$$

13a. Using ordered pairs (38.5, 182) and (45, 200), the slope is about 2.77.

  b. Answers will vary. Sample: $H = 2.77L + 75$

  c. about 214 cm

Practice Test 2

Section One

There are seven multiple-choice questions in this section. Work the problem in the area marked "Scratch work." Circle the letter of the correct answer.

1. The area of the circle enclosed in the square is 8π square units. What is the area of the square?

   A. 64 square units   **B.** 32 square units   **C.** 16 square units   **D.** 8 square units

   Scratch work

2. If the average of x and y equals the average of x, y, and z, then express z in terms of x and y.

   A. $x + y$ **B.** $2(x + y)$ **C.** $\frac{x+y}{2}$ **D.** $\frac{x+y}{3}$

   Scratch work

GO ON TO NEXT PAGE

Practice Test 2
(continued)

3. The measure of the sides of four triangles are given. Which one is *not* a right triangle?

   A. 5, 12, 13   **B.** 8, 15, 17   **C.** 9, 40, 41   **D.** 12, 15, 18

Scratch work

4. Which equation is graphed below?

   A. $y = 2$ **B.** $x = 2$ **C.** $y = x + 2$ **D.** $y = -x + 2$

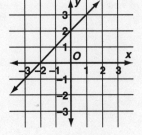

Scratch work

GO ON TO NEXT PAGE

Practice Test 2
(continued)

5. Use the pattern in the table shown below to determine the unit digit of 3^{15}.

Power of 3	3^1	3^2	3^3	3^4	3^5	3^6	3^7	3^8	3^9	3^{10}	...	3^{15}
Unit Digit	3	9	7	1	3	9	7	1	3	9	...	?

A. 1   **B.** 3   **C.** 7   **D.** 9

Scratch work

6. In the equation $B + 12 = P$, B represents Bob's test score, and P represents Pablo's test score. Which sentence describes the relationship between the test scores?

A. Bob's test score is 12 points higher than Pablo's.

B. Pablo's test score is 12 points higher than Bob's.

C. Pablo's test score is less than Bob's.

D. There is no relationship between the test scores.

Scratch work

GO ON TO NEXT PAGE

Practice Test 2
(continued)

7. In a family of two children, which outcome has the greatest probability?

    A. 1 boy and 1 girl   **B.** 2 girls

    C. 2 boys   **D.** They all have the same probability.

Scratch work

 Algebra 1

Practice Test 2
(continued)

Section Two

This section contains four questions for which you will provide short answers.
Work the problem in the area marked "Scratch work."

8. A ball rebounds $\frac{2}{3}$ of its height after every fall. If it is dropped from a height of 48 feet, how high will it bounce after the third bounce?

Scratch work

9. Determine the next two numbers and draw the next two shapes in the pattern below.

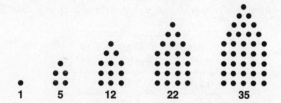

| 1 | 5 | 12 | 22 | 35 |

Scratch work

GO ON TO NEXT PAGE

Practice Test 2
(continued)

10. Line p is parallel to line t, and lines ℓ and m intersect at point P on line t. If $\angle 1$ measures 80° and $\angle 2$ measures 30°, find the measure of $\angle 3$.

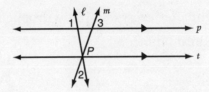

Scratch work

11. The members of Student Council surveyed 80 seniors to determine the amount they would be willing to pay for a yearbook. The results are shown in the table below. If there are 600 in the senior class, about how many would buy a yearbook that costs $18.50?

Amount Willing to Pay for Yearbook	
no more than $15	8
no more than $17	30
no more than $19	32
no more than $21	10

Scratch work

GO ON TO NEXT PAGE

Practice Test 2
(continued)

Section Three

This section contains two open-ended problems. Demonstrate your knowledge by giving a clear, concise solution to each problem.

Your score on these problems will depend on how well you
- *can explain your reasoning.*
- *show your understanding of the mathematics in an organized manner.*
- *use charts, graphs, and diagrams in your explanation.*
- *show the solution in more than one way or relate it to other situations.*
- *investigate beyond the requirements of the problems.*

12. ACT, a long-distance telephone service, charges $2.20 for the first minute and $0.63 for each minute after the first. For the same call, MT&I, another long-distance service, charges $1.90 for the first minute and $0.68 for each minute after the first. Be sure to explain your reasoning as you answer the following questions.

   a. When is the cost of both calls the same?

   b. Which company offers the better price for a 20-minute call?

GO ON TO NEXT PAGE

Practice Test 2
(continued)

13. Fifty students were surveyed as to the amount of allowance they received each week. The results of the survey are shown in the chart below.

Amount of allowance	$5	$10	$15	$20	$25
Number of students	21	12	5	8	4

    a. Which measure of central tendency — mean, median, or mode — best represents the data? Why?

    b. How might each measure of central tendency be used to further a particular point of view?

END OF TEST
You may go back and work more or check your answers.

Practice Test 2

Scoring Guide

Level	Criteria
3 Superior	• Shows thorough understanding of the concepts of *systems of equations* and *measures of central tendency*. • Uses appropriate strategies to evaluate and model expressions. • Computations are correct. • Written explanations are exemplary. • Diagrams are accurate and appropriate. • Goes beyond requirements of the problems.
2 Satisfactory, with Minor Flaws	• Shows understanding of the concepts of *systems of equations* and *measures of central tendency*. • Uses appropriate strategies to evaluate and model expressions. • Computations are mostly correct. • Written explanations are effective. • Diagrams are mostly accurate and appropriate. • Satisfies all requirements of the problems.
1 Nearly Satisfactory, with Serious Flaws	• Shows understanding of most of the concepts of *systems of equations* and *measures of central tendency*. • May not use appropriate strategies to evaluate and model expressions. • Computations are mostly correct. • Written explanations are satisfactory. • Diagrams are mostly accurate and appropriate. • Satisfies most requirements of the problems.
0 Unsatisfactory	• Shows little or no understanding of the concepts of *systems of equations* and *measures of central tendency*. • May not use appropriate strategies to evaluate and model expressions. • Computations are incorrect. • Written explanations are not satisfactory. • Diagrams are not accurate or appropriate. • Does not satisfy requirements of problems.

Practice Test 2

Solutions
Section One

1. B

2. C

3. D

4. C

5. C

6. B

7. A

Section Two

8. 14.2 feet

10. 70°

11. about 315 students

9.

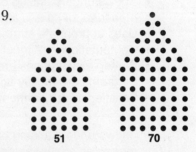

Section Three

This section contains two open-ended problems which allow for alternate solutions, differing explanations, and expressions of personal opinion. What follows are sample solutions that will often vary greatly from correct responses by students. The rubric provided with each unit will usually be a better scoring guide than direct comparison of student answers with answers given here.

12a. at 7 minutes

  b. ACT

13a. The mode or median represents the amount received by about half the students.

  b. A parent might use the mode to justify a lower amount. The median could be used to justify receiving more than $5 since half of the students receive $10 or more. The mean could be used to get the greatest possible "average" amount.

Practice Test 3

Section One

There are seven multiple-choice questions in this section. Work the problem in the area marked "Scratch work." Circle the letter of the correct answer.

1. For nonzero numbers a, b, c, and d, $\frac{a}{b} = \frac{c}{d}$. Which of the following must be true?

A. $\frac{a}{b} = \frac{b}{c}$ **B.** $\frac{a+b}{b} = \frac{c+b}{d}$ **C.** $\frac{d}{b} = \frac{c}{a}$ **D.** $\frac{b}{c+d} = \frac{d}{a+b}$

Scratch work

2. A triangle is changed by keeping the base fixed and moving the opposite vertex parallel to the base.

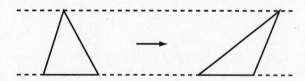

Which statement describes how the area has changed?

A. The area becomes greater.

B. The area becomes less.

C. The area is unchanged.

D. The area cannot be determined.

Scratch work

GO ON TO NEXT PAGE

Practice Test 3
(continued)

3. Sheila charges x dollars per hour to babysit. She babysits 8 hours on Saturday and 5 hours on Sunday. She also receives a $10 tip. Which expression represents the amount of money, in dollars, Sheila earns on Saturday and Sunday?

   A. $13(x + 10)$ **B.** $13x^2 + 10$ **C.** 23 **D.** $13x + 10$

Scratch work

4. Three vertices of a parallelogram are at $(2, 1)$, $(-1, -3)$, and $(6, 4)$. The fourth vertex is at

   A. $(0, 3)$ **B.** $(3, 0)$ **C.** $(-1, 4)$ **D.** $(6, 1)$

Scratch work

GO ON TO NEXT PAGE

Practice Test 3
(continued)

5. Which equation shows an incorrect use of the distributive property?

    A. $2(x + 3) = 2x + 5$ **B.** $3x + 6 = 3(x + 2)$

    C. $6(x + 4) = 6x + 24$ **D.** $5(x + 2) = 5x + 10$

Scratch work

6. Suppose a game used the spinner shown below.

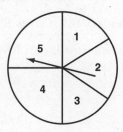

    Which game is unfair?

    A. Win by spinning a 1, 2, or 3.   **B.** Win by spinning a 4 or 5.

    C. Win by spinning a number less than 4.   **D.** Win by spinning an even number.

Scratch work

GO ON TO NEXT PAGE

Practice Test 3
(continued)

7. Video Town charges a $30 rental fee plus $35 per day for a camcorder. All-Pro Rental Services charges a $45 rental fee and $30 per day for the same camcorder. This information is summarized in the tables and graph.

Video Town $y = 30 + 35x$	
x	y
1	65
2	100
3	135
4	170

All-Pro $y = 45 + 30x$	
x	y
1	75
2	105
3	135
4	165

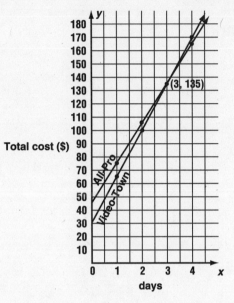

Which statement is *not* true?

A. The cost of renting the camcorder for 3 days is the same at either store.

B. It costs less to rent the camcorder at Video Town for 1 or 2 days.

C. Each additional day of rental at Video Town costs $30.

D. If you rent the camcorder for 1 week, it will cost less at All-Pro.

Scratch work

GO ON TO NEXT PAGE

Practice Test 3
(continued)

Section Two

This section contains four questions for which you will provide short answers.
Work the problem in the area marked "Scratch work."

8. Six points are marked on a circle. How many different line segments can be drawn between any combination of two points?

Scratch work

9. In the geometric sequence $1, \frac{1}{2}, \frac{1}{4}, \frac{1}{8}, \frac{1}{16}, \ldots$, find the product when the 99th term is divided by the 100th term.

Scratch work

GO ON TO NEXT PAGE

Practice Test 3
(continued)

10. How many units apart are the points at $(-11, 2)$ and at $(6, 4)$ in the coordinate plane?

Scratch work

11. The measure of the area of a rectangle is $25x^2 - 9$. Find the measure of the perimeter of that rectangle.

Scratch work

GO ON TO NEXT PAGE

422

Practice Test 3
(continued)

Section Three

This section contains two open-ended problems. Demonstrate your knowledge by giving a clear, concise solution to each problem.

Your score on these problems will depend on how well you
- *can explain your reasoning.*
- *show your understanding of the mathematics in an organized manner.*
- *use charts, graphs, and diagrams in your explanation.*
- *show the solution in more than one way or relate it to other situations.*
- *investigate beyond the requirements of the problems.*

12. Probability has many applications in baseball. Suppose Juan Garcia and Tony Brewer are the first two batters in the ninth inning. Their respective batting averages – that is, the probability that each will get a hit – are .200 or 20% and .250 or 25%.

   A. Design a simulation to find the experimental probability of both getting a hit.

   B. Tell how to find the probability of independent events. Find the theoretical probability of both getting a hit.

GO ON TO NEXT PAGE

Practice Test 3
(continued)

13. A contractor has been hired to build a deck in the shape of a rectangle. Before setting the corner posts, the contractor uses lines like the ones shown below to outline the position of the deck. Explain how the contractor can be sure that the deck is in the shape of a rectangle.

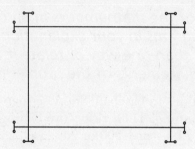

END OF TEST
You may go back and work more or check your answers.

Practice Test 3

Scoring Guide

Level	Criteria
3 Superior	• Shows thorough understanding of the concepts of *probability* and *rectangles*. • Uses appropriate strategies to evaluate and model expressions. • Computations are correct. • Written explanations are exemplary. • Diagrams are accurate and appropriate. • Goes beyond requirements of the problems.
2 Satisfactory, with Minor Flaws	• Shows understanding of the concepts of *probability* and *rectangles*. • Uses appropriate strategies to evaluate and model expressions. • Computations are mostly correct. • Written explanations are effective. • Diagrams are mostly accurate and appropriate. • Satisfies all requirements of the problems.
1 Nearly Satisfactory, with Serious Flaws	• Shows understanding of most of the concepts of *probability* and *rectangles*. • May not use appropriate strategies to evaluate and model expressions. • Computations are mostly correct. • Written explanations are satisfactory. • Diagrams are mostly accurate and appropriate. • Satisfies most requirements of the problems.
0 Unsatisfactory	• Shows little or no understanding of the concepts of *probability* and *rectangles*. • May not use appropriate strategies to evaluate and model expressions. • Computations are incorrect. • Written explanations are not satisfactory. • Diagrams are not accurate or appropriate. • Does not satisfy requirements of problems.

Practice Test 3

Solutions
Section One

1. C

2. C

3. D

4. B

5. A

6. D

7. C

Section Two

8. 15 line segments

9. 2

10. 17.1 units

11. $20x$

Section Three

This section contains two open-ended problems which allow for alternate solutions, differing explanations, and expressions of personal opinion. What follows are sample solutions that will often vary greatly from correct responses by students. The rubric provided with each unit will usually be a better scoring guide than direct comparison of student answers with answers given here.

12a. Use spinners like the ones shown at the right and conduct an experiment.

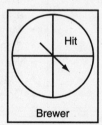

Garcia   Brewer

b. The probability of two independent events can be found by multiplying the probability of the first event by the probability of the second event. The probability of both Garcia and Brewer getting a hit is 0.2 x 0.25 or 0.05.

13. Sample answer: The contractor can measure to be sure opposite sides are equal and both diagonals are equal.

SAMPLE STUDENT WORK

Name Daniel Block   Date Nov. 3, 1994

Practice Test 1
(continued)   **Section T[**

*This section contains two open-ended proble[n]
giving a clear, concise solution to each proble[n]*

Your score on these problems will depend on
- *can explain your reasoning.*
- *show your understanding of the mathemat[*
- *use charts, graphs, and diagrams in your ex[*
- *show the solution in more than one way or[*
- *investigate beyond the requirements of the[*

12. Develop a plan for estimating the height of your s[
measuring it.

You have an excellent grasp of the problem and its concepts, and you have explained your reasoning in a clear, concise manner. Excellent diagram!

Score: 3

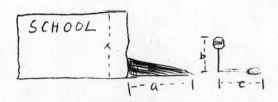

x = school's height
a = school's shadow's length
b = stop sign's height
c = stop sign's shadow's length

To find the height of my School building without directly measuring it, I would find an object, such as a stop sign, near the school.

The ratio of the heights of two objects is the same as the ratio of the lengths of the objects' shadows.

I would measure the length of both shadows and the height of the stop sign. Then I would set up a proportion and solve for x, the school's height.

$$\frac{x}{b} = \frac{a}{c}$$

$$x = \frac{ab}{c}$$

Name _Rachel Lewis_   Date _Dec. 8, 1994_

Practice Test 2
(continued)

Section Thre

*This section contains two open-ended problems.
giving a clear, concise solution to each problem.*

Your score on these problems will depend on ho
- *can explain your reasoning.*
- *show your understanding of the mathematics*
- *use charts, graphs, and diagrams in your expla*
- *show the solution in more than one way or re*
- *investigate beyond the requirements of the p*

*You have a clear
understanding of the
problem and its concepts.
You have used a table
appropriately in your
solution. Need more
explanation of your
reasoning.*

       Score: 2

12. ACT, a long-distance telephone service, charges $2.2
minute after the first. For the same call, MT&I, anotl
for the first minute and $0.68 for each minute after
reasoning as you answer the following questions.

   a. When is the cost of both calls the same?   the 7th minute

   b. Which company offers the better price for a 20-minute call?   ACT

	ACT	MT&I
1st min	$2.20	$1.90
2nd	2.83	2.58
3rd	3.46	3.26
4th	4.09	3.94
5th	4.72	4.62
6th	5.35	5.30
7th	5.98	5.98
8th	6.61	6.66
9th	7.24	7.34
10th	7.87	8.02
20th	(10 more min at $0.63) 14.17	(10 more min. at $0.68) 14.82

for a call less than
seven minutes, the cheaper
~~price~~ company would be
MT&I. For anything exceeding
seven minutes, the better deal would be ACT.

SAMPLE STUDENT WORK

Name Jason Nies   Date 12-14-94

Practice Test 2
(continued)

13. Fifty students were surveyed as to the amount of allowance
    results of the survey are shown in the chart below.

Amount of allowance	$5	$10	$15	$20	$2...
Number of students	21	12	5	8	

a. Which measure of central tendency — mean, median, or
   data? Why?

b. How might each measure of central tendency be used to
   view?

You have a good understanding of the concepts and have provided very good examples. Would like to see how you determined the mean, median, and mode.

Score: 2

A. Median, It's not the lowest allowance paid nor the highest, it's placed in the middle.

B. The mode ($5) would be used for a reference by the parents to make up the price of allowance for their child.

The mean ($11.20) would be pointed out by their child as a reasonable price for allowance.

The median ($10) would be a good compromise for both parties

END OF TEST
You may go back and work more or check your answers.

SAMPLE STUDENT WORK

Name **Karen Danko**   Date **Feb. 24, 1995**

Practice Test 3
(continued)   **Section** ?   Page 7

This section contains two open-ended probl
giving a clear, concise solution to each prob

Your score on these problems will depend o
- *can explain your reasoning.*
- *show your understanding of the mathema*
- *use charts, graphs, and diagrams in your e*
- *show the solution in more than one way*
- *investigate beyond the requirements of th*

12. Probability has many applications in baseball. S
    first two batters in the ninth inning. Their resp
    probability that each will get a hit – are .200 or

    A. Design a simulation to find the experimenta

    B. Tell how to find the probability of independent events. Find the theoretical probability of
       both getting a hit.

You have designed an excellent simulation. In it, you show that you have a clear understanding of the concepts of probability. You may want to also tell how to compute the probability from the simulation

Score: 3

A. In this simulation you want to represent both men getting up to bat. Start with two bowls, one to represent each batter. Put 4 blue marbles (represents no hit) and one red marble (hit) in the bowl for Juan Garcia. Put one red marble and 3 blue marbles in the bowl representing Tony Brewer. The number of marbles in each bowl represents the players' batting averages. With your eyes closed, draw one marble from each bowl. Record the data and do this at least 10 times. Possible outcomes could be:
(hit, hit) (hit, no hit) (no hit, hit) (no hit, no hit).
After recording the data, figure the probability of both men getting a hit.

B. To find the probability of independent events, you multiply the probability of the first event by the probability of the second event. The theoretical probability of both players getting a hit is 5%, or a 1 in 20 chance.

Additional Practice: Enhanced Multiple-Choice

There are forty enhanced multiple-choice questions in this section. Work the problem in the area marked "Scratch work." Circle the letter of the correct answer.

1. The side of one square is 3 inches long and the side of another square is $1\frac{1}{4}$ feet long. The ratio of the areas of the two squares is

   A. 1:5   **B.** 1:25   **C.** 12:5   **D.** 144:25

Scratch work

2. If $x > 1$, which of the following increases as x increases?

   I. $x - \dfrac{1}{x}$ **II.** $\dfrac{1}{x^2 - x}$ **III.** $4x^3 - 2x^2$

   A. I only   **B.** II only

   C. I and III only   **D.** I, II, and III

Scratch work

GO ON TO NEXT PAGE

Additional Practice: Enhanced Multiple-Choice
(continued)

3. How many real roots does the equation $2x^2 - 5x - 7 = 0$ have?

    A. one   **B.** two

    C. none   **D.** cannot be determined

Scratch work

4. The ratio of the area of a circle to its circumference is

    A. $\dfrac{2}{r}$ **B.** $\dfrac{r}{2}$ **C.** π **D.** $\dfrac{\pi}{2\pi}$

Scratch work

GO ON TO NEXT PAGE

Additional Practice: Enhanced Multiple-Choice
(continued)

5. The number of days in w weeks, d days, and h hours is

   A. $7w + d + 24h$ **B.** $\frac{w + d}{7} + 24h$

   C. $7w + d + \frac{h}{24}$ **D.** $7w + \frac{d - h}{24}$

Scratch work

6. There are 2 flavors of yogurt, 3 kinds of toppings, and 4 kinds of syrup. How many different combinations of yogurt, topping, and syrup (one of each) can be ordered?

   A. 6   **B.** 9   **C.** 12   **D.** 24

Scratch work

GO ON TO NEXT PAGE

Additional Practice: Enhanced Multiple-Choice
(continued)

7. A mail-order card company charges 50¢ for each greeting card plus a handling charge of $1.50. Which sentence could be used to find n, the number of cards ordered, if the total charge was $9?

A. $0.5n + 1.5 = 9$

B. $0.50n + 1.50n = 9$

C. $9 = 50n + 1.50$

D. $9 = (0.5 + 1.50)n$

Scratch work

8. Which tessellation unit would be formed by translating the change made on the square below?

A.

B.

C.

D. none of these

Scratch work

GO ON TO NEXT PAGE

Additional Practice: Enhanced Multiple-Choice
(continued)

9. If a line passes through the point at (0,2) and has a slope of 4, what is the equation of the line?

A. $x = 2y + 4$ **B.** $x = 4y + 2$ **C.** $y = 4x + 2$ **D.** $y = 2x + 4$

Scratch work

10. The graph below shows the relationship between the speeds of Car A and Car B.

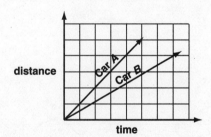

Choose the sentence that best describes the relationship.

A. The speed of Car A is greater than the speed of Car B.

B. The speed of Car B is greater than the speed of Car A.

C. The speed of Car A is equal to the speed of Car B.

D. There is not enough information to decide.

Scratch work

GO ON TO NEXT PAGE

Additional Practice: Enhanced Multiple-Choice
(continued)

11. Which graph shows $y = 2x + 2$?

A. 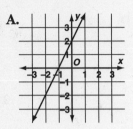 **B.** 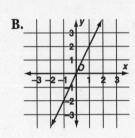 **C.** 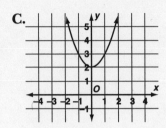 **D.**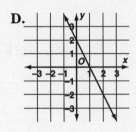

Scratch work

12. Which expression is *not* the difference of two perfect squares?

   A. $x^2 - 1$ **B.** $y^2 - b^2$ **C.** $9m^2 - 25n^2$ **D.** $4x^2 - 8$

Scratch work

GO ON TO NEXT PAGE

Additional Practice: Enhanced Multiple-Choice
(continued)

13. Which figure does *not* belong? In each figure, lines *a* and *b* are parallel.

A.

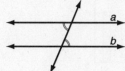

B.

C.

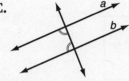

D.

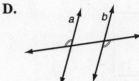

Scratch work

14. Which ordered pair is a solution of the system $y = x + 3$ and $3y + x = 5$?

A. $(1, 4)$ **B.** $(2, -1)$ **C.** $(-5, 0)$ **D.** $(-1, 2)$

Scratch work

GO ON TO NEXT PAGE

Additional Practice: Enhanced Multiple-Choice
(continued)

15. Which graph would you expect to show the results of rolling a fair die 1000 times?

A.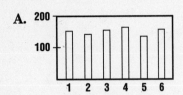

B.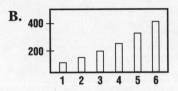

C.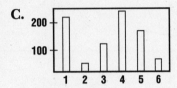

D.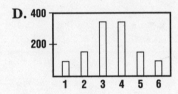

Scratch work

16. If $x @ y = x^2 - y^2$, then $3 @ (-2) =$

A. 5   **B.** 10   **C.** 13   **D.** 25

Scratch work

GO ON TO NEXT PAGE

Additional Practice: Enhanced Multiple-Choice
(continued)

17. If $\triangle BIG \cong \triangle TOP$, which pair of corresponding parts are *not* necessarily congruent?

A. $\overline{BG}, \overline{TP}$ **B.** $\overline{IB}, \overline{OP}$ **C.** $\angle G, \angle P$ **D.** $\angle I, \angle O$

Scratch work

18. The sales of the 15 largest American businesses for a recent year are given below.

Company	Sales (in billions)	Company	Sales (in billions)
Amoco	21	IBM	60
Chevron	25	Mobil	48
Chrysler	35	Occidental Petroleum	19
Du Pont	33	Phillip Morris	26
Exxon	80	Proctor and Gamble	19
Ford Motor	92	Shell Oil	21
General Electric	49	Texaco	34
General Motors	121		

Which values are outliers?

A. none   **B.** 19   **C.** 121   **D.** 19 and 121

Scratch work

GO ON TO NEXT PAGE

Additional Practice: Enhanced Multiple-Choice
(continued)

19. What is the measure of the diagonal of a square if the area is $25x^2$?

   A. $5x$ **B.** $5x\sqrt{2}$ **C.** $10x$ **D.** $5x^2$

Scratch work

20. Line p is parallel to line q.

$c° - a° =$

   A. $0°$ **B.** $100°$ **C.** $120°$ **D.** $150°$

Scratch work

GO ON TO NEXT PAGE

Additional Practice: Enhanced Multiple-Choice
(continued)

21. A section of a graph without the x- and y-axes is shown below.

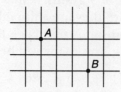

If point A has coordinates $(4, 6)$, state the coordinates of point B.

A. $(4, 7)$ **B.** $(4, 1)$ **C.** $(9, 2)$ **D.** $(7, 4)$

Scratch work

22. In $\triangle ABC$, $AB = 8$ and $BC = 12$. Which one of the following cannot be the measure of $\overline{AC}$?

A. 5   **B.** 8   **C.** 12   **D.** 20

Scratch work

GO ON TO NEXT PAGE

Additional Practice: Enhanced Multiple-Choice
(continued)

23. The weights of boxes of cereal filled by machine are normally distributed. The weight is 510 grams with a standard deviation of 4 grams. A machine at the end of the production line checks the weight of the boxes before they are shipped to the stores. If a box weighs more than 522 grams or less than 498 grams, it is sent back to the beginning of the line to be emptied and reused. Of 2,000 boxes, how many will be sent back for this reason?

A. 0 **B.** 4 **C.** 20 **D.** 80

Scratch work

23. Jane has four pieces of copper tubing to make a triangular base for her art project. The lengths of the pieces of tubing are 2 inches, 4.5 inches, 5.8 inches, and 10.2 inches. How many different triangles can Jane make?

   I. 2 in., 4.5 in., and 5.8 in.

   II. 2 in., 4.5 in., and 10.2 in.

   III. 2 in., 5.8 in., and 10.2 in.

   IV. 4.5 in., 5.8 in., and 10.2 in.

A. I only **B.** II and III only **C.** I and IV only **D.** I, II, III, and IV

Scratch work

GO ON TO NEXT PAGE

Additional Practice: Enhanced Multiple-Choice
(continued)

25. A spinner and the results of 20 spins on the spinner are shown below.

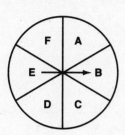

Outcome	Tally	Frequency
A	III	3
B	II	2
C	Ж	5
D	IIII	4
E	Ж	5
F	I	1

What is the experimental probability of spinning a C?

A. $\dfrac{1}{2}$ **B.** $\dfrac{1}{4}$ **C.** $\dfrac{1}{5}$ **D.** $\dfrac{1}{6}$

Scratch work

26. The graph of the equation $y = 4x + 8$ is

A. a horizontal line   **B.** a vertical line

C. a line that rises to the right   **D.** a line that falls to the right

Scratch work

GO ON TO NEXT PAGE

Additional Practice: Enhanced Multiple-Choice
(continued)

27. Which expression gives the area of the figure below?

A. $x^2 + 1$ **B.** $x^2 + 2x + 1$ **C.** $x^2 + 3$ **D.** $x^2 + 3x$

Scratch work

28. The high temperatures for a week in April were 56°F, 58°F, 60°F, 63°F, 58°F, 62°F, and 70°F. What was the median temperature?

A. 58°F   **B.** 61°F   **C.** 60°F   **D.** 63°F

Scratch work

GO ON TO NEXT PAGE

Additional Practice: Enhanced Multiple-Choice
(continued)

29. Which statement is true about the relationship between $m \angle 2$ and $m \angle 1$?

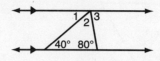

A. $m \angle 2 < m \angle 1$

B. $m \angle 1 < m \angle 2$

C. $m \angle 1 = m \angle 2$

D. There is not enough information.

Scratch work

30. The geometric mean between 12 and 18 is

A. x, where $\dfrac{12}{x} = \dfrac{x}{18}$

B. x, where $x = \dfrac{12 + 18}{2}$

C. the same as the arithmetic mean

D. 15

Scratch work

GO ON TO NEXT PAGE

Additional Practice: Enhanced Multiple-Choice
(continued)

31. The top, front, and side views of a figure are given below.

 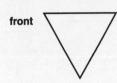 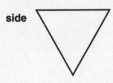

What is the figure?

A. cone   **B.** cylinder   **C.** sphere   **D.** rectangular prism

Scratch work

32. The figure below is a grid showing how a fire spread in a certain region.

If, at the start of the fire, the forest ranger had given an accurate probability factor for the spreading of this fire, what would the probability factor have been?

A. $\frac{1}{6}$ **B.** $\frac{1}{4}$ **C.** $\frac{1}{3}$ **D.** $\frac{3}{4}$

Scratch work

GO ON TO NEXT PAGE

Additional Practice: Enhanced Multiple-Choice
(continued)

33. A car is traveling at a constant speed. Which graph represents the distance traveled with respect to time?

A.

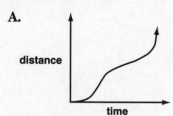

B.

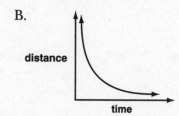

C.

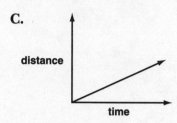

D.

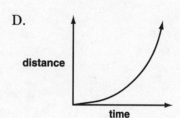

Scratch work

34. Which expression represents a number that is doubled and then increased by 3?

A. $(2 + n) + 3$ **B.** $2n + 3$ **C.** $n^2 + 3$ **D.** $2n - 3$

Scratch work

GO ON TO NEXT PAGE

Additional Practice: Enhanced Multiple-Choice
(continued)

35. If $x > 0$, $y > 0$, and $x < y$, then $y - x$

   A. is positive   **B.** equals $x - y$

   C. is negative   **D.** cannot be determined

Scratch work

36. The map of a small college campus is shown below.

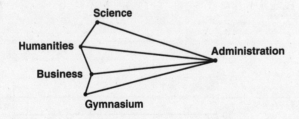

Suppose you want to tour the campus in the most efficient way possible. That is, you want to see each building and walk on each sidewalk only once. From which building would you want to start?

   A. Administration   **B.** Humanities

   C. Business   **D.** Humanities or Business

Scratch work

GO ON TO NEXT PAGE

Additional Practice: Enhanced Multiple-Choice
(continued)

37. The value, in cents, of q quarters, d dimes, and n nickels is

    A. $q + d + n$ **B.** $40(q + d + n)$ **C.** $25q + 10d + 5n$ **D.** 40

Scratch work

38. The graph shows the life expectancy for males and females.

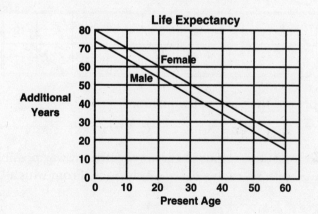

To about what age can a 20-year old male expect to live?

    A. 55   **B.** 60   **C.** 75   **D.** 80

Scratch work

GO ON TO NEXT PAGE

Additional Practice: Enhanced Multiple-Choice
(continued)

39. The area of a square is found by using the formula $A = s^2$. Which graph shows this relationship?

A.

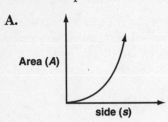

B.

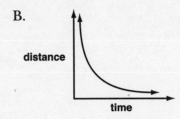

C.

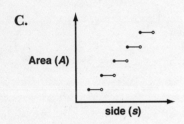

D.

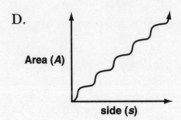

Scratch work

40. The table shows a relation between x and y as a set of ordered pairs.

x	0	1	2	3	...	7	...	10
y	−3	−1	1	3	...	11	...	17

Which equation expresses the same relationship?

A. $y = x - 3$ **B.** $y = 2x - 3$ **C.** $y = x$ **D. A., B.,** and **C.**

Scratch work

GO ON TO NEXT PAGE

Additional Practice: Constructed-Response

*This section contains twenty questions for which you will provide short answers.
Work the problem in the area marked "Scratch work."*

1. A gardener for a park district has to prepare three circular gardens for planting by covering them with peat moss. One garden has a diameter of 12 feet, one has a radius of 8 feet, and the third has a diameter of 20 feet. If each bag of peat moss can cover 160 square feet of ground, how many bags of peat moss will the gardener need?

Scratch work

2. Two planes left Kennedy Airport in New York City. One plane flew to London at a rate of 600 mi/h for 6 hours. The second plane flew in the opposite direction to Los Angeles at a rate of 650 mi/h for 3.5 hours. What is the distance between Los Angeles and London?

Scratch work

GO ON TO NEXT PAGE

Additional Practice: Constructed-Response
(continued)

3. The average of six numbers is 10, and the average of ten other numbers is 6. Find the average of all sixteen numbers.

Scratch work

4. Sal's wages vary directly as the number of days he works. If his wages for 5 days are $26, how much would they be for 12 days?

Scratch work

GO ON TO NEXT PAGE

Additional Practice: Constructed-Response
(continued)

5. The sail of a certain type of hang glider consists of two congruent isosceles triangles joined along the keel so that a 90° angle is formed at the nose of the sail.

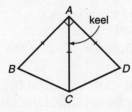

In order to construct such a sail, what must be the measure of ∠BCD?

Scratch work

6. The measures of the four angles of a quadrilateral are $x - 15$, $x + 35$, $x + 20$, and x. Find each measure.

Scratch work

GO ON TO NEXT PAGE

Additional Practice: Constructed-Response
(continued)

7. The *pitch* of a roof is the angle the roof surface makes
   with the horizontal, or level, line. Although the pitch is
   an angle measure, carpenters describe the pitch of a
   roof by using a pair of numbers. The diagram at the
   right illustrates a roof with a 5-12 pitch. That is, for
   each 12 inches of run, there is a 5-inch rise.

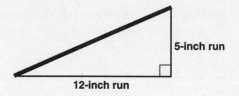

Suppose that a carpenter knows that roof AB shown below has a 5-12 pitch. If a beam is
placed 14.4 feet from A and 9.6 feet from C, find the pitch of roof BC.

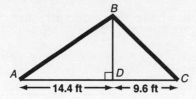

Scratch work

8. The charge for shipping a package is 75 cents for the first 4 ounces and 9 cents for each
   additional ounce or part of an ounce. Find the weight of a package that costs $1.83 to ship.

Scratch work

GO ON TO NEXT PAGE

Additional Practice: Constructed-Response
(continued)

9. Solve the equation $3x + 4(x + 1) = 5x - 8$.

Scratch work

10. One evening, the candy counter at the Cineplex sold 532 buckets of popcorn for $1489.50. A large bucket sells for $2.25, and a jumbo bucket sells for $3.75. How many jumbo buckets of popcorn were sold?

Scratch work

GO ON TO NEXT PAGE

Additional Practice: Constructed-Response
(continued)

11. In science lab, Alex attaches a weight to the bottom of a spring and hangs the spring from a free-standing hook. He pulls the spring down a distance of 27 centimeters and allows it to rebound freely. He records how far the weight drops after each successive rebound in the table shown below. How far would the weight drop after the next rebound?

Distance the Weight Drops
27 cm
18 cm
12 cm
8 cm
5.3 cm

Scratch work

12. What number is 0.3% of 62.7?

Scratch work

GO ON TO NEXT PAGE

Name _____ Date _____

Additional Practice: Constructed-Response
(continued)

13. Hank Aaron, who played baseball at Milwaukee and Atlanta from 1954 to 1976, hit more home runs than any other major league player. The number of home runs he hit each year is given below.

13	27	26	44	30	39	40	34	45	44	24	32
44	39	29	44	38	47	34	40	20	12	10	

Make a frequency table of the data.

Scratch work

14. Draw a box-and-whisker plot of the data in question 13.

Scratch work

GO ON TO NEXT PAGE

Additional Practice: Constructed-Response
(continued)

15. During the morning rush hour, a bus arrives at the bus stop at Indianola and Morse Roads every seven minutes. A bus will wait for thirty seconds before departing. If you arrive at a random time, what is the probability that there will be a bus waiting?

Scratch work

16. At a certain time of the day, Luanna's shadow is 8 feet long. Luanna is 5 feet 6 inches tall, and the oak tree in her yard is 44 feet tall. If Luanna stands in the shadow of the tree so that the end of her shadow coincides with the end of the tree's shadow, how far from the tree will Luanna be standing?

Scratch work

GO ON TO NEXT PAGE

Additional Practice: Constructed-Response
(continued)

17. In the figure below, ∠*ABC* is a straight angle, and $\overline{DB}$ is perpendicular to $\overline{BE}$. If ∠*ABD* measures *x* degrees, write an expression to represent the degree measure of ∠*CBE*.

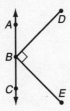

Scratch work

18. The corner is cut from a rectangular piece of cardboard as shown below. Find the area of the remaining cardboard.

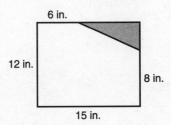

Scratch work

GO ON TO NEXT PAGE

Additional Practice: Constructed-Response
(continued)

19. An airplane can travel 1716 feet in 3 seconds. Find the speed of the plane in miles per hour.

Scratch work

20. A gallon of water evaporates from a 9-gallon drum of 4% salt solution. What is the percent of salt in the remaining solution?

Scratch work

Additional Practice: Open-Ended Problems

This section contains ten open-ended problems. Demonstrate your knowledge by giving a clear,
   concise solution to each problem.

Your score on these problems will depend on how well you
* *can explain your reasoning.*
* *show your understanding of the mathematics in an organized manner.*
* *use charts, graphs, and diagrams in your explanation.*
* *show the solution in more than one way or relate it to other situations.*
* *investigate beyond the requirements of the problems.*

1. Juan and Maria have calculators. Juan starts at zero and adds 2. Maria starts at 100 and
   subtracts 3. If they push their keys at the same time, will their displays ever show the same
   number at the same time? If so, what number is it? Be sure to explain your reasoning.

GO ON TO NEXT PAGE

Additional Practice: Open-Ended Problems
(continued)

2. Explain why you think bees form honeycombs with hexagons instead of octagons.

hexagon   octagon

Additional Practice: Open-Ended Problems
(continued)

3. Pilots know that as they fly higher, the air gets colder. Through experimental testing and data accumulated over the years, weather observers and meteorologists have found that for each 1000-foot increase in altitude, there is a 2°F drop in temperature.

   a. Suppose the ground temperature is represented by s. Write a formula that would help a weather observer find the atmospheric temperature (t) at a given altitude (a).

   b. Find the atmospheric temperature 12,500 feet above an area where the ground temperature is 68°F.

GO ON TO NEXT PAGE

Additional Practice: Open-Ended Problems
(continued)

4. The owner of Maple Grove Campground wants to update her facilities to provide more recreational opportunities for campers. She interviews 300 campers and lists the 8 favorite recreational activities of men, women, and children, as shown in the table below.

Campers	Activities
Men	basketball, swimming, fishing, boating, bicycling, hiking, jogging, frisbee golf
Women	Hiking, tennis, jogging, swimming, aerobics, walking, bicycling, volleyball
Children	rollerblading, basketball, volleyball, bicycling, frisbee golf, skateboarding, swimming, miniature golf

Use a Venn diagram and sound reasoning to determine some new activities she could include at her campground. Explain your reasoning.

GO ON TO NEXT PAGE

464

Additional Practice: Open-Ended Problems
(continued)

5. Sandra is giving Timothy information about roof trusses and braces made up of right triangles. In drafting, a T-square and triangle are used to draw right angles. Timothy wonders what information he needs to ensure that the right triangle he draws with a compass, ruler, and protractor is unique.

    a. If Sandra says that the measure of the horizontal leg is 3 and the measure of the hypotenuse is 6, does the information determine a unique right triangle? Explain. If it does, describe how Timothy can construct the triangle. If not, give a counterexample.

    b. Timothy knows that the measures of the acute angles of a right triangle are 47° and 43°. Does this information determine a unique triangle? Tell how you know. If it does, describe how to construct the triangle. If not, give a counterexample.

    c. Is a unique right triangle determined when the length of the vertical leg is 10 cm and the angle opposite the leg measures 35°? Justify your answer. If it does, describe how to construct the triangle. If not, give a counterexample.

GO ON TO NEXT PAGE

Additional Practice: Open-Ended Problems
(continued)

6. Describe a situation that might be represented by the graph below.

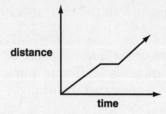

GO ON TO NEXT PAGE

Additional Practice: Open-Ended Problems
(continued)

7. Area models can be used to illustrate factoring polynomials. Consider $2x^2 + 3x + 1$. First represent it by the area models shown below.

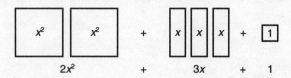

Then use the area models to form a rectangle as shown at the right.

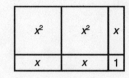

a. Name the factors of $2x^2 + 3x + 1$.

b. Use an area model to find the factors of $3x^2 + 4x + 1$. Explain each step.

c. Draw an area model for a polynomial. Then write the polynomial and its factors.

GO ON TO NEXT PAGE

Additional Practice: Open-Ended Problems
(continued)

8. The graphs of each group of equations have at least one characteristic in common. Name the characteristic(s) and then graph each group of equations on the same axes to verify your answer. Then write an additional equation for each group that shares the characteristic you have named.

a. $y = x$, $y = 3x$, $y = 5x$

b. $y = 2x$, $y = 2x + 1$, $y = 2x - 3$

c. $2y = 6x$, $4y - 12x = 0$, $3x - y = 0$

d. $2x - 4y = 12$, $3y + 2x = -2$, $x + y = 0$

GO ON TO NEXT PAGE

Additional Practice: Open-Ended Problems
(continued)

9. The table below shows the differences, in inches, between the actual July rainfall and the mean rainfall over the past thirty years for a certain region. A positive difference means that the rainfall was greater than the mean; a negative difference means that the rainfall was less than the mean.

Year	1	2	3	4	5	6	7	8	9	10	11	12	13	14	15
in.	0.26	0.36	0.16	0.16	0.16	0.26	-0.64	-0.54	-0.54	-0.44	-0.34	-0.54	-0.54	-0.64	-0.54

Year	16	17	18	19	20	21	22	23	24	25	26	27	28	29	30
in.	0.16	0.26	0.36	0.36	-0.46	-0.46	-0.46	-0.04	-0.1	-0.1	-0.11	0.06	0.54	0.36	0.36

Does the data suggest that next July will be a dry month or a wet month? Explain your reasoning by showing a graph of the data.

GO ON TO NEXT PAGE

Additional Practice: Open-Ended Problems
(continued)

10. The following questions are related to the formula $d = rt$ where d represents distance, r represents rate, and t represents time.

    a. Every day at lunchtime, Kelli walks 30 minutes before returning to work. On cool days she walks more briskly than on warm days. Does the distance she walks vary directly or inversely with her rate of walk? Justify your answer.

    b. At the Indianapolis 500 auto race, each car finishing the race travels 500 miles. Does the average speed of the cars finishing the race vary directly or inversely with the time taken to complete the race? Justify your answer.

    c. On an interstate highway Mr. Grant sets his cruise control at 65 miles per hour. Does the distance he travels vary directly or inversely with the time traveled? Justify your answer.

    d. Write a word problem illustrating inverse variation. Solve and give the meaning of the answer.

Answers

Additional Practice:
Enhanced Multiple-Choice
(pages 431–450)

1. B	21. D
2. C	22. D
3. B	23. C
4. B	24. C
5. C	25. B
6. D	26. C
7. A	27. B
8. B	28. C
9. C	29. B
10. A	30. A
11. A	31. A
12. D	32. B
13. C	33. C
14. D	34. B
15. A	35. A
16. A	36. D
17. B	37. C
18. C	38. C
19. A	39. A
20. B	40. B

Additional Practice:
Constructed-Response
(pages 451–460)

1. 3 bags

2. 5875 miles

3. 7.5

4. $62.40

5. 135°

6. 65°, 115°, 100°, 80°

7. $7.5 - 12$

8. greater than 15 ounces, but less than or equal to 16 ounces

9. -6

10. 337 large buckets

    195 jumbo buckets

11. 3.5 cm

12. 0.1881

13.

Number of Home Runs	Frequency
10–19	3
20–29	5
30–39	7
40–49	8

14.

15. $\frac{1}{14}$

16. 56 feet

17. $(90 - x)°$

18. 162 square inches

19. 390 miles per hour

20. 4.5%

Answers

Additional Practice: Open-Ended Problems (pages 461–470)

These problems allow for alternate solutions, differing explanations, and expressions of personal opinion. What follows are sample solutions that will often vary greatly from correct responses by students. You may want to modify the Sample Scoring Guide on page 424 to use for evaluation. Such a scoring guide will usually be better than direct comparison of student answers with answers given here.

1. The displays will show the same number at 40.

2. Hexagons fit together to form a tessellation by themselves. A tessellation with octagons would need to include squares.

3a. $t = -0.002a + s$

 b. 43°F

4. Since swimming and bicycling are common to all three groups, the owner would probably want to include these activities at her campground. She may also want to include hiking, jogging, basketball, frisbee golf, and volleyball since these are recreational activities that two of the three groups enjoy.

5a. Yes, HL says that a unique triangle is determined by the hypotenuse and a leg. Construct by drawing a horizontal segment measuring 3 and a vertical segment. Place the point of a compass at the end of the horizontal segment where the acute angle will be formed and swing an arc 6 units long. The point where the arc intersects the vertical segment is the third vertex of the triangle.

 b. No, he would need to know the measure of at least one side since an infinite number of similar triangles fit this description. Two are shown at the right.

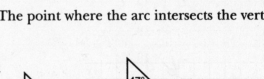

 c. Yes, LA says that a unique triangle is described by a leg and an acute angle. Construct by drawing a vertical segment measuring 10 cm and a horizontal segment. Use a protractor to draw a 55° angle at the end of the vertical segment where the acute angle will be formed and extend the segment to meet the horizontal segment.

Answers

Additional Practice: Open-Ended Problems (continued)

6. A car is traveling on a freeway at a constant speed when it stops for a time due to an accident on the road ahead. After the accident is cleared, the car can proceed at a constant rate again.

7a. The factors are $(2x + 1)(x + 1)$.

b. $3x^2 + 4x + 1$

The regions form the rectangle below.

The factors are $(3x + 1)(x + 1)$.

c.

$x^2 + 2x + 1 = (x + 1)^2$

8a. All pass through the point at $(0, 0)$.

b. All are parallel lines.

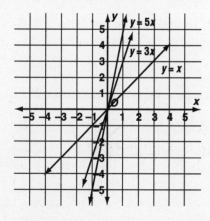

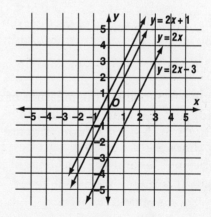

The graph of $y = 10x$ also passes through the point at $(0, 0)$.

The graph of $y = 2x + 3$ is also parallel.

Answers

Additional Practice: Open-Ended Problems (continued)

8c. They are the same line.

d. All pass through the point at $(2, -2)$.

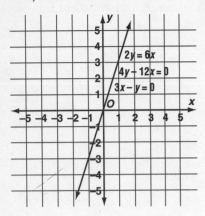

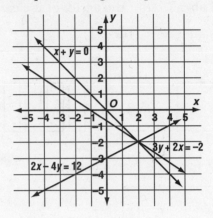

Another equation is $4y = 12x$.

Another equation is $y = x - 4$.

9. The data in the table is shown in the bar graph below.

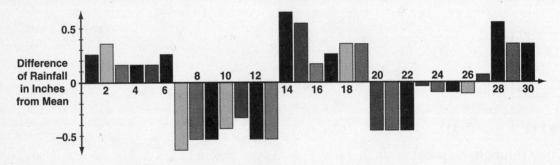

It appears that there are cycles of six or seven years in which rainfall alternates between above and below the mean. The data suggest that next July will probably be a wet month.

10a. Directly, because as her rate increases, the distance increases in a proportional amount.

b. Indirectly, because as the rate increases, the time decreases in a proportional amount.

c. Directly, because as her rate increases, the distance increases in a proportional amount.

d. Mrs. Berg allows $40 a week for groceries. If she bought 10 items this week, what was the average price per item? The items bought averaged $4 each. If she had bought more items, the average price would have been less.